HOSPITAL CITY

Donated by

Warren Kump M.D.

HOSPITAL CITY

BY JOHN STARR

THIS EDITION HAS BEEN SPECIALLY PREPARED FOR
THE ALUMNAE ASSOCIATION OF THE BELLEVUE
SCHOOL OF NURSING, INC., SPONSORS OF THIS WORK.

CROWN PUBLISHERS, INC.

NEW YORK

CONTENTS

THE HOSPITAL WITH A HEART

On the East Side of New York between Twenty-sixth and Thirtieth streets, a few blocks below the United Nations building, sprawls a city within a city. Its crowded buildings, an arresting mixture of style and period, run back all the way from First Avenue to the East River. This is Bellevue, most famous of all hospitals and a byword to millions who have never laid eyes on its smoke-bleared tiers of brick and stone.

Look at it closely, this great and forbidding house of refuge. It has more doctors, more interns, more operations, more apparatus, and a greater range of maladies to cope with than any other institution of its kind on earth. In all aspects it reflects the complexity of the world's greatest human swarm.

The old lady struck by a cab as she crosses Fifth Avenue on the way to the Public Library is brought here to be mended. The hoodlum drilled in the back as he races down a Greenwich Village alley here finds refrigerated rest. The watchman discovered huddled at the bottom of a garment-center freight-elevator well, the stout commuter taken by a coronary on a Grand Central ramp, the epileptic who swallows his tongue in front of the Princeton Club on East Thirty-ninth—all find their way here. So it is, too, with the skinny Puerto Rican girl from Harlem with white patches on her palms, and the Lascar seaman from the West Street docks whose lungs have hemorrhaged.

Bellevue garners them all in, the endless casualties of cosmopolis, so long as they are sick enough, or hurt enough, or crazed enough to need urgent attention. Here crisis is the natural order of the day. Somehow room will be found, even if tents have to be pitched on the grounds, or mattresses laid in the corridors. For Bellevue policy is: you must pay something if you can, but if you cannot, come anyway.

No matter how many new laboratories, wards, and pavilions are added to its already huge plant, Bellevue can never quite keep pace with New York's enormous need. Misery and disease spawn far faster than the hospital appropriations made by the board of estimate. Year in, year out, the Bellevue authorities find themselves at odds with economy-minded administrations. Always the great city of pain and surcease by the river finds itself short on sheets, drugs, bedding, bathrobes, mops, iron lungs, nurses, porters, and space. Yet always, somehow, it gives its patients the most concentrated medical attention of any hospital on record.

Bellevue has been investigated countless times, now pilloried, now praised. It is a dramatic index of New York's social consciousness. Suicides, murders, and strait-jacketed indignities beyond mention have occurred within its walls. So, too, have some of medicine's greatest advances, perhaps more than in any other single institution of its kind. Its power for good has left a clear and permanent imprint on the metropolis. There is scarcely a public health reform, an improvement in slum clearance, or an advance in the treatment of psychotic, alcoholic, and sex offender in which Bellevue has not signally figured.

Bellevue is a peculiar combination of old and new, of ultramodern operating rooms and dark, peeling corridors. Most hospitals have loud-speaker systems; Bellevue still depends on a bell system installed in 1911. But if, to live, you must have a cancerous pituitary removed, a Bellevue surgical team can do it. For whatever this greatest of city hospitals may be short on, it is certainly long on brains and skill. Doctors vie to work here.

Roughly 1,500 patients come every day to Bellevue's out-patient clinics, and the average daily caseload on the wards runs around 2,700. Each night of the week about 25 sufferers are admitted, and from 50 to 100 more are treated in the emergency ward. Besides these, about 20 persons a night are admitted to the psychiatric pavilion. Last year more than 3,000 babies were born in Bellevue, and some 2,500 people died there.

All told, Bellevue's steady population is around 10,000. This figure includes 1,000 female and 1,700 male patients, 1,000 visiting physicians, and a house staff of 469 interns and resident doctors. In addition, there are 582 new graduate nurses, over 300 practical nurses, 1,300 attendants, and 1,890 other salaried personnel, among them technicians, therapists, dietitians, cooks, administrators, secretaries, cleaners, clerks, guards, and police-men. And, supplementing these, a volunteer staff of 1,000 men and women also serves Bellevue.

To operate Bellevue for one year costs the city nearly $17,000,000—$14,000,000 for payroll, $1,300,000 for food, and $1,150,000 for laboratory and surgical supplies. To get these funds requires unremitting effort, for it is almost a political tradition to resist pleas from Bellevue.

Of the eighty-two approved medical schools in the United States, four are integrally tied in with Bellevue: the First Division is operated by Columbia University College of Physicians and Surgeons; the Second Division is the purlieu of Cornell University Medical College; New York University has the Third Division; the Fourth Division is traditionally called the Open Division, although it is now affiliated with N.Y.U. Post Graduate Medical School. Each of these divisions functions autono-mously and has its own medical and surgical services, but administrative control of the whole institution comes from Bellevue's superintendent, who is appointed by the city of New York. The teaching staffs of the four medical schools are the doctors who supervise treatment of patients in Bellevue's wards, and every one of these eminent doctors is an unpaid volunteer, his only reward the privilege of doing research at Bellevue.

Bellevue is really three hospitals in one: a general hospital, sixth largest in New York; a tuberculosis hospital of 382 beds; and a psychiatric hospital with 630 beds. The general hospital houses surgical patients in addition to general medical patients, and also patients needing such special services as pediatrics, gynecology, and rehabilitation. It has a total bed capacity of 1,733. Ninety-two percent of the 7,000 hospitals in the United States have fewer than 500 beds.

Bellevue has its own prison, mortuary, and fire department. It publishes seven newspapers. It has a Sunday school and a nursery school. In one building is housed a state Supreme Court, where judges can commit psychiatric patients to state mental hospitals, with only relatives present during the harrowing procedure.

In Bellevue, at certain seasons of the year, you can attend the Rodeo or the Ringling Brothers, Barnum and Bailey Circus. You can see a current movie or, perhaps, a Broadway play. There are four lending libraries, and two public schools operated by the New York City Board of Education. P.S. 401, known as the "School Without a Schoolhouse," serves most of Bellevue's children, but P.S. 16 takes care of those at the psychiatric pavilion.

Bellevue is not the only charity hospital in New York. There are many others, and in addition the city helps to support all voluntary or nonprofit hospitals within its boundaries. But Bellevue is the city's special concern, perhaps because of the long and stormy relationship between the city and the old gray pile on the East River.

The battered old hospital has an enduring fascination for all those who have ever worked in it. Among the men and women who have been associated with Bellevue, there is a bond that lingers throughout their lives. Wherever they go, whatever they do, they are conscious that having been a part of Bellevue marks them as different, and as perhaps a little better than most in the ranks of those who serve the sick.

The story of this fabulous institution is best told in the lives of the men and women who made it the most famous hospital in the world, a breeder of great men and women, of great ideas and greater legends.

CLOACA REIGNS SUPREME

Bellevue Hospital has its roots in the early decades of the eighteenth century. This century, the so-called Age of Reason, in its medical aspect was a period of consolidation. That is, between 1700 and 1820, or thereabouts, the medical discoveries of the preceding hundred years or more underwent development and elaboration in many scattered directions.

Overshadowing the whole intellectual life of the age were the laws of Newton. Out of Newtonian physics swiftly arose a mechanistic and highly rational concept of the universe, and also of man, its principal feature. This point of view, via contributing disciplines, particularly chemistry, carried over into medicine. Among the elite minds of the century, at least, the idea of man as a machine was coming into focus.

At the time of Bellevue's inception, several key medical advances had already been accomplished. William Harvey had done his pioneer work on the circulation of the blood. Another Englishman, Thomas Sydenham, had reawakened a long neglected interest in close clinical observation and restored the useful idea that each disease is an entity in itself with its own peculiar symptoms. Marcello Malpighi, one of many brilliant Italians, had explored the capillaries and laid the groundwork for the science of embryology. The Dutchman, van Leeuwenhoek, had demonstrated the existence of microorganisms and evolved rudimentary microscopic techniques. And many

6

other Europeans besides these pathfinders had contributed basic discoveries of a medical or related nature as part of the new belief that the physical world was lawful and the forces of nature subject to human understanding and control.

Meanwhile, at the turn of the eighteenth century Boerhaave, at the University of Leyden, had shown the value of a methodical approach to the art of healing, an approach that drew severally on chemistry, physics, botany, zoology, and other sciences. Boerhaave's ideas were brought to Edinburgh by Pitcairne and Munro, and this Scottish center of learning soon dominated British medicine. Then, first through John Morgan, and later through Benjamin Rush, both of whom attended Edinburgh, the Boerhaave system was introduced at the University of Pennsylvania.

But these names and institutions represent the highlights of medical history. In point of actual everyday practice, during the early 1700's American medicine was in exceedingly low estate. Cataract-couchers, lithotomists, and tooth surgeons flourished. If it was the century of John Hunter, it was also the century of the charlatan. Most doctors learned what little they knew of the mysteries of the human frame through apprenticeship to some established physician, chirurgeon, or barber-surgeon. There were no licenses or compulsory examinations. The chemistry of the body was a blank page.

The therapeutic side of medicine was a gruesome mishmash, necessarily so since nothing was known of germs, viruses, cell chemistry, and the like. Bleeding was universally practiced, an outgrowth of the humoral theory of Aristotle and Galen. Disease meant that something bad and nasty was in the blood. Bleeding reduced the malign substance or unbalance of humors.

Surgery and bonesetting, however, were relatively much more advanced than internal medicine and pathology, if the then existing primitivities can be so named. Vesalius, and later Baglivi and others, had made remarkably complete studies and drawings of the gross human anatomy. And so the surgeons, at least, had something dependable to go on. Ambroise Paré, a humble French military surgeon, had shown positive genius in developing rational techniques for the handling of gunshot wounds with the help of ligation. Still, asepsis was unknown. Surgeons operated on one patient after the other without even thinking to wash their hands. No one was sure whether pus was a desirable or an undesirable feature of healing. Despite the work of such intuitively gifted minds as van Helmont's, the simplest physiological processes remained a mystery.

As for Colonial America, here even more than in Europe early eighteenth-century medicine was a hodgepodge of quackery, folklore, and a few genuine but as yet uncoordinated insights. American medicine started from scratch, a circumstance that only later turned out to be an advantage. Such was the situation when, in 1734, a momentous chain of events was set in motion. This year, by order of Mayor Robert Lurting, the common council of New York appointed a committee to pick a site for a municipal workhouse, or catchall.

The council's plans specified a yard, a garden, and a burial ground. The building was to be made of stone, and was to be called the Publick Workhouse and House of Correction of the City of New York.

No one, of course, foresaw New York City's spectacular growth. The site selected, a flowery meadowland well out in open farming country, was thought to be irrevocably remote from genteel view. Yet in a few short decades New York's present City Hall was to go up on the same spot. But at that time the workhouse grounds were bordered on the west by Cortlandt Street and, above this sleepy thoroughfare, by Kings Farm. To the south and east, some distance off, lay Beekman Swamp, not to be drained and put to cultivation until 1740. To the north and east ran Park Row, then the beginning of the highway to Boston.

After leisurely cogitations, in December, 1735, a certain John

Roomer was given £80 for materials and fifty gallons of rum to stimulate his carpenters and masons. By March, 1736, Mr. Roomer had put up a drab two-story, steep-roofed building, 24 feet wide by 56 deep. Down in the cellar a whipping post for disobedient slaves was installed, along with spinning wheels and looms. A gloomy iron cage was provided for the unruly or demented. The first floor was given over to a dining room and the warden's quarters. Finally, one more facility was set up, in accordance with the council's decree that "the upper room at the west end of said house be suitably furnished as an infirmary and for no other use whatsoever."

This tiny infirmary was the seed from which grew the mighty oak of Bellevue.

The first superintendent was John Sebring. His official title was Keeper of the House of Correction and Master of the Workhouse and Poorhouse. This honorific suggests the variety of services covered by the one small institution. Sebring's salary was £30 a year with board and lodging. In addition, he collected fees for detaining and punishing recalcitrant slaves and indentured servants.

In the same building were lodged paupers, children, and helpless old people, the miscreant and the demented. The term "workhouse" was no misnomer. The rebellious were put to hard labor. Pauper inmates taught young orphans how to sew, knit, spin, weave, and work leather and iron.

The upper west room infirmary contained six beds. Its first medical officer was a Dr. John Van Beuren, whose salary was £100 a year, out of which he was expected to supply his own medicines and dressings. Dr. Van Beuren served at the infirmary until about 1765, at which time he was succeeded by his youngest son Beekman, who was holding the position at the outbreak of the Revolutionary War.

Actually, nothing at all memorable occurred at the city workhouse until the great fire of 1776, when New York almost burned to the ground, leaving thousands homeless. Very suddenly the institution had some three hundred destitute and sick people to take care of. It is interesting to note that although New York was very shortly rebuilt in a great burst of civic energy, nothing was done to improve or add to the only city refuge. However, the housing boom initiated by the fire was kept in motion by a steadily rising influx of population, and the city began to move out toward the little stone building near Kings Farm, thus steadily bringing the facility into public notice. Broadway became the main thoroughfare, Wall Street the center of fashion. The party of the decade was a ball given after President Washington's inauguration ceremony, which took place on the balcony of Federal Hall at Broad and Wall. Later, this balcony for many years adorned the entrance to Bellevue.

Presently—in 1794—New York suffered the first of a series of yellow fever epidemics which were to continue for more than eleven years. Yellow fever, a disease of the American tropics, had been first noted in the Barbados in 1647. Throughout the country there were some thirty-five serious outbreaks of this dreaded virus affliction between 1702 and 1800. Endemic in the West Indies and throughout tropical America, yellow fever is the type of disease which epidemiologists tell us is spread by the influx of susceptibles.

The main carriers of the disease in nature are monkeys, from which animals it is transmitted to humans by the *Haemagogus* mosquito. Once established in the human bloodstream, it can then be further transmitted by *Aëdes* mosquito, which tends to live near human habitations.

At any rate, in 1794 a citizens' committee demanded that the city provide some place of isolation for victims of the epidemic. Since yellow fever was no respecter of economic or social station, the authorities responded with alacrity. For £2,000 the city council bought part of the estate of a Mr. Brockholst Livingston, on the East River opposite the Three-Mile Stone. This large property had once been part of the Kip's Bay Farm owned by Jacobus Kip. (At this time Kip's Bay was a considerable indentation in the river; in later years much of the cove was filled in.)

In 1772 the farm had passed into the hands of Robert Leake, who named it Belle View. In 1783, after the Revolutionary War, it had come into the possession of Lindley Murray, who changed the spelling of the name to Bellevue. The main building on the property was a two-story house with an attic. It was in this house that the city proposed to take care of the victims of the yellow fever epidemic. This structure became the first of many to bear the famous name of Bellevue.

Yellow fever cropped up again and again to prostrate the city. An account of conditions at Bellevue during the 1795 epidemic has come down to us in the diary of a Dr. Alexander Anderson, who in September of that year was engaged as house surgeon at a salary of $4.00 a day. Dr. Anderson was not yet twenty-one years old. His brief medical career proved extremely arduous.

An early entry in the diary tells us that there were six patients in the hospital—or pesthouse, as it was then plainly called. A steward and his wife, an ancient gardener, a Negro handyman, and three nurses—one colored, two white—made up the personnel. Presently the first of many new patients arrived, "in shocking condition after ten days of the disease, vomiting blood by the mouthful and dying within two hours."

More and more victims were fetched up from town in carts, and dumped into the young doctor's lap. One young girl Dr. Anderson treated "by the application of a large blister, and pouring down medicines." Needless to say, she soon died. Soon the nurses began to quarrel, and Dr. Anderson confides that he is beginning to think of resignation. Finally he did cry quits and entered private practice, but was persuaded to return during the even more severe epidemic of 1798. This was a still worse experience. The fever raged unchecked. Carpenters were kept busy day and night making cheap pine coffins, though many people protested they could not afford the inflated $4.00 asking price.

Hardly had Dr. Anderson settled down to his second stint at Bellevue than his brother was taken sick and died. A few days later, his father fell violently sick and he, too, failed to survive. Then, the following day, Dr. Anderson was horrified to see yellow fever symptoms developing in his wife. The next week was a nightmare. Dr. Anderson lost his wife, his daughter, and his mother. Shattered, he turned the pesthouse over to a Dr. Douglas, retired from medicine, and took up the printing trade.

Meanwhile, at Bellevue, Dr. Douglas had been stricken but lived to tell the tale. Although there were no cases of infection among the sixteen nurses and other emergency attendants, and although Dr. Douglas attributed his illness to having visited friends in a part of town where the fever was widespread, by this time Bellevue had come to be popularly regarded as a "house of death."

During the Great Epidemic of 1798, a total of 2,086 people out of a population of 36,000 died of yellow fever in New York. This grim experience resulted in the formation of a joint committee "to investigate the causes, progress, and probable means of preventing the return of the fever." The committee was made up of representatives of the common council, the health commission, the chamber of commerce, and the medical society. The committee's most useful finding was "powerfully and earnestly" to recommend a new water system.

During the eighteenth century the water supply in nearly every American city, as in urban centers the world over, was heavily polluted. People who lived in the Age of Reason either developed a resistance to germs unknown in our hygienic times, or abruptly paid the consequences. Drinking water in New York came mostly from wells teeming with lethal microbes. Pigs roamed Broadway, rooting in the mud. Porters earned a modest competence carrying silken ladies and tightly-trousered dandies across quicksands of muck. A sewer ran through Maiden Lane and the Fly Market to the East River. At Pearl Street a bridge arched over this shameless conduit. Here passers-by paused to ponder the view of a slow, black river of sewage dotted with the bloated bodies of small dead animals. At night unwary pedestrians drowned in ill-constructed cesspits.

In a situation where Cloaca reigned supreme, epidemics simply ran their course, killing off the weak and debilitating the strong. The prevailing tendency was to hold tight and pray. When the 1798 scourge had passed, Governor Jay declared November 26 as Thanksgiving Day, though always before the day had come much earlier, during harvest-time. Thus was established a precedent that in due course became nationally accepted.

Among other desperations of the period was childbirth, which, thanks to the total lack of asepsis, only too often ended in puerperal fever and other dismal complications. In this connection, in 1799, an interesting innovation was announced in the daily papers.

> A lying-in ward has been established in the Almshouse of the City of New York. The cases which occur there are numerous enough to answer the purpose of public instruction. Accordingly, there is delivered a course of lectures on the subject of obstetric art, including the anatomical, physiological, and practical parts, by Valentine Seaman, M.D. As this establishment is particularly and exclusively devoted to the education of females, it will be easy for women who practice, or intend to practice, midwifery to avail themselves of the excellent opportunities which are hereby held out to them.

Dr. Seaman was in the van of his profession. Before undertaking to teach obstetrics, he had campaigned, against violent opposition, for the use of Jenner's cowpox vaccine. Now he was bitterly criticized for his obstetrics project. All public levels recoiled from the prospect of having men preside over an act so intimately female as parturition. But again Dr. Seaman persisted, and the following year published the first book on midwifery by an American author. On the title page he calls himself "physician extraordinary to the lying-in ward in the Almshouse." The little volume bears the quaint title *The Midwives' Monitor and Mothers' Mirror*. And so, to the forerunner of Bellevue Hospital belongs the honor of establishing the first wards in New York for expectant mothers, and of giving the first hospital instruction to women in the art of midwifery.

All this while, yellow fever and pollution notwithstanding, the city was growing by leaps and bounds. Just before the War of 1812 its population had reached 76,000. The old farm building at the original Kip's Bay site was proving inadequate to house the drunks, vagrants, indigent sick, and other by-products of the busy social process. Accordingly, in 1811 a special meeting of the common council was called to consider an offer from the heirs of the Kip family to sell a part of the old Kip's Bay Farm adjacent to the alms- and pesthouse. A committee was authorized to purchase this site at a price not exceeding $3,500 an acre, and to build a new almshouse and prison. This whole area, incidentally, had interesting historic associations. Still fresh in people's minds was the delaying action fought here during the Revolutionary War, against Howe's languid redcoats after they had crossed the East River in small scows from the then sylvan Queens shore.

Dr. John Francis, first graduate of the College of Physicians and Surgeons, and destined shortly to become a member of the staff of the projected institution, describes the new Bellevue site as it then appeared:

> On the Eastern side of the island was the well known Kip's Farm, preeminently distinguished for its grateful fruits, the plum, the peach, the pear and apple, and for its classic culture of the *Rosaceae*. Here the elite often repaired, and here our Washington, now invested with presidential honors, made an excursion, and was presented with the Rosa Gallica, an exotic first, introduced into this country in this garden.

The city paid $22,494.50 for this property. Alderman Hoghland received $100 for the plan which he drew up for the new layout. The cornerstone, now preserved in the southeast corner of one of the chapels of the present Bellevue Hospital, was laid on July 29, 1811, by the Honorable DeWitt Clinton, mayor of New York.

In 1811 work on the new almshouse made rapid progress, and over $45,000 was spent on construction. But the next year came the War of 1812, and most of the work ceased, not to be resumed for two more years. Finally, at high noon on April 29, 1816, the members of the council with their families and friends met by the river. The Reverend John Stanford, chaplain of the almshouse, opened the dedication ceremony with a prayer in the new chapel, which measured 65 by 45 feet, and had a ceiling 30 feet high.

The new facility, on which over $421,000 had been lavished during its five years of building, consisted of several structures. The main one, its long dimension paralleling the river, was made of the gneiss rock familiar to anyone who has watched skyscraper excavations in Manhattan. This edifice was a combination house of correction and poorhouse, with prisoners housed in wings at either end, one wing for whites, and the other for colored people. In the main body of the building were workshops, schoolrooms for destitute children, rooms for paupers, and cells for the insane.

North and south of this main building were two small brick hospitals, one for women, the other for men. Each contained six rooms, or wards. There was also a deadhouse or morgue, and two enginehouses adjacent. Somewhat removed was the superintendent's house, with a greenhouse, icehouse, and summerhouse attached. A bakehouse, washhouse, soap factory; a building for carpenters, blacksmiths, and oakum pickers; a barn, a carthouse; and houses for stewards and gatekeepers completed the plant. A gray stone wall ten feet high enclosed the whole grim affair, which was named the Bellevue Establishment.

· III ·

SOME GENERALITIES AND
SOME EARLY NAMES

The term "hospital" comes, through the Old French, from the Latin *hospitalis,* which originally meant a place of rest and entertainment. This fact is pointed up by the many offshoots of the original root, such as "host," "hospice," "hostler," "hospitable," and the like. The word "hospital" to designate a place where the sick are tended came into common usage about the eleventh century, in great measure through the charitable work of the Knights Hospitallers.

The Hospitallers were, so to speak, the medical corps of the Crusaders, military monks whose order was founded in Jerusalem in 1048 to care for poor pilgrims in the Holy Land. Originally they called themselves the Knights of the Hospital of St. John in Jerusalem. Later, having retreated from one Mediterranean city to another under Moslem pressure, they settled on Malta. As the Knights of Malta they lost their medical connection.

All this is by way of saying that for many, many centuries the care of the sick and indigent in Western countries was the exclusive province of the Church, as reflective of the Christian creed of charity and good works. It is from the early monastic system of refuges and asylums that modern hospitals such as Bellevue are directly descended.

In the history of hospitals the very first signs of a shift from monkish to secular auspices appeared in the distant, pre-scientific past. This occurred when, as a natural result of the human ferment, ties formed between the monastic hospitals and the universities, themselves dominated though never entirely controlled by the Church. Thus the stage was set, when all Western society became secularized during the Renaissance and the Reformation, for a shift to civic management of places of asylum. This tendency was particularly strong in the large cities, where social and economic change was most pronounced. Christ's Hospital in London, for example, and the Hôtel de Dieu in Paris illustrate the typical metamorphosis.

As a natural consequence of secularization, the connection between hospitals and centers of learning was extended and formalized. This process went hand in hand with the emergence of medical colleges as separate entities within the universities. Meanwhile, the Church resisted free medical inquiry, at least for a time, on the grounds that it was a tampering with God's highest handiwork, man. Among other things the Church strongly disapproved of anatomical research and the dissection of the human body. For, once dissected, how restore the body for Resurrection's trump?

For hundreds of years, therefore, and well into the nineteenth century, hospitals were in the main thought of as custodial institutions where people mostly went to languish and die rather than to be cured. Perhaps only in times of plague and epidemic were such asylums principally devoted to the care of the ill. As a rule the very poor, the lost, the vagrant, the misfit, and all the myriad wasted souls of the human process figured at least as prominently on hospital rolls as did the sick.

The change from a monastic to a secular control was by no means a happy consummation in all respects. The nuns and brothers who worked with the sick were, in their way, trained people. Most important, they had a vocation. And wherever their services were dispensed with, there was no one to replace them. Only uneducated men and women from the lowest orders of society could be recruited to work for a pittance at so arduous and disagreeable a task as nursing.

Then there was another consideration. Poor people are more often sick than those with money. But in the medieval concept neither poverty nor sickness was thought undesirable. Indeed, suffering was felt to be a strong guarantee of post-mortem reward. This whole point of view was violently reversed when Western society became secularized. In the new ethos, to be poor was to be reprehensible. And since the poor were so often sick, disease also came to be thought of as somehow wrong or evil. So strong, in the new age, was this feeling of stigma about disease that it lingers to this day in respect to mental disease, cancer, syphilis, and some others. But the important thing here is that, for reasons of taboo as well as for reasons of poor pay, hospital work was long considered to be only for the lowest of the low.

When the first American hospitals came into being in Philadelphia, Boston, and New York in the eighteenth century, they all had almshouse associations or antecedents. However, American hospitals, as it proved, had one advantage over those in older countries. They might be held back by lack of medical knowledge and social consciousness, but they were not hamstrung by a fixed social order. A great deal of hypocrisy hid the democratic principle. But it was definitely at work.

At any rate, at the time of Bellevue's inception, nurses were taken from the dregs of society, often from the almshouse population itself. "Ten-day drunks" from the workhouse did much of the dirty work. It can be imagined that with them solicitude for the patient was rather casual. Dickens' Sairey Gamp, the bibulous midwife and nurse of *Martin Chuzzlewit,* is as good a prototype as any.

The Sairey Gamps of the eighteenth century were medical scapegoats. They were chevied by substantial citizens serving on face-saving or emergency committees. It did not, of course, occur to these good people to step into the breach as a matter of Christian example. The nurse-slaveys of the spitals were also bullied by visiting physicians and surgeons, by the dressers who changed the bandages, and by grafting hospital authorities who begrudged them their food.

And so, for a variety of reasons, progress in hospitals occurred only by fits and starts. Pressure would build up to a crisis. Taxable people, under bitter protest, then dug into their pocketbooks, and momentary relief ensued. But again more pressure built up. So it goes to this very day, though on a much higher and more detached level.

Often it was the doctors themselves who initiated reform, now campaigning from behind the scenes, now in the public forum. In some instances their motives were humanitarian and Hippocratic. But the need for better professional facilities also contributed to their zeal, a desire for better operating paraphernalia and a common pool of instruments, for proper space in which to exchange information and give instruction, for free and tranquil opportunity to dissect and experiment. From the public at large they could almost always count on misunderstanding and opposition.

Dr. John Jones, son of Welsh emigrants, and in the last half of the eighteenth century one of New York's foremost practitioners, was typical of the progressive and inquiring type of physician who paved the way for the Bellevue tradition during the earlier almshouse period. Born in 1729 in Jamaica, Long Island, Dr. Jones studied medicine at Paris, Leyden, and Edinburgh. Among his colleagues he soon earned the reputation of being something of a rebel. Unlike most of the profession, he believed that all aspects of medicine were integrally connected, and that a physician should not prescribe for a disease unless he had an idea of how the body functioned. Dr. Jones and his friends, Dr. John Bard and Dr. Peter Middleton, were the first exponents in this country of the idea, stemming from Boerhaave, that both anatomy and pathology were requisites of a good medical training. As early as 1750 Jones, Bard, and Middleton got hold of the corpse of a criminal, injected dye into the blood stream, and laid out the organs for the instruction of their private students. This is the first recorded instance in America of teaching anatomy by actual dissection.

Dr. Jones is also remembered, along with the second Dr. Van Beuren, as a strong believer in the use of the Jenner cowpox to prevent smallpox. So uncertain were the aftereffects of the rude dosages then given that sometimes the preventive was as bad as the disease. As a result public sentiment against vaccination was strong, and during one interval Governor Clinton of New York forbade its use. But Dr. Jones, among other innovators, persisted, and even inoculated Washington's troops, apparently with success, for later he became personal physician both to the General and to Benjamin Franklin.

Dr. Jones was an almost eccentrically bluff man who scorned all show. He would not wear a wig or have his hair cut in a special professional manner. In those days the fashionable physician, following the English style, wore a powdered wig, a red satin or brocade coat, short breeches, buckled shoes, a three-cornered hat, and the indispensable gold-headed cane. The physicians of Paris were even more elaborately outfitted, and the dean of the Paris faculty affected an ermine cape. Colonial sentiment against these fripperies was especially strong in Boston, rather less so in New York.

In those days leading surgeons like Dr. Jones or Dr. Bard enjoyed a great deal of prestige in the community, and in their leisure characteristically turned their minds to other scientific pursuits, such as botany or astronomy, or explored the theoretical side of their own field. This was typical of the encyclopedic mentality of the times. Dr. Bard, for instance, was not content to abide by the convention then prevailing of treating a disease according to some all-inclusive principle. Returning to the ideas promulgated long before by Sydenham, he maintained that to understand and treat a disease its symptoms must be rigorously studied. Since Dr. Bard was New York's leading physician, and since he had gathered about him such vigorous personalities as Dr. Jones and Dr. Middleton, his word carried weight in the profession. Thus the trend toward enlightenment was kept alive.

Dr. Bard instructed his son Samuel in medicine, as was the custom of the time; then sent him abroad to study. The young man returned with glowing tales of medical instruction at the universities. In 1767 young Bard, backed by his father and his father's colleagues, Jones and Middleton, petitioned Governor Colden of New York for permission to open a medical school in New York City. In due course His Majesty George III "was graciously pleased to grant the said humble request of his said loving subjects." Shortly afterward the petitioners opened the doors of King's College Medical School; later—during the Revolutionary period—King's College was renamed Columbia College. This occurred just two years after the establishment of the Medical School of the College of Philadelphia, and almost fifteen years before Harvard Medical College was organized.

Samuel Bard, again aided by Jones and Middleton, also made an attempt to found a New York hospital in 1771. While under construction at Broadway and Pearl Street, the building burned to the ground, within view of the nearby almshouse. The project was particularly interesting because it followed the new pavilion plan for hospitals then coming into favor abroad.

The medieval hospital had been a vast and lofty hall, vaulted upon columns and well lighted. Later, to save space in crowded cities, hospitals were built several stories high around an inner court. This method made for poor light and ventilation. The Ospedale Maggiore at Milan, for example, had nine courts and accommodated 3,500 patients. The new pavilion plan, which came from France, visualized wards housed in wings of not over three stories, exposed to light and air on three sides, and connected by a continuous structure containing the administrative and other facilities.

Another influential figure of the early almshouse period was Dr. Richard Bayley, educated in London and Paris and esteemed abroad for his work in pathology. At Columbia Dr. Bayley established the first pathology laboratory in this country. An ardent Royalist, he fought on the British side during the Revolution, and remained a nonconformist and Tory sympathizer his life through. He was an impressive man, tall and patrician, who freely expressed his vitriolic contempt for popular fears and superstitions hindering the progress of knowledge.

When Dr. Bayley needed bodies for his anatomy classes, he went out and got them, although the possession of even the smallest part of a cadaver meant fine or imprisonment, and possibly lynching. It was Bayley who touched off New York's first important riot, the affair of the "Doctors' Mob."

Earlier, in 1763, the city had become greatly aroused when an attempt to snatch the body of a Negro hanged for rape was prevented by an aroused citizen. About the same time a Dr. Samuel Clossy was officially dissuaded, in view of the popular temper, from giving a private course of lectures on anatomy. In 1788 the free Negroes and slaves of New York had a petition drawn up begging the common council to stop doctors and students from digging up their dead. A few days later an ad appeared in a New York paper offering a $100 reward for the discovery or apprehension of body-snatchers who had removed a fresh corpse from Trinity Churchyard. The story grew in the telling. Rumors spread that pretty young girls were being incontinently dug up. Digging up Negroes was one thing, white bodies another. Excitement ran high.

Such was the situation one mild spring afternoon in 1788 when Professor Bayley was doing one of his masterful dissections before his class at Columbia. The students must have been completely absorbed, for one of them carelessly placed a disembodied arm on the window ledge to dry, and forgot all about it. Some boys playing in the street saw the grisly object and one of them climbed a ladder leaning against the wall to get a better look. Down the ladder he came, agog. Quickly the word spread that Dr. Bayley's students were making sport with human limbs.

Within an hour a mob had formed, stormed Bayley's laboratory, destroyed his priceless specimens of morbid anatomy, and collected assorted legs, arms, trunks, and entrails to give them proper burial. Then the mob went after more exciting game— the students, and the doctors who had led them into ghoulishness.

By the time Mayor Duane and the sheriff arrived, the mob had grown ugly. The sheriff spirited the students to the safety of the almshouse jail across the way and locked them in overnight. Meanwhile, Duane stayed to reason with the rioters, with apparent success. But by the following noon the mob had reformed and was in full cry. This time the rioters were out to destroy the whole medical profession. They found battering rams and stormed the jail, screaming, "Throw us the doctors!" Luckily the stout door held and the students fought them off at the windows. Mayor Duane called on the militia, but the mob was too strong for them.

Now there was no choice. The troop of regular soldiers garrisoning the city was ordered out. Advancing with fixed bayonets, they forced the insurgents back from the jail. In the action old Baron von Steuben was rolled in the dust and lost his famous temper. "Damn it, Duane," he cried, "fire! Then follow with the steel!" The troopers fired, and when the smoke settled, five men were dead and eight others wounded. The next afternoon the frightened young doctors were taken out to the country until the city quieted down.

The Doctors' Mob Affair attracted wide attention. From Paris, Thomas Jefferson wrote that he feared Europe would consider it proof that the Colonies were ruled by mobs and that it would weaken America's position on the Continent.

A year after the riot, an act was passed "to prevent the odious practice of digging up and removing for the purpose of dissection dead bodies interred in cemeteries or burial places." This blow to the teaching of medicine was somewhat softened when the legislators expressed the hope that "science might not be injured by preventing the dissection of proper subjects." But, despite legislation, New York City continued to be the most active body-snatching center in the United States. With the advent of railroads, some bodies were even exported to supply the wants of schools elsewhere. When John Collins Warren and his father opened their dissecting room in Boston in 1806, for a short time they were able to obtain an adequate supply of bodies for dissection from local sources. But as the number of medical schools increased throughout New England, the supply diminished, and the Warrens turned to New York for bodies "at a great expense of money and a great hazard of being discovered." The price for a New York cadaver was then $25.00.

As time went on the city's population, together with its production of unclaimed bodies, grew faster than the medical need for cadavers. In fifty years the situation was happily eased, as evidenced by a complaint made against Bellevue Hospital in 1848 by Alderman G. H. Burse. A certain Dr. Reese, the complaint said, was selling the bodies of dead patients as a sideline. The price for corpses was "fixed by said resident physician at $5.00." Such are the beneficent results of mass production.

· IV ·

PHYSICIAN AND BOTANIST

When, in 1816, the mayor, board of aldermen, and other city notables met at the opening exercises in the chapel of the Bellevue Establishment, they waxed eloquent and self-gratulatory over the new facilities, and no doubt actually believed them to be adequate for years to come. But, in truth, even on its opening day Bellevue's resources were hopelessly limited. Nearly two hundred patients were regularly crowded into the almshouse hospital; yet the staff consisted of only two visiting doctors and two interns.

The visiting physicians made it a rule to attend the hospital twice a week. Two interns were left on the scene to compound prescriptions, give postoperative care to surgical patients, and keep an eye on the whole installation. Even the prison was under the medical staff's supervision. Nevertheless, as always in the history of Bellevue, a few great medical personalities were on hand to carry the banner of progress. One of these was David Hosack (1769–1835), whose career was a landmark in American medicine at the time of the clipper ship during the mercantilist period.

A tall, robust man with piercing black eyes and a deep voice, David Hosack was virtually unique among his colleagues in having had a fine classical as well as a thorough medical education. He attended Columbia, was graduated from Princeton, and studied medicine in London. Later he became a pupil of Dr. John Bard and of Dr. Richard Bayley, principal in the first Doctors' Mob Affair. He was, in fact, studying under Dr. Bard when the disturbances occurred, and would have been killed by the mob while hurrying to the dissecting rooms to save whatever specimens remained, had not a friend of his father's, a Mr. Mount, dragged him to safety.

According to a contemporary, Dr. Hosack looked down on surgery and anatomy as inferior sciences, his chief interest being materica medica. This prejudice he implanted in all his pupils, none of whom, it was said, ever patiently and thoroughly dissected an arm or leg. However, while he was a visiting consultant at Bellevue, Dr. Hosack performed several remarkable operations, and much of his reputation, in actual fact, came from his surgical successes.

As early as 1795 Dr. Hosack experimented with the injection method of treating hydrocele, a serous, watery swelling of the lining of the testes. The treatment consisted of injecting irritating substances, probably either iodine or carbolic acid, thus promoting scarring and adhesion of the *tunica vaginalis*. The serum then no longer had room to collect. Needless to say, this procedure is no longer used, but it was a promising innovation in these early days.

Dr. Hosack's most celebrated surgical feat, however, and the first operation of its kind in America, was the ligation of the femoral artery for aneurysm, after Scarpa's method. This operation, carried out in 1808 at Bellevue, is worthy of mention, for surgery of the femoral artery even today can be a quite ticklish affair.

An aneurysm is a dilatation of a blood vessel, commonly an artery, caused when disease weakens the wall. The sac clots with blood and a tumorous mass forms. The problem is to restore the arterial flow either by excision of the bulge, or by the insertion of some object, say a fine wire, to ensure free passage.

Dr. Hosack proceeded in this fashion. First, to allay pain, he gave a hundred drops of laudanum. Then he cut into Scarpa's triangle in the midfront of the thigh, exposed Hunter's canal, and separated the aneurysmal artery from the vein and nerve. He then tied off the artery in two places about an inch apart above the aneurysm. This ligation of the third largest artery is the operation's memorable feature. It then appears that he boldly cut into the swelling, cleared it of obstructive matter, and somehow restored the arterial wall, by sewing or some alternative method. We are told that the patient—who must have been a remarkably vital person not to have his aneurysm aggravated by such drastic incision!—three months later was walking about.

Dr. Hosack's theory of medicine anticipated Hahnemann's homeopathic ideas. That is, he believed in presenting medicine in small doses. He frowned on the free use, so common in his day, of such poisonous drugs as mercury. Whereas most of his colleagues bled their patients on any excuse, he was cautious with his lancet. He combated fevers by cold washes, purgatives, and starvation. He was the first to point out the importance of the circulatory system in fever conditions. He noted the pathological changes in diphtheria and differentiated three stages in the disease.

Hosack's favorite treatment for the relief of angina pectoris was to have the patient inhale ether. He strongly supported vaccination, requiring it of his patients and the inmates of Bellevue Almshouse. He was among the first to insist upon the necessity of isolation in certain diseases. His attitude on contagion was largely responsible for the beginning of a strict system of quarantine at seaports, especially to guard against cholera.

Since David Hosack also played a tremendously important part in improving medical education in New York, it will be instructive to look back on what had been happening in the half-century since Drs. Bard, Jones, and Middleton received their charter for a school of medicine at King's College. This school, which had started so auspiciously, by the turn of the century was in a state of imminent collapse. In 1807 a group of doctors seeking to remedy this decline organized a new medical school, the College of Physicians and Surgeons. Six years later the newcomer absorbed the old medical school at King's, or Columbia College, as it had come to be called.

Valentine Seaman became the first professor of surgery at the College of Physicians and Surgeons, which was the direct precursor of the present Columbia University medical school. Samuel Bard, still active and vigorous, joined the faculty and later became the school's second president. David Hosack was appointed professor of surgery and midwifery. These men of the faculty of Physicians and Surgeons wrote the first really promising chapters in the history of medicine in America— and in Bellevue.

By any standards and in any age David Hosack would have been a remarkable man. In the New York of the early nineteenth century he was a colossus. Washington Irving said of him, ". . . Dr. Hosack, DeWitt Clinton, and Bishop Hobart are the tripod upon which our city stands."

He also had that faculty, typical among men destined to lead their fellows, of being at the right place at the right time. In 1794 when he was returning from his medical studies in London aboard the ship *Mohawk,* typhus struck among passengers and crew. Young Dr. Hosack, the only medical man on board, took over, and did not lose a single patient. The grateful passengers, one of whom was Thomas Law, brother of Lord Elinburgh, published an unsolicited vote of thanks in a New York daily newspaper. Not content with this passing show of gratitude, Law insisted on introducing young Hosack to his whole circle, which included General Alexander Hamilton and Aaron Burr. Presently Dr. Hosack was physician to both these prominent men. This association quickly proved to be both profitable and politic. Dr. Hosack's earnings from his first year's practice in New York amounted to about $1,500, a remarkable sum for a youthful and inexperienced doctor.

About this time Dr. Hosack attracted the notice of Dr. Samuel Bard. In short order Bard had placed the up-and-coming young physician in charge of his entire practice when he moved to the country for the summer. Hosack did so well that Dr. Bard proposed a partnership, looking to his own retirement from the profession. Just three years after hanging out his shingle Dr. Hosack found himself enjoying one of the largest and most remunerative practices in New York.

Once again lady luck smiled on the young Hosack. Scarlet fever had attacked several members of General Hamilton's family. Hamilton was summoned home from Philadelphia by an urgent letter informing him of the hopeless condition of one of his children. Riding most of the night, the General on arrival rushed to the child's sickroom to find his son, so it is recorded, perfectly well and in a sweet sleep. Who but Hosack could have cured the child—with a spirits of ammonia bath and a twenty-four-hour vigil at bedside?

After the death of Dr. Hosack's first wife, in 1797 he married Mary Eddy of Philadelphia. Nine children were born of this happy union, one of whom, Alexander, became a leading practitioner like his father.

The Hosacks' home became a mecca, we are told, for distinguished European visitors and Americans of note. Dr. John W. Francis, in his book of reminiscences of old New York, tells us that Dr. Hosack's "house was a resort of the learned and enlightened from every part of the world. No traveler from abroad rested satisfied without a personal interview with him."

Fine arts had a fascination for this man of catholic interests, and he was among the founders of the American Academy of Art to which Rembrandt Peale, Stuart, and Trumbull belonged, and which in 1828 became the National Academy of Design. He encouraged the inventor-artist Samuel F. B. Morse by commissioning anatomical paintings for anatomy classes.

All his life he kept up an association with DeWitt Clinton, a onetime Columbia classmate, and served his friend in a medical capacity.

In Thomas A. Emmett, brilliant Irish lawyer and cousin to the great patriot Robert Emmett, Hosack had a powerful friend who stood by him all through his troubled later years. Hosack was also one of the very few who found nothing to laugh at in "Fulton's Folly." As close friend and physician, he gave the inventor every encouragement. Washington Irving, William Cullen Bryant, Fenimore Cooper, and the poet Halleck regularly attended the Saturday night soirées at the Hosacks'.

A young student visting in New York in 1828 had this to say about one of these elegant gatherings:

> I was surprised to find a large assembly of gentlemen and ladies, the former including eminent artists, scientists, and authors, to whom I was presented by the host. Supper was served in a spacious dining room at fifteen minutes of eleven o'clock. The menu embraced every available delicacy and the wines were the best quality. The conversation most animated. It was after midnight when the party separated.

Dr. Hosack was one of the founders in 1804 of the New York Historical Society, of which he served as president from 1820 to 1828. Yet with all his associations with the great and near-great, his closest friend was Philip Hone, the honest and witty ex-auctioneer who became the gentleman mayor of New York in 1826.

Though Dr. Francis' description emphasizes Dr. Hosack's gentleness and charm, Dr. Hosack was far from unrealistic. He was called to attend both Hamilton and Burr on the occasion of the famous duel across the Hudson, and when the affair was over, accompanied the wounded Hamilton to his home. His subsequent administrations to the dying general made him late for one of his Saturday evening soirées. "It were as well had Burr also received a ball," he said to the company that evening, "for both were dangerously ambitious men and badly needed silencing. However, it matters little except that I am late for supper." This comment, incidentally, may have been apocryphal, for a few years later it was Dr. Hosack who lent Burr the money to flee the country.

Dr. Hosack's parents died about the beginning of the nineteenth century, and left him with more means than he knew what to do with. With his legacy he purchased and established the Elgin Botanical Gardens, the first in America, and a monument to his passionate interest in materia medica. When Hosack went abroad, he was chagrined to find how little he knew of the rapidly advancing science of botany, the field in which the theory of evolution was then being anticipated. In Sweden he obtained duplicate specimens from Linnaeus' herbarium and brought them back to New York.

The Elgin Gardens, according to the *New York Times*, were "situated on the middle road, now Fifth Avenue, between Bloomingdale and Highbridge, and a distance from the city of three and one-half miles." Hosack paid $5,000 for the twenty-acre tract, which extended roughly from what is now Forty-first Street to Fifty-first Street, bounded east and west by Fifth and Sixth avenues. Between Fiftieth and Fifty-first streets he built a country cottage, hothouses, and an administrative hall for scientific meetings.

In what today is the very heart of Manhattan, he planted a garden containing 2,000 plants, including everything from catnip and potato tansy to date plum, Malabar plum, walnut, garlic, and camomile. In proper season he fed his students strawberries, which cost $5.00 a box. In the course of time no less than sixteen species of plants were enrolled in botanical nomenclature in the genus *Hosackia*.

The expense of maintaining this immense collection began to drain Hosack, and he appealed to the state to buy the property. He wrote later:

> Finding my expenses for these several purposes and outlays far exceeded the calculations I had formed, and that these

expenses were more than prudence would justify, especially
with an increasing family of children, and being still desirous
of perpetuating the benefits of the institution, I at once
resolved to offer it to the state at a fair and equitable
valuation.

Undoubtedly he could have sold off the property in city lots,
but by holding off until it was taken as a single parcel he made
real estate history of vast benefit to others.

Upon the suggestion of friends, he made one more application to the state, and this time the bill went through. But when
settlement was made, even though the appraisal had been made
for something in excess of $103,000, Hosack received less than
$75,000.

The garden gradually deteriorated owing to the failure of
the state to provide sufficient funds for its maintenance. Some
years later the state granted the property to Columbia College,
and for a long period of time the land was a drain upon the
slender resources of that institution. In 1857 Columbia sold
a strip to the Dutch Reformed Church, and in 1906–7, the entire
block bounded by Forty-seventh and Forty-eighth streets and
Fifth and Sixth Avenues. However, Columbia held onto the
remainder of the tract, and in 1929 it was leased for the development of Rockefeller Center. Its value today is in excess
of $100,000,000.

· V ·

DR. HOSACK EMBATTLED

As we have indicated earlier, one of the most serious public health problems in Dr. Hosack's day was recurrent epidemics of yellow fever. This virus scourge, in the early days of the Republic, killed more people than all other ailments combined and created a great deal of bitter controversy in medical circles.

In the spring of 1819 a French ship from Martinique arrived in New York with several crew members prostrated by the disease. The vessel was promptly quarantined and kept anchored off Governors Island for the prescribed twenty-four days. At the end of this period the quarantine officer inspected the ship and found the captain dead. Shortly after, the quarantine officer himself, together with five of his staff, came down with the fever, and in a few days all were dead. This was characteristic of the virulent infectiousness of the malady, and the complete inability of the medical profession to combat it.

The deadly affliction spread to the city and settled in the same slum area where the Great Plague of 1795 had started. This section was a huddle of dilapidated shacks on the west side of Old Slip at the tip of Manhattan near South Street. Here the poorest people were housed. The ground was low and marshy, and the city's main sewer emptied into the river nearby. At low tide, river muck and sewage bubbled gaseously in the sun. So powerful a stench rose from these hideous deposits that the tenement-dwellers of Old Slip, inured as they were to unpleasantness, boarded up windows facing the river.

Actually, of course, it was the *Aëdes* mosquito that was the key offender in spreading the disease, and this vector was completely unsuspected. But a gross lack of hygiene made for increased susceptibility, and so it was at least a constructive move when Dr. Hosack insisted that the people of the Old Slip section be evacuated to Fort Richmond on Long Island. A jerry-built hospital for fever victims was thrown up at Fort Stevens, near Hell Gate, and placed under the supervision of Bellevue physicians. These doctors, despite the overload of work throughout the city, managed to visit it at least twice a week.

But then, within a matter of days, Dr. Hosack and his weary colleagues were faced with an entirely different epidemic crisis. Typhus, a lice-borne rickettsia disease in which—unlike yellow fever—personal hygiene and domestic cleanliness are of basic importance, broke out in the already panic-stricken city. That one summer 1,850 cases were reported. Bellevue bulged at the seams. Patients were admitted and died before they could be taken to the wards. Coffins were stacked ready in the corridors.

In at least one case, that of Joe Young, a colored man in Ward Five, the orderlies behaved with unseemly haste. A Bellevue physician, John Ridder, wrote in his diary:

> As I passed a shuttered coffin I heard a most horrible groan. In these surroundings of pestilence and death it was as much as the mind could bear. My friend and I prized up the lid and found there a man still quick with life, although most pitifully wasted by the fever.

Thereafter began a practice that has ever since obtained at Bellevue: the orderlies were told to move no moribund patients from the wards until a physician had officially declared them dead.

Dr. Hosack strove with might and main to keep the combined epidemics from decimating the city. He bombarded the council with demands for a general cleanup. Among other innovations, he urgently recommended the filling in of the city's countless cesspools, and the installation of public sewerage and water systems. Despite personal associations with the principals of the enterprise, he excoriated the Manhattan Company of Burr and Hamilton for its failure to provide the water it had so confidently promised. He drew up a plan for rigid quarantine inspection and isolation, and forced the council to consider it.

In the process he learned the painful lesson driven home to so many other Bellevue men in the ensuing years—that you cannot fight City Hall. Once the danger had subsided, the politicians reneged on many promises made under stress. Disillusioned, Hosack gladly returned to his teaching duties at Physicians and Surgeons.

Hosack was one of the first and most ardent advocates of medical ethics. Although his style is somewhat stiff by our standards, his advice to young medical students, as it appeared in the *Journal of the Medical Society of New York,* is still sound:

> Continue to study medicine all your lives. Add to your present acquirements a knowledge of the improvements medicine is daily receiving. To omit such opportunities of improvement, thereby depriving the sick of the benefits that would be derived from such researches, cannot be considered from any other point of view than a critical neglect of duty.

Dr. Hosack's teaching career was not without its trials, and more than once he had occasion to draw heavily on his reserves of moral strength. For some years jealousy had been building up among the non-teaching doctors of the city; that is, among those who either could not obtain teaching posts at the College of Physicians and Surgeons, or who had been dropped from the faculty for one reason or another. The members of this disgruntled faction were able to enlist the college trustees on their side. When the trustees submitted a scathing report on Physicians and Surgeons to the Board of Regents, the faculty became so incensed that they replied with a report of their own. This memorable report appeared in 1826, and was signed by David Hosack, Wright Post, William J. MacNevan, Valentine Mott, and John W. Francis—the flower of New York's medical profession.

This interesting document clearly reveals the confused state of medical education in the early 1800's. It said, in part:

> . . . the number of students has diminished nearly one-fourth this session and the mortifying fact is fled over by the Trustees without explanation. They cannot charge it against the Professors, for these are the same men with whom the college lately flourished, and as yet they have in no wise relaxed in assiduity, declined in reputation nor lost any portion of their credit with the votaries of the physic.
>
> The fault does not lie at their door—it is solely the result of the mischievous intermeddling of the Trustees, of their assuming powers beyond what is allowed them and falling of consequence into personal altercations with students. During some of these dissensions they have attempted to make students confess against themselves, and others were asked to inform against their comrades which, if any has been seduced to do, would probably among young men of their age and spirits be followed by duels and bloodshed.
>
> We cannot obey two masters. To you, the Regents, we pay a willing obedience but have an invincible aversion to being controlled by the present agitators or their abettors on the Board of Trustees.
>
> As the income of the college is derived from students, the Regents will have the goodness to observe that every calculation founded upon that resource is at best uncertain and already is rapidly diminishing and must, under the continued attacks of the present Trustees, shortly cease altogether. With the decrease of students will also fall the earnings of the Professors so that the plan of finance first suggested by the Treasurer of paying the current expenses and debts of the college in great part out of their emoluments is very unsubstantial. It appears to the Professors to possess so little solidity that they have come to the firm determination of calling in immediately the monies that are due to them before the college property by age, dilapidation or other misfortune shall fall any further in value.
>
> Motion for referring their application for repayment of

this debt to a committee was negatived by the Trustees so that they have no more hope from that quarter. The most welcome settlement to the Professors would be an immediate repayment of the debt, but if this be not practicable, they are willing that skillful and indifferent persons shall value the estate and they will accept such valuation.

The professors' claims against the school amounted to over $30,000. They were finally settled in 1830 by the payment of only $13,000.

In the *New York American* of March 4, 1826, a Mr. Spence gave a further report to the state senate. He stated that the trustees had run the college into debt by mismanagement, and had violated the orders of the Regents since they "created cabals among other physicians of the city . . ." He recommended that the trustees be removed and the charter of the college be revised.

The editor of the *American* commented on Spence's report:

If, as the report states, the Trustees seem to be placed in the institution for no earthly purpose but to superintend funds to which they in no way contribute, and to recommend pupils whom they do not instruct, it certainly becomes an imperative duty of the legislature forthwith to reorganize the establishment.

The professors' next communication to the Board of Regents is dated April 11, 1826:

We, the undersigned Professors and Officers of the College of Physicians and Surgeons in the City of New York . . . are fully persuaded that we best consult our self-interests by withdrawing altogether from the institution.

The plot thickened when, in the *New York Evening Post* of August 8, 1826, this advertisement appeared:

The late professors of Physicians and Surgeons having seen fit to withdraw from that institution, without thereby intending to relinquish their accustomed functions, have organized another medical college in which all but two of the former faculty take part, and the remaining vacancies were filled by gentlemen of distinguished fame and acknowledged ability.

The officers of this new college were David Hosack, president; Samuel L. Mitchill, vice-president; Peter S. Townsend, registrar; and the professors were David Hosack, Professor of the Institute and Practice of Physical Medicine; William James MacNevan, Professor of Therapeutics and Materia Medica; Valentine Mott, Professor of Surgery; John W. Francis, Professor of Obstetrics and Forensic Medicine; John D. Goodman, Professor of Anatomy and Physiology.

It was further announced in the October 1 issue of the *New York Spectator* that the new school had become affiliated with Rutgers College of New Brunswick, New Jersey, and that a new building had been erected for the school on Duane Street across from New York Hospital.

Alexander H. Stevens was one of the few well-known men who remained on the faculty of Physicians and Surgeons. Despite the enmity between the two groups of doctors, Stevens seems to have remained a good friend of Dr. Hosack's, for he was in attendance at the latter's death. Stevens afterwards became a leader in the American Medical Association and was one of its early presidents.

The new Rutgers College Medical School soon affiliated with the College of Geneva of New York in order to strengthen its position with the state legislature. This should have ended the matter, but the trustees of Physicians and Surgeons were unwilling to forgive or forget. They and their following in the profession held numerous protest meetings and kept the state legislature in a ferment with their claims that the new school violated the laws of New York, and that as a consequence its degrees were not valid.

In an unprecedented move Dr. Hosack retained the services of his friend Thomas A. Emmett, the famous Irish lawyer, and in November of 1827 the following note appeared in the *New York Evening Post*:

To the public: As attempts have been made on the validity of the degrees of Rutgers Medical faculty of Geneva College, it is deemed sufficient to submit to the public this following opinion of eminent counsel.

"We have deliberately examined the charter of Geneva College and the acts relating to the different colleges in this State, and have no hesitation in saying that diplomas granted by Geneva College to those who shall study medicine with Rutgers Medical Faculty of that College are good, effective, and valid to every purpose for which a medical degree is legally requisite, and equal to that of any medical college in this State." *Signed* Thomas A. Emmett and J. O. Hoffman.

But even the great Irish advocate could not turn the tide. The legislature, under intense pressure from the group of doctors who had started the row, declared Rutgers' degrees null and void. Sadly the medical faculty of Geneva College issued the following statement, which was signed by Drs. Hosack, Mott, and Francis:

> The undersigned late professors in the Rutgers Medical Faculty of Geneva College, in answer to numerous inquiries both epistolary and verbal, announce that they have resolved to suspend for the present the exercise of their collegiate duties as Professors in the different departments of medical science, unwilling to controvene the laws of the State or the decisions of its courts, which have recently declared the Geneva College does not possess the power of establishing a medical faculty in the city of New York.
>
> Let it suffice that more than two thousand pupils have been educated under their care and direction during their entire collegiate labor, but the authorities of the State, which, right or wrong, they are bound to obey, having seen proper to deny them protection in order to sustain a monopoly, and to prevent by legislature that competition so necessary to the free development of talent, they now withdraw from the task of official and public instruction, wishing to those who come after them all the success they may merit, unimpeded by those envious arts which may interfere with their usefulness.

Thus, a narrow little group of men by their willful jealousy almost destroyed some of the greatest medical figures of the age. The bitter result of the struggle was to reduce the College of Physicians and Surgeons from the leading American medical school to a pitifully third-rate affair. Not for more than a generation did medical education in New York regain its prestige.

There was a revealing aftermath which placed the disgruntled doctors in an even more unfavorable light. In 1849 there appeared a remarkable little pamphlet titled *The History of the New York Kappa Lambda Conspiracy.* In it the anonymous author presented some convincing proof of the existence of a secret medical society devoted to furthering the advancement of its members over outside physicians in every way. It quoted the *American Lancet* of October 18, 1830, as denouncing this secret club and named some of its members. From the College of Physicians and Surgeons: Drs. Alexander Stevens, Edward Delafield, John Watts, J. M. Smith, and John Beck. Of the doctors who did not teach at the college, the following were named: Drs. Daring, Ludlow, Moore, Cheseman, Ives, Paine, G. Smith, Rodgers, Hoffman, Johnson, and Kissan. All of these were prominent men of the day.

Dr. Beck and Dr. Ludlow brought suit against the *Lancet* but the jury threw their libel claims out of court.

The pamphlet reveals that an investigation by the New York Medical Society at the request of Dr. Hosack and Dr. Francis showed beyond a doubt that the secret organization did exist and that there were no medical qualifications for membership. It embraced men prominent in the city council, as well as four professors and two-thirds of the trustees of Physicians and Surgeons, eight surgeons of the New York Hospital, four of the five doctors from the New York Dispensary, and seven of the nine physicians from the Lying-In Hospital.

After the imbroglio resulting from the split in the faculty of Physicians and Surgeons, more than ever Dr. Hosack was a marked man in the public eye, and every move he made aroused comment. Such was the case when, after his second wife's death, he married a wealthy Philadelphia widow.

There was also much adverse and caustic criticism, particularly about his botanical venture, but at least a part of the press took his side. One Sunday supplement devoted to thumb-nail sketches of New York's rich and prominent citizens summed up his career in a way that pretty much stands the test of time:

But few names will shine in the annals of medical history brighter than Dr. Hosack's. Whatever may be said about his foibles as a man, his superior practical talent, sagacity, bold-ness, and decision as a bedside practitioner and the invalu-able lessons he has left will live forever while truth and com-mon sense prevail. He was a man reckless and extravagant in money affairs, and as he often said, his embarrassments were perpetually bringing him to the verge of bankruptcy.

In later years, happily or unhappily for him, a sudden flow of wealth poured profusely into his lap by his marriage with the rich widow of Henry A. Costloff, by which he real-ized the immediate possession of over a half a million of personal property alone that nearly turned and intoxicated his excitable brain and impetuous temperament. Converting that and portions of a large estate come from Mrs. Costloff into new purchases in his own name, he hoped to give a solid and permanent basis to the opulence from which he naturally and modestly designed to enrich his own children by a former wife.

At Hyde Park he laid out his lawns and grounds with a luxuriousness that surpassed the English gentry, and spared no expense transplanting full-grown trees from the side of mountains to form a ready-made forest of scenery upon his own plantation.

Together with this property he made large investments in insurance stocks, but in his avidity to become a Croesus it seemed as if an evil star would rob him of all. The dreadful conflagration that laid waste 600 houses in one night swal-lowed up nearly every insurance agency in the city. The shock caused apoplexy and he perished, and since his death the terrible depression has left his own children with but a few thousand, barely enough to support them, and even much of that has been melted away.

So much for a self-made man whose father was a humble redemptioner that worked out his apprenticeship in the Roosevelt family, and became rich and richly endowed his favorite son, David, and then set him up in practice by pur-chasing out Dr. Samuel Bard. But for David's marriage with a widow of extreme wealth, he would have been now and for years hence at the head of his profession and of eminent use-fulness, all of which was arrested by the influence of gold.

Dr. Hosack was not a great contributor to medical science; he was a great practitioner. But that he was a genuine exponent of the scientific method may be inferred from his famous statement that "principles of the medical practice must be gained through accurate observations, judicious experiment, and cautious induction from the facts which they present." Of this credo Dr. William Welch, the great Bellevue pathologist of the nineteenth century, once said, "We can add nothing more, and nothing better, today."

· VI ·

PROGRESS OUT OF PESTILENCE

Among the many pandemic diseases which have swept in waves over the face of the earth Asiatic cholera is of comparatively recent date. Typhus, smallpox, yellow fever, dysentery, and the Black Death have very ancient historic records. The Black Death (bubonic or pneumonic plagues) is mentioned by Rufus of Ephesus as widespread in Syria, Egypt, and Libya in the second century A.D., and its recurrence throughout the Middle Ages is a matter of detailed record.

The first historic mention of Asiatic cholera, by a Portuguese who spoke of the disease as "the worst kind of flux," goes back only to 1517. The disease is caused by a comma-shaped microorganism of a bacterial nature called the *Vibrio comma*. Cholera victims suffer from great prostration. They waste away under the effects of an intense diarrhea, uncontrollably passing watery, rice-type stools. They also quickly take on a characteristic livid, pinched expression, which is unmistakable not only to doctors but to all those who have even had contact with the affliction.

In any event, after long quiescence a wave of cholera began in India in the early part of the nineteenth century, traveled all over Asia and Africa, then went underground. But suddenly, after a six-year lapse, the disease awoke to renewal activity and swiftly moved as far afield as Britain in the west and Japan in the east, and so quickly back to India, the original source. About 1832 the western phase of the epidemic reached New York.

43

The advent of cholera had been fearfully anticipated by the medical profession of New York. They had begged for hospitals to be set up in strategic locations. But the city administration, as usual, dragged its feet. The politicians were callous to disease and all alarms and excursions connected with it. For half a century as many people as could afford to had been leaving the city during the summer to escape epidemics of one kind or another. In the warm months business as a matter of course slowed down to a walk, and trade and shipping were in good measure suspended. Now the aldermen were warned that cholera was imminent. This information evoked yawns and calculated indifference.

When the first cases were reported, the city fathers initially pressured the board of health into declaring the symptoms indicative of nothing more serious than diarrhea, or summer complaint. But *Vibrio comma* was not to be denied by mere wishful thinking. More and more deaths occurred daily, and the board of health was forced to establish emergency hospitals. But after this had been done, the people refused to have their sick go to them on the grounds that the board of health was totally incompetent. The situation became so grave that on Friday, August 13, 1832, by order of the mayor the city observed a "day of humiliation and prayer."

Meanwhile, between June 27 and July 7, 1832, 555 cases of cholera had been admitted to Bellevue, and 334 of them had died by August 8. The stricken lay on the floors, crying for water. Often there were as many as 40 bodies at a time in the deadhouse, as the morgue was long known. In all, Bellevue received 2,000 cases that summer, over a sixth of all the victims, and recorded 600 deaths.

At last the invasion of *Vibrio* ran its mysterious course, and once again the doctors compared, studied, deduced, and just plain guessed at a cause or cure. But they were stumped. They could do no more than subscribe to the innocuous findings that appeared in an international booklet signed by leading American and European physicians of the day. As preventive measures the booklet advised ". . . regularity in meals, in exercise, in all the affairs of life; and a tranquil and happy mind. Keep the feet warm and dry and at all costs avoid the night air."

Boerhaave had said the same thing more succinctly a hundred years earlier. When the great Dutch doctor died in 1739, he left an elaborately bound volume with a note announcing that it contained the world's sum total of medical knowledge. All the pages in this volume were blank except one on which Boerhaave had written in his fine, backward-sloping script: "Keep the head cool, the feet warm, and the bowels open."

With the end of the pestilence the fortunes of both the medical profession and of Bellevue Establishment went into a marked decline. The cholera epidemic ushered in fifteen years of corruption and frustration for doctors and institutions alike.

The city council of this period became known as the "City Stepfathers" and the "Forty Thieves." They did their best to live up to these epithets. Among other things, they appropriated a strip of almshouse land west of First Avenue and another below Twenty-sixth Street, which they caused to be sold at auction and, through dummies, bought for themselves at ridiculously low prices. Physicians' groups protested and offered to purchase the land at a fair price that they might build a medical school on it. To this proposal the politicians turned a deaf ear.

At Bellevue the post of resident physician was repeatedly filled by incompetent political appointees. Bellevue employees followed the corrupt example set from above. Cows and chickens ceased to exist at the Almshouse. Either supplies were sold or the purchase money pocketed. Hospital property was exchanged for liquor by both inmates and employees. All that kept the Establishment from being sold off stone by stone was death itself. The mortality rate became so staggeringly high that the newspapers smelled a lurid story. The resultant clamor frightened the politicians into appointing a commission to investigate.

The commission's report to the board of aldermen was the famous "Record No. 32," and it was as damning as words could make it:

> The female part was found in good order, furnishing a silent rebuke to the contrast in the other parts of the building. The adult males were in filthy and ragged condition. The sick were in every part of the house, and, with the above exception, the whole department exhibited evidence of neglect of the public interest and want of a proper regard to the subjects of misfortune.
>
> Complaints of poor and scanty provisions, and of unheeded applications for relief were numerous and voluntary. Many were without shirts and destitute of sheets and blankets, and such bedding as there was was not clean. In the building assigned to colored subjects was an exhibition of misery and its concomitants never witnessed by your commissioners, nor in any public receptacle for even the most abandoned dregs of human society. Here were scenes of neglect and filth, of putrefaction and vermin.
>
> Of system or subordination there was none. The same apparel and the same bedding had been alternately used by the sick and dying, the convalescent, and those in health; and that, for a long period. The situation in one room was such as would have created contagion when the warm season came on. The air seemingly carried poison with every breath.

The steward of this house had been a hungry villain. The commissioners found but few provisions left—no meal or flour or potatoes, and very little rice. No coal and little wood remained. The carpenters and tinsmiths, the spinners and weavers, all were idle because no materials were at hand to work with. The farm was neglected, and there was no straw and very little hay, no oats or any other grain. The cattle were lean and ill-favored. All swine and poultry were claimed by the officers as their private property.

There were 265 patients in the wards of the hospital, over half of them psychotics. These people were unconscionably neglected. All the buildings, from cellar to garret, abounded in filth. The lack of proper ventilation deprived the wretched inmates even of fresh air. The seriously ill were without "garments used next to skin," and females in a high state of fever were found with nothing but a blanket to cover them.

Benjamin Ogden, who had served previously as head of Bellevue, was asked to return, and accepted the challenge. Dr. Ogden took charge on Friday, May 12, 1837, and in his report he gives his side of the story. He tells how the night before his arrival eight nurses and servants had gone off without permission, leaving the sick to provide for themselves as best they might. He then goes on to say:

> . . . the whole concern was filled with typhus from top to bottom. They [the patients] were lying in their filthy blankets, destitute of sheets and pillow cases, and in some chronic cases, they had not had a change for three months. Requisition had been made by my predecessor again and again, but no notice had been taken of it. No clothing for the patients—not a change was to be found—and there had not been any Indian meal nor poultices for three weeks, and no rags to dress the wounds.

The report caused a sensation in the newspapers. The aldermen made speeches blaming the authorities at the Almshouse for the sorry state of affairs, and did nothing whatever to correct them.

These lamentable conditions persisted until 1847 when, as usual, a catastrophe forced the politicians to act. Another typhus epidemic, again journalistically remembered as the "Great Epidemic," struck the city. In June alone sixty to eighty victims were brought daily to Bellevue—in buggies, wagons, wheelbarrows, and pushcarts. The Army pitched eighty tents on the grounds and the patients in them did better than in the fetid wards of the hospital itself.

Doctors from the city and medical students volunteered to live in the hospital and help out. They paid high for their dedication. Within thirty days nine of them were dead.

Public reaction seemed destined to follow the pattern characteristic of all the previous epidemics: first panic and frantic pleas to the doctors to "do something"; then, as the onslaught slackened, a return to apathy. But now, for the first time in Bellevue Establishment's brief history, appeared a man who would not be downed by social and political inertia.

Dr. James R. (Jimmy) Wood was then in his thirty-fifth year. He was a great physician—but he was also a man with enough political acumen to deal with City Hall on its own harsh terms. In addition, he loved Bellevue and was determined to make it the best hospital in the land.

Almost singlehandedly he forced the board of aldermen to appoint another investigating body, and kept the public health issue alive until their recommendations were carried out. Perhaps the most important of the innovations backed by the forceful Dr. Wood—a board of visiting physicians and surgeons was placed in charge of the hospital. Their names are all famous in the early history of New York medicine: John W. Francis, Valentine Mott, Alexander Vaché, Willard Parker, William Van Buren, Alonzo Clark, F. Campbell Stewart, Alexander Stevens. And, of course, Dr. Jimmy Wood.

These men were finally able to separate Bellevue from the Almshouse. They opened the hospital to medical students, who were permitted to accompany physicians and surgeons on their rounds. They reduced the death rate from 30 to 9 per cent. It was they who initiated the teaching and clinical tradition at Bellevue which, in later times and on into the present, had made this hospital unique.

The most important result growing out of the transfer of the hospital to a new medical administration was the board's decision to set up a teaching program. Promoting this innovation was a task made for Dr. Wood. He began his campaign by judicious "plants" in the press. A statement in the *Evening Post* suggested that repeated offers had been made to open Bellevue's stores of knowledge to the city, but the administration had turned thumbs down. A little later another article appeared in the *New York Journal of Medicine* which said, in part:

Bellevue Hospital with its one thousand patients must be made accessible to students of medicine and that, too, without delay. It's a crying shame that such a wide field for clinical instruction should be lost to the city, to science, and to the world, merely to subserve paltry party political purposes, to give to some favorite a monopoly of private teaching in that great establishment.

Having set the stage by these and other clandestine means, Jimmy Wood went to City Hall, and just one year after the Medical Board had taken over the hospital, Wood had an amphitheatre where he could really undertake a teaching program. On Friday, March 2, 1849, Dr. William Van Buren, before thirty students, held the first public clinic, where he performed a brilliant operation for bladder stone. On this occasion Dr. Wood was quoted by the *Evening Post* as being "very grateful to our honorable Mayor and to the Board of Aldermen without whose generosity and loyal support the amphitheatre could never have come into being."

· VII ·

ORGANIZER AND PATHOLOGIST

By 1850, when he had reached thirty-seven, Dr. Jimmy Wood had established a benevolent despotism at Bellevue. He had so mesmerized City Hall that the council had agreed to abolish the office of governor of the Almshouse, a valuable political plum of many years' standing, and to establish an elective hospital board of governors. The first governors were men of experience and of distinction, among them William T. Pinckney, Simeon Draper, and Francis Tillou. They immediately undertook a study of hospital management at home and abroad, from which many improvements eventually resulted.

Dr. Wood had a passion for detail, plus a conviction that if a job had to be done, he could probably do it better than the next man. In a short time he knew more about the organization of the hospital than anybody on the board. Soon he became the actual head to whom decisions affecting the institution's ever increasing affairs were naturally referred.

Dr. Wood's ultimate goal was to make Bellevue one of the world's great medical teaching centers. Looking around for help, he found it in Alonzo Clark. These two men, associated with Bellevue for many years, did more than any others to shape its future course.

For Dr. Clark, Bellevue was a magnificent laboratory for his microscopic studies and work in applied pathology. And for Dr.

Wood, who was to achieve international fame as a surgeon, the old hospital afforded a priceless opportunity for autopsy of patients dead from a wide variety of causes. These autopsies not only enabled him to plan future operations, but also established a precedent for checking diagnosis.

Wood and Clark shared the same dream. They were determined to transform this disorderly catchall for paupers, psychotics, and criminals into a great medical school.

Wood's first move in this direction was to charm City Hall, in 1857, into giving up its long political monopoly and to open Bellevue to all students of medicine. Next, he organized the hospital into three medical and two surgical house services. He hired and trained a woman to supervise the nurses, still "ten-day drunks" serving out sentences for inebriation often coupled with prostitution.

The first twelve interns were chosen by competitive examinations, for a period of eighteen months. With characteristic stinginess the city government had neglected to provide quarters for them. They were jammed together wherever the warden could find room for them, and given the same food as the almshouse prisoners.

The young students protested, and when their complaints went unanswered, took to baiting the warden unmercifully. The warden, a large, obtuse man who invited youthful challenge, retaliated by cutting the inadequate rations still further. One afternoon an intern was cleaning his pistol and, seeing one of the famous Bellevue cats passing in the hallway, took a shot at it. The warden was just behind the cat. Convinced that the ball was meant for him, he collared the intern and dragged him before the board, demanding his instant dismissal.

Mr. Simeon Draper, president of the board, read the young man a stern lecture and put him on probation. Later, Draper stopped the intern in the hallway. "I am convinced that you planned to bag that cat for the pot," he said. "If I were not, I should certainly have dismissed you for poor marksmanship in missing so fair a target as the warden."

Dr. Wood was determined, in the interest of furthering medical instruction, to make it easy and legal to obtain anatomical specimens, the lack of which was hampering every medical school in the land. For four years he fought to get a measure known as the "Bone Bill" through the state legislature. This bill was a direct "appeal to the people of the state of New York to legalize the dissection of the dead." It was finally passed in 1854, legalizing the dissection of the unclaimed paupers who died in the hospitals. At last the dead in the city's graveyards could sleep undisturbed, no longer troubled by nocturnal raids.

This measure was long overdue in the United States. England had already passed such a law some years before, although not without strong opposition in Parliament. Sir Astley Cooper had defended it dramatically, declaring, "Gentlemen, pass the bill or not, I will have the bodies that I need for dissection, for I hold in my hands the keys that would unlock any vault in your Kingdom!"

Two years later, in 1855, Dr. Wood presented to the mayor and the board of aldermen his prize specimens of morbid anatomy. Next, he used his persuasive powers with the board to tear down the disreputable old deadhouse and build a two-story pathology building, the second floor of which would make an excellent home for his collection.

Among Wood's rare specimens in pathological and comparative anatomy was an especially fine assortment of diseased bones, the equal of which could not be found either in this country or abroad. One of the specimens that brought Wood international notice was a diseased lower jaw which he himself had removed from a young German girl. This operation, at that period, was one of the greatest triumphs of American surgery.

When the girl entered Bellevue, her jaw was so badly infected that it was a month before Wood could operate. During the operation his chain saw broke. Wood grasped the bone with his forceps and tried to divide it, but found that there was no articulation. He was obliged to remove the entire right side of the jaw. The infection then spread to the left side and began to secrete "intolerably offensive pus." After waiting another month until the position of the new jaw was firmly fixed, Wood operated for the second time and removed the remainder of the affected bone. The moment the bone was divided, the central portion which still remained at the chin dropped off into the hand of his assistant, and in the ensuing excitement the girl swallowed her tongue. Wood grasped the tongue with forceps, pulled it out, and tied it to her cheek, thus saving her from suffocation.

Within a week new bone had formed and the contour of the face was back to normal. In time, the girl had an entirely new lower jaw, with only two almost invisible scars on her cheeks. This regeneration of the lower jaw was so admired by European surgeons that the president of the German Congress of Surgeons asked Wood to send specimens of bone reproductions to Berlin.

Wood was the first physician in New York to devote himself entirely to surgery, a luxury he could afford since he had private means. It was not until the eighties that a surgeon could support himself without relying to some degree on medical practice.

Dr. Henry Mann Silver, whose surgical career at Bellevue followed and overlapped Jimmy Wood's, tells us what the clinic was like when Wood operated in the early days:

> Wood would enter the amphitheatre wearing a black silk gown buttoned tightly about the neck and wrists. Over the left breast was a boutonniere of bright flowers. Accompanying him was his house surgeon wearing any old coat. In the buttonhole of Wood's left lapel were many well waxed silk ligatures, no special care having been taken where the silk and wax had been kept.
>
> On a side table was arranged a most elaborate display of highly polished instruments with beautifully turned ivory handles. If, during an operation, an instrument did not please Dr. Wood, he would hurl it to the floor and berate the maker,

should he happen to be present. The ether was administered by a junior assistant, from a cone improvised from a towel and a folded newspaper with a wad of absorbent cotton within. No special preparation of the surgeons, assistants, patient, instruments, or dressing was made for the operation.

A good part of Wood's fame rests on a nerve operation, the removal of Meckel's ganglion for the relief of *tic douloureux*. Prior to 1879 he had performed one-fourth of all operations of this delicate nature. Hundreds of doctors and students came to watch him. With an assistant holding a lantern just above the patient's head to light up the incision, the spectators filed past, each pausing to stare into the opening. For the first time in medical history they could see the superior maxillary nerve at its point of exit from the skull. As one of Wood's students said, "He extended operative surgery far beyond our grandest conception of its limits."

For twelve years Dr. Wood made haste slowly, always encouraging his students, by his own dynamic example, to practice close clinical observation, exchange ideas freely, and check preoperative diagnoses, when opportunity arose, by postoperative pathological examination, or autopsy. Always the final objective of making Bellevue a great teaching center lurked in the back of his mind. At long last, in 1860, on the eve of the Civil War, he set in motion what was to be a momentous chain of events.

On December 18 of that year, the first recorded suggestion for a new school of medicine appeared in the minutes of the Bellevue Medical Board. This suggestion stemmed directly from intensive behind-the-scenes campaigning by Dr. Wood and his progressive faction. "At the request of the Commissioners of Public Charities and Corrections," the minutes read, "'a committee from the Medical Board at Bellevue Hospital has been appointed to examine and report on the institutions under the control of the Commission."

Dr. Isaac E. Taylor, as chairman, and Dr. James R. Wood constituted a subcommittee and, in their report to the Board, pointed out that "it becomes an important question whether ere many days elapse Bellevue should have, nay ought to have, connected with it an established college for the education of young men, independent of a clinical hospital, thus making it one of the larger schools and hospitals united together."

Thanks to Wood's persuasive diplomacies, the commissioners granted the request for the new school, and gave permission to erect a college building on the hospital grounds. On April 2, 1861, ten members of the medical staff of Bellevue hospital were appointed for the first faculty. They are names to remember: Stephen Smith, Principles and Practice of Surgery; F. H. Hamilton, Surgery of Bones and Accidents; James R. Wood, Operative Surgery and Surgical Pathology; Alexander B. Mott, Surgical Anatomy; Louis A. Sayre, Orthopedic Surgery; L. E. Taylor, Fordyce Barker, and George E. Elliot, Obstetrics; W. B. McReady, Materia Medica and Therapeutics; and J. W. S. Gouley, Anatomy. The faculty was later completed by the appointment of the following men: Austin Flint, Principles and Practice of Medicine; Austin Flint, Jr., Physiology; R. O. Doremus, Chemistry and Toxicology.

It was at least a beginning.

While the doctors had concentrated on getting the medical setup straightened out, the physical facilities of the hospital continued to be in a sorry state. The following story appeared, 1860, in *Harper's Weekly*. It was briskly entitled "Rats in the Hospital."

> We give herewith a picture of the beds in Bellevue Hospital in this city, in one of which the newborn child of Mary Connor was bitten by rats on Monday morning, April 23. All the hospital authorities state the building is swarming with rats, as many as forty having been killed in the bathtub in one evening, and Mary Connor herself mentions that in her agony she felt them running over her body.
>
> The following is Dr. Alexander Haddon's account of what he is pleased to call the "unpleasant occurrence":
>
> "Mary Connor, an unmarried woman, aged 31 years, was

admitted to Bellevue Hospital Sunday afternoon. She stated
that she expected to be confined soon but could not specify
how soon. She had no pains and made no complaint. She
walked unassisted to the ward appropriated to women who
come here to wait for their confinement. The ward was occupied at the time by twenty other women patients, and by
the nurse who had charge of the ward.

"At six o'clock Monday morning, I was called by the nurse
to see the woman. I immediately went to the ward, found the
woman who was expected by the nurse to be soon confined, as
follows: lying on a bed between two other beds, not five feet
from either. Both beds were occupied by waiting women. I
asked of her condition. She stated she thought her child was
born. I immediately examined, and found the child beneath
the hips of the mother, in a lifeless condition, and mutilated,
apparently by rats. In the position the child was, life could
not have existed more than a few minutes. The mutilation
without doubt had occurred after the death of the child.

"She stated that she complained of feeling slightly ill to a
patient on her left, but thought she would be worse before
she was better and did not want the doctor sent for. She fell
asleep and was conscious at one time that something was
running over her, which she supposed to be a cat. She again
went to sleep, and, on waking, she was observed to be uneasy
by one of the women, who told the nurse. I was at once sent
for. The woman was not in a feebled condition when I first
saw her. (*Signed*) Alexander Haddon, Intern."

The new commissioners have taken up the matter. They
have work before them if they intend to do their duty. Not
only the rats, but the officials, need some sweeping out.

It was not entirely for lack of effort that such deplorable
degradations obtained at Bellevue. Society was not then ready
to support in decent measure a city hospital catering almost
entirely to very poor people. Nor, indeed, is it entirely ready
to do so today. The fact is, Dr. Jimmy Wood had a job on his
hands rivaling the labors of Hercules. He could not, with all
his will and energy, make equal advances in all directions. His
accomplishments lay not so much in providing custodial improvements for the patients, as for initiating long-range
improvements in the medical regime. Greedy political oppor-

tunists who had been milking Bellevue appropriations for years opposed him at every turn. And time and time again his own profession resisted forward-looking changes. But his purpose never faltered, and with the passage of the years his love of Bellevue only waxed stronger.

VIII

TWO MORE PATHFINDERS

Dr. James Rushmore Wood exemplifies the dawn of a much more hopeful and scientifically purposive phase in Bellevue's long growth. This change, in a wider sense, reflected the rapidly developing scientific grasp of the nineteenth century and the first glimmerings of a social consciousness. But before exploring the lives of doctors who brought this now imminent unfolding to bear on Bellevue, it is important to look back on two other great figures of the transitional period.

The first of these two somewhat older contemporaries of Dr. Wood was John Wakefield Francis; the second, Valentine Mott. Francis and Mott also contributed a great deal to the betterment of Bellevue. Like Wood, through example and persuasion and long hours given over to teaching, they did much to seal public acceptance of Bellevue as a true hospital and a clearinghouse for medical knowledge and experiment. In their careers we clearly see the emergence, from the crude and groping medical life of the eighteenth century, of a new attitude, a new climate of thought. Like Wood, they represent what might be called a stage of scientific premonition, a first glimpsing of the time of fruition when Pasteur, Lister, Koch, Roentgen, and other giants liberated medicine from its basic uncertainties.

John Wakefield Francis (1789–1861) was a physician of German and Swiss descent, born in New York. Throughout his medical career he was consulting physician at Bellevue. He taught materia medica at the College of Physicians and Surgeons, and was professor of obstetrics and medical jurisprudence at the short-lived Rutgers Medical College. He wrote several books, one quaintly called the *Anatomy of Drunkenness*, and collaborated with Dr. Hosack on a medical register.

But much more important than any of his strictly medical accomplishments and his years of work at the Bellevue Establishment was his ethical influence, his medical style. People interested him. He was at home in all walks of society and became the very prototype of the all-wise family doctor. His manner and presence elevated the profession in public estimate, and restored public confidence badly shaken by the repeated failure of medicine to cope with yellow fever, typhus, and smallpox. He was a genial force, bringing light and comfort wherever he went. And he loomed as a shining example of integrity in an age when the newspapers were filled with the ads of quacks and charlatans.

Dr. Francis studied under Hosack, and modeled himself on his gifted teacher. But he had a quality of compassion and a feeling of affection for common people which Hosack lacked. Dr. Francis was perfectly at home in the disreputable Five Points district, where the "Red Nag" gang and the "Bloody Bashers" held sway. In this depressed section of Manhattan abounding in thieves, gangsters, pimps, and paupers, Dr. Francis moved freely and made many friends. He doctored the children of the poor, gave them alms out of his own pocket, and often attended their weddings and funerals.

Dr. Francis belonged to the plague years. He watched his father die of yellow fever, and during the epidemic of 1798 was himself so ill from the disease that his coffin was brought into the room and made ready to receive his body. Years later he said of this incident to Valentine Mott, who was his lifelong friend, "I remember thinking at the time that my parents showed a

certain lack of confidence in my ability to conquer disease—
a feeling I sometimes unhappily discern in my patients today."

Dr. Francis revered Hosack, and after the latter's death continued the Hosack tradition of Saturday soirées. He once introduced Edgar Allan Poe to his guests as "My friend 'The Raven,'
down from his doortop to pick at crumbs with us." Poe wrote
of Francis in the *Ladies Book* in 1846, ". . . the most genial man
that can be conceived. His conversation is a sort of Roman
Punch made up of tragedy and the broadest of all possible
farce."

Like Hosack, Dr. Francis made himself a part of the artistic
life of New York. He appears among the celebrities of Gotham
in Halleck's play *Fanny*. And Rembrandt Peale insisted on
painting his portrait.

At the time of Charles Dickens' American lecture tour, Dr.
Francis, an ardent patriot, was incensed by the author's slurs
on his beloved country. When he was called to examine the
great man's sore throat to tell him whether he should speak
that night, he refused to go. Dickens' manager appealed to his
sense of duty as a physician, and reluctantly Francis consented
to make the call. "After all," he said, "if I could save Pug Mosley
[a triple murderer whose life Francis had saved] for hanging,
perhaps I can do the same for this fellow."

Mayor Andrew Mickle, a member of Francis' church, tells of
meeting the little physician on the church steps and hearing
him mutter in great annoyance to himself. It seems that one of
his best patients had just been delivered of a baby, and Francis
had not even suspected the pregnancy. He had been out of
reach at his favorite coffeehouse, the Bread and Cheese Club,
when the belated summons came. Another doctor in the neigh-
borhood had delivered the child. Francis expressed himself
explosively:

> It's the cursed hoopskirts! There was a time when I could
> look around me in the church and form some idea of what
> my income might be during the year, but now since these

monstrosities have become the fashion I can no longer judge the condition of the women—to say nothing of their conformity, which used to so please me. When my services are needed I sit gossiping over a pot of ale, while some young breakbones collects my rightful fee.

Dr. John Roosa, in *The Old Hospital and Other Papers,* relates how on one occasion Dr. Francis sent his annual bill though he had not visited the house professionally during the entire year. The bill was paid promptly, but when the head of the family met Dr. Francis he remarked, "Doctor, I got your bill the other day, but I don't remember that any of us has been sick this year." "Very likely not," the bluff physician retorted, "but I stopped several times at the gate and inquired of the servants how all of you were."

Dr. Francis loved to write. His papers cover a wide range of subjects, from accounts of the New York Historical Society's early days to pen portraits of his fellow physicians. He made such a reputation as a writer that he was offered $10,000 for his autobiography. His writing was as pithy and straightforward as the man. The following excerpt was addressed, on the eve of the Civil War, to his Bellevue students:

> It is fortunate, gentlemen, that here at the Bellevue and Almshouse Establishments you will never lack of cases of every form and type of disorder, and subjects of surgical appliance too numerous for specification. New York is not only the city of excess in taxation but she is the place of the ample provision for the acquisition of knowledge in almost every department of human pursuit.
> . . . I need not give assurance to you and to the scholar who aims at linguistic studies that upward of eighty different tongues or languages may be heard in our cosmopolitan residence, an index that in the types or forms of disease, she is not less remarkable. I leave you to draw the inference.

Of autopsies, he wrote:

> When, as a priest of medical science, you enter the temple once inhabited by a human soul, let the proceeding be decorous, mar no more than you are required to do, and when you retire, leave as few traces as may be of your presence.

As a medical man, Francis, following Valentine Mott's example, inaugurated clinical lectures at Bellevue which marked the real beginning of Bellevue as a teaching center. He was also one of the founders of the New York Academy of Medicine, of which he was president for two separate terms.

Dr. Marshall Hall pronounced Francis the most representative physician of the generation. He died, as quaintly and puckishly as he had lived, of an infected carbuncle.

When Valentine Mott was appointed consulting surgeon on Dr. Wood's newly organized Medical Board of Bellevue in 1847, he was sixty-two years old and at the height of his fame. A large, aloof man in black coat and white neckcloth, his skill, high fees—sometimes as much as $1,000 for an operation—and social position were legendary. During the first fifteen years of the new Bellevue, his work lent the hospital a world reputation.

Mott was born in Hempstead, Long Island, the son of a Quaker doctor who had studied under John Bard. He was a cousin of Valentine Seaman, in whose office he took his first training. He had studied in most of the famous clinics of Europe and counted as his friends the illustrious surgeons of the Continent.

His students at the College of Physicians and Surgeons idolized him. They never missed a lecture and they liked to hang about the dissecting room and listen to his grave-robbing stories. Dr. Francis, who had a deep affection for Mott, delighted in giving his own version of some of these stories.

> When Mott was not yet quite thirty, he dressed in the clothes of a poor workingman, which must have tried the soul of this most dignified of men, and seated on a produce cart, he drove out of town and met at the appointed hour certain rakish companions who entered into this rash business with him. Pulling up at the side of a burial field, Mott waited patiently until eleven bodies had been stowed away carefully in this unique hearse, concealed by an appropriate amount of clothing to suggest a ragman's load. Then, alone in the dead of night, at the imminent risk of life and reputation, Mott drove through the half-lit lanes down Broadway

to Barclay Street to the Medical College, where he deposited his load of care.

Mott's students loved to hear him tell about one of his visits to Paris, where he was invited to witness a private operation by a well-known French surgeon for the removal of a malignant tumor of the neck, involving the deep jugular vein. Dr. Mott claimed that never had he seen anybody but a butcher cut as did this French doctor. Almost immediately the jugular vein was severed. Mott instantly placed his finger on the vein and stayed the flow of blood. But in a few minutes the jugular was cut a second time. The patient, an elderly gentleman, was losing pints of blood, and only the smallest portion of the tumor had been removed. The French doctor filled the wound with lint, made his closure, and pronounced the operation complete. About a week later Mott met the surgeon and asked him how his patient fared. The doctor shrugged his shoulders, turned his head to one side, and said gravely, "Oh, yes, poor old fellow. He grew pious all of a sudden and made his way to Paradise." Such anecdotes, of which Mott had a fund, had a tremendous appeal during this chauvinistic and self-defensive period when the new Republic was beginning to spread its wings.

The great problems confronting early American surgery were fourfold: the lack of complete and precise knowledge of human anatomy; a means of controlling hemorrhage; anesthesia; and the control of postoperative infection. Dr. Mott made a valuable contribution to the solution of the second of these problems, the control of hemorrhage, particularly by ligation.

Dr. Mott's first brilliant achievement was a successful ligation, or tying-off, of the innominate artery, a large blood vessel arising, just above the heart, from the arch of the aorta and in part supplying the brain. In 1818 the obstacles to tying off a vessel so large and so intimately connected with the central nervous system seemed insurmountable. It was only after much preliminary anatomical research that Dr. Mott decided to proceed.

The surgeon, at this period, had no idea what would happen when half the brain's blood supply was suddenly cut off. Mott was anxious and tense as he ruthlessly tightened the ligature around the great arterial trunk. Nothing untoward happened, at least for the time being. The patient lived for many days, but eventually died of a secondary hemorrhage.

But Mott had proved that ligation of the big arteries was at least feasible. Yet forty more years had to pass before a New Orleans surgeon not only ligated the innominate, but pulled the patient through. Hearing of this, Mott exclaimed: "Now I can die happy!"

In 1827 Dr. Mott ligated the primitive iliac artery for the first time in American medicine. In 1828, he performed an entire exsection of a cancerous collarbone. He regarded this as the most difficult and dangerous operation he had ever performed, for to do it he had to work his way through a net of arteries and veins, and avoid cutting into the sac containing the lungs. The patient lived to become a well-known minister. The operation was performed on the eve of the anniversary of the Battle of Waterloo, and Mott always referred to it as his Waterloo operation.

Twelve years afterward Mott again cut out a cancerous clavicle, and this time applied 40 ligatures and tied off 138 large arteries, more than any surgeon had done before.

Mott was fond of showing his pupils the beautiful set of surgical instruments designed and given him by Sir Astley Cooper, the greatest English surgeon—scalpels and forceps with handles of oak from Old London Bridge and blades from its iron. Mott was able to handle instruments with either hand with equal dexterity.

Dr. Mott's chief attention was directed not so much to the study of the individual organs which make up the body as to the relation which these organs bear to each other when they present problems in surgical procedure. In later years, when teaching surgery at the College of Physicians and Surgeons, he ended each term by demonstrating on a cadaver all the operations which could be performed on a human being. It was he, too, who introduced the use of the medical chart that hangs at the foot of each patient's bed and gives the physician the clinical picture at a glance.

In 1841, in answer to the city's tremendous expansion, the New York University College of Medicine was established, with Dr. Mott as first member of the new faculty. By this time the city had completely recovered from the great fire of 1835, which had destroyed thirty acres of downtown New York, and the population had reached the half-million mark. Broadway was now paved all the way to Fulton Street, and P. T. Barnum had opened his famous American Museum at the corner of Broadway and Ann. Pigeon-shooting and trotting races were the fashion, and Dr. Mott was an enthusiastic follower of these sports.

Only one unpleasant incident marred the great surgeon's career. Having come to the aid, in 1841, of a colleague who had lost a patient through what the man's family held to be gross negligence, for a time Dr. Mott was in the headlines. Statements and counter-statements appeared, amid a welter of mutual recrimination which the newspapers did their best to foment. In the end, Dr. Mott withdrew into Olympian dignity and refused henceforth to discuss the case. "I consider that I acted in all good conscience," he declared, "and there's an end to it."

Mott, a stauch Union man, felt strongly about the Civil War, which occurred during the last four years of his life. Asked at the commencement of the rebellion what his prognosis was, he said:

> Sir, I grant you that the body politic has been severely lacerated, and I doubt not that the wound will heal eventually, but it will be by the "second intention." There will always be a scar to mark the union of dissevered parts.

At the very end of the war, he was appointed by the Union government to make an official visit to the Andersonville prison. The experience shocked him.

> You can form no idea of the poor, shriveled, wasted victims. In the whole course of my surgical experience, not excepting the most painful operations on deformed limbs, I have never suffered as much in my life at the sight of anything. I care not what it is, it unnerved me, I felt sick.

Dr. Mott was a great admirer of Abraham Lincoln, and the President's assassination came as a profound shock to him. His barber was shaving him when he got the news. He went at once to his wife in an adjoining apartment, exclaiming, "My dear, I have received such a shock—President Lincoln has been murdered." After a moment he added, "I am ill." Less than two weeks later he was dead; the diagnosis, typho-malarial fever (*sic*).

In his eulogy of Mott, Dr. Samuel Gross, the famous Philadelphia surgeon of a later generation, noted only one fault in the man. "As a lecturer," wrote Gross, "he is said to have occasionally been too egotistical." But fulsomeness and ego were typical failings of the times, a period of which Emerson remarked: "The American Eagle is well, but beware the American Peacock." Mott's writings are undeniably windy. Yet during the fifteen years he served at Bellevue he made it one of the most progressive and resourceful operating theaters of the day. In the entrance hall of Bellevue, opposite the stone on which Washington stood as he took his oath of office, is a tablet to his memory.

IX

BETTER HEALTH FOR ALL

In 1850, when Dr. Jimmy Wood was organizing and expanding his new medical school and consolidating Bellevue's reputation as a progressive surgical center, Dr. Alonzo Clark was in charge of the lying-in ward, as the maternity section was then known. Holmes of Boston and Semmelweiss of Vienna had yet to make their epochal demonstration that puerperal, or childbed, fever could be controlled by asepsis. As for the pathogens actually causing this dreaded infection, nothing at all was known. Dr. Clark conceived the idea of using opium to deal with the malady, apparently on the theory that the galloping inflammation would slow down to a walk if the body were drugged into quiescence.

While Dr. Clark was experimenting with this novel strategy, a new intern, fresh from Geneva and Buffalo Medical Colleges and a farm near Skaneateles in Upper New York State, was assigned to his ward. The young man's name was Stephen Smith. He was a slender fellow, and looked very youthful indeed to the ward chief. Nevertheless, Dr. Clark gave him Draconian instructions to narcotize his unfortunate women patients "within an inch of their lives." The new intern followed his superior's instructions to the letter. By sheer good luck, none of his first five charges died.

This good luck and ability to face boldly up to any situation remained with Dr. Stephen Smith throughout an immensely long and crowded medical career, studded both with surgical successes and battles against corrupt politicians and public inertia. It would seem that he was a marked man from the very start. As an intern he wrote a monograph on the "Statistics of Rupture of the Bladder" which, when it came out in the *New York Journal of Medicine,* immediately attracted favorable, even excited, notice. Later, Dr. Smith was to write other and increasingly important works, notably a *Handbook of Surgical Operations,* which for many years was a standard reference for the whole profession. But it was in the field of public health that he achieved his greatest fame. The reforms which he launched practically singlehanded were of immense benefit not only to New York but to the nation as a whole. He lived to be within a few months of the century mark, and was busy and interested in human welfare to the end. The name of Stephen Smith is one of the most illustrious in the annals of Bellevue.

Young Dr. Smith's initiation into the complexities of public health problems began during his internship at Bellevue. A mild typhus epidemic appeared in the city. The willing young doctor was assigned the thankless task of taking charge of an improvised tent hospital on Blackwell's Island. Earlier, while a medical student, he had nearly died of typhus, but this baleful memory did not deter him. Let him tell about the episode in his own language:

I served a two years term of service on the intern medical staff of Bellevue Hospital, 1850 to 1852, where large numbers of typhus cases were treated. I was placed in charge of the tents on Blackwell's Island, by the Commissioners of Charities. Soon after entering upon the service, I noticed that the patients were continually admitted from a single building in East 22nd Street. Impressed with the importance of closing this fever nest, I visited this tenement, and was not surprised at the large number of cases of fever which it had furnished our hospital.

It is difficult to describe the scene that the interior of the house presented. The building was in an extreme state of dilapidation generally, the door and windows were broken, the cellar was partly filled with filthy sewage, the floors were littered with decomposing straw which the occupants used for bedding. Every available place, from cellar to garret, was crowded with immigrants, men, women, and children. The whole establishment reeked with filth and the atmosphere was heavy with the sickening odor of deadly typhus. I found that the house was never visited by anyone who claimed to be either agent or owner, but that it was a resort of vagrants, especially of the more recent and destitute immigrants, and that they came and went without let or hindrance, generally remaining until attacked by the prevailing epidemic fever, when they were removed to the fever hospital.

I brought the condition of this tenement to the owner's attention, and explained its menace to the public health as a fruitful fever nest. But this prominent man was very angry at what he declared was an interference with the management of his property, and asserted in the most emphatic manner that as the house yielded him no rent, he wouldn't spend a dollar for the benefit of the miserable creatures who had so wrecked the building.

Then I visited the office of the *Evening Post* and explained the matter to Mr. William Cullen Bryant, then editor of that newspaper. He was at once interested in the failure of the city government to remedy such a flagrant evil. In the absence of laws and ordinances, Mr. Bryant proposed to make the case public in all of its details, and for that purpose, suggested that the police should cause the arrest of the delinquent owner, and he would send a reporter to make notes of the case. The charge was made against the landlord, and he was required to appear at the Jefferson Market court.

On entering the court, he was confronted by the reporter, pad and pencil in hand, who pressed him with questions as to his tenement house. Greatly alarmed at his situation, the owner inquired as to the purpose of the reporter and was informed that Mr. Bryant intended to publish the proceedings of the court in the *Evening Post* and to expose his thievishness.

The man begged that no further proceedings be taken and promised the court that he would immediately make all the necessary improvements. He promptly vacated the house and made such a thorough reconstruction of the entire establishment that it became one of the most attractive tenements in that East Side district. For many years that house continued to be entirely free from the ordinary contagious diseases of the tenement houses of the city. It's an interesting fact that the landlord subsequently thanked me for having compelled him to improve his tenement house where he had secured first-class tenants who paid well.

Thus Dr. Smith early discovered the key to public health reform—the power of public opinion. Henceforth he realized that if he could enlist the aid of people with enough influence and intelligence to force their will on an indifferent City Hall, there was no limit to what he could accomplish. At that moment he began a planned campaign which started to bear fruit eleven years later.

Meanwhile, in due course Dr. Smith became a visiting surgeon at Bellevue. He quickly became known for his courtesy and gentleness with his patients, at a time when a brusque, or even forbidding, bedside manner was considered proper. When operating, he did not, like so many, flourish his scalpel or engage in whiskery theatrics. In all ways he was ahead of his time.

Among other things, Dr. Smith was early converted to the doctrine of surgical asepsis as expounded by Lister, and stuck to his guns despite witticisms and mordant comments from many of his colleagues. Though it is almost unimaginable today, less than a hundred years ago a considerable part of the medical profession scoffed at scrubbing and boiling, or any form of sterilization. Dr. Smith was among the first to alter this situation. At an early date he resolved, to his own satisfaction, the relative merits of wet and dry healing, a question hotly debated in his youth. He found, after experimenting with asepsis, that his incisions remained relatively free from pus, and healed quickly and cleanly. Others, convinced by the evidence of their eyes, followed suit.

But all this while he never lost sight of what privately had become his larger objective: to reduce the incidence of disease in New York by cleaning up the city. The very sight of fat politicians, he once confided, made his hackles rise. He sensed that first they must be subdued before the physical situation could be dealt with. His first serious step toward this end was to recruit interested doctors and laymen into a group who called themselves the Sanitary Association.

Just prior to and through the Civil War years, the Sanitary Association regularly introduced health bills in the city legislature, bills which were as regularly defeated or tabled. Chief source of opposition was the city inspector's office, which would have had no jobs to sell had Dr. Smith's proposals gone through. However, far from discouraging Dr. Smith, this resistance only steeled him to greater effort.

Coming out even farther into the open, he became prime mover in the organization of the Citizens' Association, which had a membership of a hundred of the city's most prominent figures, and Peter Cooper as its president. Dr. Smith saw to it that two investigating committees were appointed, one on law, the other on medicine.

He now ran headlong into the Tweed ring. This was Boss Tweed's heyday, the most corrupt period in New York history, when five men were hired to do the work of one, with all growing fat on the municipal payroll.

Dr. Smith's inquiries soon revealed the fact that New York had no effective sanitation administration at all. There were several departments with health-connected duties, but all were staffed by politicians without the least knowledge of public health, or even interest in it. There was a board of health only when the aldermen were summoned to meet as such. And Mayor Fernando Wood had so poor an opinion of this board that when a cholera epidemic was threatening, he is reported to have said, "I will not convene the Board of Health, for I consider it more dangerous to the city than the cholera itself!" In addition to the board, there was a health commissioner, with practically no well-defined duties. The city physician attended a few cases of sickness among the poor.

The real boss of the city's sanitation setup was the head of the street cleaning department. This fortunate fellow had an appropriation of slightly less than a million dollars a year. One of the duties of his department was to make a periodic sanitary inspection of the city, and for this purpose he appointed a full-time crew of "health wardens" complete with badges and special privileges. At the insistence of the Citizens' Association a committee of the legislature tested the qualifications of these ubiquitous gentlemen, and found that 20 per cent of them were tavern-owners and more than half the rest had trained for their work by serving drinks in New York's bars. One health warden was asked to define the word "hygiene" and responded with this gem: "The vapor which rises from stagnant water." Another was asked to describe his procedure when he was called to examine a case of contagious disease. "I make everybody come out in the street," he answered, "and I give my orders there, which are to burn sulfur. I never go into the house; it might spread the disease."

Under pressure from the Citizens' Association, yet another commission was appointed to make a sanitary inspection of the city. But this time the commission consisted of a team of competent physicians supervised by Stephen Smith, together with such prominent men as August Belmont, John Jacob Astor, Dr. Willard Parker, and Hamilton Fish. The politicians did not dare interfere.

Under Smith's plan they divided the city into twenty-nine districts. For nearly a year, flying squads of physicians swooped down on the tenements of the East Side, the slaughterhouses, the pestilential dark alleys, and the dead ends where disease flourished. They brought in information that rocked the city and threatened to topple the administration. This volunteer sanitary inspection of a great city was regarded by European health authorities as the most remarkable in the history of municipal reform.

Dr. Smith struck while the iron was hot. The association, in 1864, published his report in a 500-page volume, and Smith saw that it got the widest distribution possible. Publication costs were $22,000, but it was to save the city billions, to say nothing of countless human lives.

The memos from the commission's inspection teams on which Dr. Smith based his famous report make shocking reading in any age. The inspector of the Eleventh Ward says:

> As a rule the streets are mainly dirty and offensive and the gutters obstructed with filth. The filth of the streets is composed of house slops, refuse vegetables, decayed fruit, store and shop sweepings, ashes, dead animals, and even human excrement. These putrefying organic substances are ground together by the constantly passing vehicles, and are driven by the wind in every direction. This street filth and domestic garbage is a well recognized cause of diarrheal diseases and fevers. . . .
>
> The privy at the rear of a tenement house on West 22nd Street is used by 42 persons. It has five subdivisions, one for every two families. The compartments are so small that a person can scarcely turn around in them and so dark that they have to be entered in artificial light. Under such circumstances, the emanations of the excrementious matter of 42 persons can find no escape. The privy cellar is worse than a Stygian pit.

The inspector of the Sixteenth Ward says:

> New York has a vast number of special nuisances which are a constant danger to its public health. There are nearly two hundred slaughterhouses, many of which are in the most densely populated districts. To these places droves of cattle, hogs, and sheep are constantly driven, rendering the streets filthy in the extreme, and from the slaughterings flow blood and refuse of the most disgusting character. In certain popular sections of the city are fat-boiling, entrails-cleansing, and tripe-curing establishments which poison the air for squares around with their stifling emanations. To these must be added hundreds of unclean stables, immense manure heaps, etc.
>
> . . . It is estimated by the City Inspector that 18,000 persons live in cellars . . . many of [which] are below tide water. . . .
>
> These are the places in which we most frequently meet with typhoid fever and dysentery during the summer months. It is estimated the amount of sickness of all kinds affecting

the residents of basements and cellars compared with that
occurring in an equal number of inhabitants above ground
is in a ratio of about 3 to 2.

Ragpickers' Row is described this way:

> The houses are of wood, two stories with attic and base-
> ment. The attic rooms are used to deposit the filthy rags
> hung up to dry, sending forth their nauseous stench to all
> the neighborhood.
> The tenants are all German of the lowest order, having
> no national or personal pride. They are exceedingly filthy
> in person and their bed clothes are as dirty as the floors they
> walk on. Their food is of the poorest quality and they have a
> peculiar taste for the association of dogs and cats, there being
> about 50 of the former and 30 of the latter. The whole num-
> ber of apartments is 32, occupied by 28 families. They
> number 120 in all, 60 adults and 60 children.

On the wave of public indignation that ensued, in 1866 the
legislature tamely passed the famous Metropolitan Health Law
drafted by Dr. Smith. This model sanitary code not only contained a comprehensive set of health rules but created a board
of health with power to enforce them. The code was so far-
reaching that Stephen Smith, when he was appointed first
health commissioner, had almost absolute power over the city's
hygienic behavior. One of the wags at City Hall suggested that
if the shah of Persia really wanted to play the despot, he should
appoint himself commissioner of health.

Dr. Smith filled the office of commissioner of health in New
York from 1868 to 1875. During this time he helped set up a
new bureau of vaccination, and began a national campaign
that resulted, in 1871, in the formation of the American Public
Health Association. By now Stephen Smith was attracting international attention, earning a reputation to be honored much
later, during the Cleveland administration, when Smith of
Bellevue was sent to Paris to represent the United States at a
world public health conference.

But in the interim a vast amount of clean-up work confronted Dr. Smith in New York. He wielded his newly won

powers with a ruthless hand. One of his colleagues of that period, Dr. Charles F. Chandler, in his reminiscences describes a typical public health situation of the time, and Dr. Smith's method of attacking it. The incident unfolded after word came that cholera was rife in Memphis, and could certainly be expected in New York unless preventive measures were taken.

One of the first attacks was on the public market, which was found to be in a filthy condition. The butchers had been permitted to build out to the middle of the street all around Washington Market. The flooring over the pavement was defective and bones and pieces of meat fell through and putrefied, tainting all the food sold in the market. For forty years this condition had existed and, to a greater or lesser degree, the same conditions existed at Fulton and Center markets.

Dr. Smith and the Medical Inspectors insisted that, with cholera threatening us, these evils must be corrected at once. Orders were issued directing the butchers to remove immediately all those portions of the three markets which extended beyond the curbstone. They laughed at the orders and paid no attention to them. The Board then called upon the Department of Public Works to remove the booths. Again we were ridiculed. Then Dr. Smith and I mobilized a force consisting of all the Sanitary Inspectors, 150 mechanics and laborers, with the necessary carts, and 360 policemen. Between 8 o'clock at night and 9 o'clock in the morning, we tore down everything in Washington Market outside the curbstone around the entire block and carted this material to the junkyards. Before 10 o'clock we had the street cleaning department sweeping the pavement upon which the sun had not shown for 40 years. . . .

The city was sued for $59,000 damages by the market people for this destruction but the courts decided that the complainants had no case and that they were trespassing in the public highways.

Dr. Smith and I took part in several other warlike acts, such as correcting the offensive treatment of offal, the rendering of dead animals, the scavenger nuisance, and like complaints. Some of these nuisances were entrenched by time, or contracts with the city which the owners thought impregnable, but we declared the contracts void for non-fulfillment and stopped the nuisances by force. The city was sued for over $600,000 because of the acts of the Board of

Health in warding off cholera, but the courts sustained the Board in every case.

The way in which Dr. Smith handled the smallpox epidemics was typical of him. During the winter of 1874 there were 3,000 cases of smallpox and 1,200 deaths. The difficulty in dealing with the disease resulted from the concealing of cases in the tenement houses until each primary case produced half a dozen additional cases.

The smallpox hospital on Blackwell's Island was in charge of the Department of Charities and Correction. It was not properly equipped for the welfare of the patients. The nurses were largely recruited from the women's end of the island, the so-called "10-day drunks." The result was that the hospital had such a bad reputation that everyone shunned it.

The condition of things reached the Legislature, and on January 12, 1875, the Board of Health was directed to take the hospital under its exclusive charge. Dr. Smith immediately suggested that most radical reform must be made in the hospital to overcome the existing prejudice against it. His first step was a master stroke. He went to Catholic Archbishop McClosky and asked him for a corps of Sisters of Charity to take possession of the hospital and run it. The Archbishop was astounded but, as the importance of it was explained by Dr. Smith, he yielded and sent over 14 Sisters to take charge.

They asked if they might have a chapel in the hospital and were assigned a suitable room. More than that, Smith purchased a considerable number of photoengravings of the famous Madonnas and other sacred subjects and sent them over nicely framed. Everything was done to make the Sisters comfortable and contented. As the name "Smallpox Hospital" was unpalatable, Dr. Smith proposed the name of "Riverside Hospital," and this continued to be its name until it was removed.

There had been some complaint about a cart backing up to a tenement house door to take away a patient so, at Dr. Smith's suggestion, a fine second-hand coupe was purchased, sporting a pair of gray horses and a driver in livery. As soon as it became known that the Sisters were in charge of the hospital, and that the patients were well treated, all opposition to going there disappeared, and there was no more concealing of cases.

Especially remarkable, considering the wear and tear of his incessant labors throughout many decades in the field of public health, is the fact that Dr. Smith, with a heavy operating schedule, found time to continue all this and to write solid medical works on the side. Not only this, he also helped organize a number of great hospitals, including Roosevelt in New York and Johns Hopkins in Baltimore. In later life he became deeply interested in public welfare and in the mass economic problems which gave rise to slums and disease-ridden living conditions. It was he who drafted the original bill for the State Care Act of 1890. He was also a pioneer in improving conditions in the state mental hospitals, and once served as state mental health commissioner.

Public relations expert, lobbyist, and organizing genius, humanitarian, and physician—Dr. Stephen Smith was all these. As a physical specimen, too, he was a marvel. At the age of ninety-eight, a year before his death, he delivered a half-hour lecture standing before a large audience, and was able to make his voice carry to every corner of the hall. Even at Bellevue, which attracts powerful personalities, Dr. Smith stands out as a tremendous figure of a man.

· X ·

AN ILL WIND

It is an ill wind, the old saw goes, that blows no good, and such is the case of war in the history of medicine. Wars have always precipitously introduced advances in preventive medicine and surgical practice, from the days of the French barber-surgeon, Ambroise Paré, down to the most recent times when, in the Korean War, new and virulent forms of bacillic dysentery were diagnosed and dealt with. Epidemics flourish during wartime, gross and gaping wounds must be handled as a matter of course, the problem of shock arises in acute form. Nerving itself to meet the challenge, the medical profession accomplishes miracles impossible to conceive under peacetime conditions.

The Civil War acted as a great stimulus on American medicine, bringing into focus situations of a magnitude never before dreamt of. Bellevue figured prominently in providing medical men to care for the Northern troops, and reaped benefit from lessons learned during the seemingly endless conflict.

When war broke out in 1861, Stephen Smith was just beginning his long fight for public health reform. Drs. Mott, Francis, Wood, Clark, and others, were struggling to get the new Bellevue Medical College off to a flying start. Meanwhile, the old hospital was suffering, as usual, from lack of space and nursing care. Again patients were sleeping in the corridors. A new medical service had been added, and a new wing to the old central building. But these small additions were trivial in the face of the city's need. Plans had been drawn for a new operating amphitheater on top of the almshouse, but again this was a mere stopgap measure.

A brochure describing the Bellevue Medical College at the onset of the Civil War tells us that the hospital had 1,200 beds, with 500 more on Blackwell's Island. Much was made in the prospectus of the clinical material available to aspirant medical students. The drug department annually dispensed, we discover, about 135,000 yards of surgical gauze, 50 bales of oakum, and 1,000 pounds of ether. Medical students, to qualify for a degree, had to study privately for three years with a regular "respectable practitioner of medicine" and, in addition, take two full courses of medical lectures at Bellevue. Of the 200 students regularly studying under Bellevue house surgeons, 20 were chosen each year as interns. The only compensation was experience.

All this would suggest that Bellevue was a rigorous training ground. And it is a fact that when hostilities broke out between North and South, Bellevue's wide experience proved of incalculable value to the Federal cause. Young doctors and interns from the hospital flocked to the colors. Bellevue organized a condensed course in military surgery. Dr. Stephen Smith, always indefatigable and timely, rushed to press a pocket-sized text called *A Handbook of Operative Surgery* which became a standby in the field hospitals.

Overnight New York took on the appearance of an armed camp. From platforms in Union Square prominent citizens exhorted the populace to contribute money to the cause, or join the colors. Crowds drifted restlessly about the streets. New York merchants financed equipment for the Seventh Regiment, originally organized in 1824. Seven days after the first shot fell on Fort Sumter, the outfit marched down Broadway in full fighting regalia to stimulate patriotic feeling.

The Ladies' Central Relief Committee, organized by Dr.

Elizabeth Blackwell, Stephen Smith's classmate at Geneva College, met at Cooper Union to enlist women nurses for the wounded soldiers. Dr. Valentine Mott accepted the chairmanship of this committee and arranged to send nurses to Bellevue for a month's training. This was the seed from which eventually grew Bellevue's great school of nursing. Mott lived to see his organization become the nucleus of the U. S. Sanitary Commission, which was the parent of the American Red Cross.

The city's mounting excitement and preoccupation with war progressively disrupted Bellevue routine. During the first month almost the entire staff left for the front, and most of the Medical Board were involved with one service or another. As casualties began to be shipped back from the battle lines, Dr. Stephen Smith went to an amputee hospital set up in Central Park, and there tackled a problem arising directly from the war. Leg amputees were having trouble with their artificial limbs. At that time surgeons cut the flaps of tissue of equal length to cover the stump, and joined them in the center. This caused the artificial limb to rest directly on the tender closure. Dr. Smith tried a very long front flap and a short one in the back, thus removing the area of closure from the pressure of the artificial limb. This method proved highly successful, and was adopted by the British Army after the war.

Bellevue became so desperately understaffed that some students and interns served as house physicians and surgeons during their entire terms. At one juncture typhus broke out again; fourteen of the staff caught it and six died.

As time went on with no Northern victory in sight, the volatile Irish immigrant class conspired to lead savage riots against the draft, which was of course felt most onerously among the poor, who had no means to buy exemption. The Irish were strongly disinclined, as they put it, to submit to one kind of slavery merely to put a stop to another. Early one morning angry crowds gathered in front of the Third Avenue enlistment office. When the drawing of names started, someone threw a brick and the great riot was on. First the mob set fire to the whole block and almost killed the provost marshal. Rival gangs from Five Points united to keep firemen from reaching the hydrants, and then overpowered the police.

By noon the disturbance had spread to Forty-sixth Street, and the mob surged through the burning city shouting its battle cry: "Kill the niggers!" For the New York Irish strenuously objected to giving up their lives to free the Southern blacks from slavery. The enraged crowd beat, knifed, and hanged Negroes, and set fire to a colored orphan asylum.

For six days the rioters freely roamed the city, and were finally quelled only when the Seventh Regiment was returned on the frantic plea of the mayor to Secretary of War Stanton. Bellevue, meanwhile, had taken on the appearance of a field hospital. The exhausted staff probed gunshot wounds, cleaned cuts and abrasions, and set fractured limbs until they were ready to drop. The official count of deaths due to the riot was set at a thousand. But this figure was actually too low, in view of the fact that the gangs from Five Points and elsewhere took care of their own dead and wounded.

The surrender at Appomattox Courthouse at last brought release from the strain and unnatural excitements of the war years. The tent hospitals disappeared from Central Park. The Sanitary Commission sponsored a fair on Fourteenth Street at Union Square, where the society belles of the city raised an enormous sum by selling kisses to the returning soldiers. The young doctors and interns drifted back, weary with the weight of four brutal years. Gradually Bellevue returned to its normal state—still overcrowded, understaffed, and desperately over-worked.

Among the doctors returning from duty with the Northern forces was Edward B. Dalton, who had interned at Bellevue two years before the war. Dalton's service record, as described by a contemporary, was very impressive. He was in the thick of action during the summer campaigns of 1864, when the Army

of the Potomac finally began to fight its way to Richmond. For
twenty-seven days out of a period of forty-five, the armies were
in contact, at the Battles of the Wilderness, Spottsylvania Courthouse, Hanover Town, Cold Harbor, and intervening points.
During this fearful melee Dr. Dalton showed his mettle as a
medical organizer by coping with a tremendous flow of casualties.

> The Army was almost constantly moving in such a manner
> as to require repeated changes in the direction in which its
> sick and wounded were to be transported. This latter duty
> was entrusted to the care of Dr. Edward Dalton.
> On May 8, Dalton was directed to establish near the city
> of Fredericksburg the first hospital depot. Here he collected
> and placed under shelter over 7,000 wounded, converting the
> city into an organization of corps hospitals and providing
> for all the immediate necessities of the medical service.
> This movement was accomplished so successfully that not
> one of the wounded was left behind nor any of the hospital
> property abandoned.
> Owing to the constant and heavy demand for transporta-
> tion of the wounded at the immediate front, Dalton com-
> mandeered a large number of Army wagons from the
> Quartermaster Department to assist in getting the wounded
> quickly from the scene of action. All the available trans-
> portation was used for the more severe cases, while many,
> wounded only in the upper extremity, were sent in squads
> on foot to Bell Plain under charge of a medical officer and
> there placed on board transports.
> This successful establishment and administration of the
> wartime hospitals on a scale much surpassing any other which
> had ever been attempted in the field won for Dr. Dalton the
> unqualified commendation and confidence of his superior
> officers.

Dr. Dalton came back to Bellevue convinced that time was
the most important factor in treating the wounded. Since the
ambulance had saved so many lives on the battlefront, why
could it not do the same in New York? He approached Stephen
Smith on the matter and found him, as always, sympathetic
toward his former students' ideas. Dr. Smith advised him to

draw up a design of an ambulance for civilian use and to list his reasons for recommending it. He, Smith, would then sponsor the plan with the commissioners of public charities and corrections.

Dr. Dalton followed this advice. In arguing the critical importance of getting patients with severe injuries to the hospital quickly, he cited the case of a colored man who was run over by a beer truck and badly mangled. He was carried to the nearest house, while onlookers tried to find a wagon or some other conveyance to take him to Bellevue Hospital. It was five hours later before anyone found a wagon to drive the man to Twenty-eight Street. The outcome was obvious; the man died. If he had been brought directly to the hospital he might have been saved.

At Dr. Smith's urging, the commissioners adopted Dr. Dalton's ambulance design and his specifications for an ambulance service. They drew up a memo stating that:

> (1) There should be provided at Bellevue Hospital two ambulances of the design recommended by Dr. E. B. Dalton in his report and it shall be the duty of the Warden to see that they are at all times in good order and fit for service.
> (2) Each ambulance shall have a box beneath the driver's seat, containing a quart flask of brandy, two tourniquets, a half a dozen bandages, and a half a dozen small sponges, some splint material, pieces of old blankets for padding, strips of various lengths with buckles, and a two-ounce vial of persulphate of iron.

Application was made to various carriage-makers for plans for a suitable vehicle, and the ambulance of the Abbott-Downing Company was accepted as closest to specifications. On June 30, the Medical Board at Bellevue held the first examinations for ambulance surgeons, and in June, 1869, the ambulance system was inaugurated.

This was the first ambulance service in the world. Bellevue preceded all other hospitals by eight years. New York and Roosevelt Hospitals followed in 1877, St. Vincent's in 1879, and the Presbyterian a year later. Paris, London, and a few English hospitals adopted the idea later on.

In her book *Darkness and Daylight,* Mrs. Helen Campbell describes the Bellevue ambulance service in those first years:

Hark! The "hurry" call has sounded. A bell in the stable instantly arouses both driver and horse. The harness, always suspended and ready to be dropped on the horse's back, is already in place. The stable doors fly open, and the ambulance is ready and rolls out before the reverberations of the five quick and imperative strokes of the signal gong have died away. The surgeon, whom another bell has summoned, is at the big archway just as the ambulance furiously dashes up, and he springs to his seat in the rear. The address is given them, the driver gathers up the reins, and with a word to the horse they are off at a mad pace. The ambulance has right of way and takes the middle of the street, the gong sounding a loud and incessant alarm as they gallop on. . . .

The ambulance itself is a triumph of ingenuity and invention. The bed in the bottom is of the softest, and on strong deep springs. The vehicle is sombre as a hearse, everything from pillows to bed, stretcher, and curtains, being dead black. About the sides within, splints are arranged, each with its lint bandage coiled about it ready for use. The stretcher is fastened securely, its iron rods strong enough to support the heaviest weight. Blankets, lint, bandages, belts for strapping down violent patients, everything that can be needed for any possible emergency is there, while the doctor's satchel holds surgical instruments and stomach-pump. Bellevue is known as "the poor man's hospital" and thus the majority of calls come in from the poorer districts and in large proportion from the vicinity of the swarming tenements on the East Side. Accidents of every nature, and the long list of casualties caused by drink, furnish abundant material, though there is a large proportion of ordinary sickness, many of these cases being complicated by the privations of poverty.

Through his innovation Dr. Dalton earned the respect of the profession, which was quick to appreciate the value of rapid transport of accident victims. In 1866 he was recommended by Stephen Smith for the position of superintendent of the newly created Metropolitan Board of Health, which embraced Manhattan, Brooklyn, Jamaica, and Flushing. Despite recurrent malaria, which he had contracted during the first Richmond campaign, Dalton did an outstanding job until the city commissioners began to play the old game of politics with him. They filled his department with party workers and so tied his hands that in 1868 he resigned in disgust.

Dalton had evidently had enough of higher command. His health was broken and he retired to California, where he died in 1872, another of the unsung heroes of American medicine.

XI

DRS. SAYRE AND JANEWAY

During and just after the Civil War, Bellevue underwent a gradual but extensive reorganization and emerged divided into four major divisions functioning as four separate hospitals, each with its own surgical and medical staffs. To these major divisions were attached various outlying services, such as the outpatient department, then called "The Bureau of Medical and Surgical Relief for the Outdoor Poor."

This last department was established two years after the war to relieve the crowded hospital of ambulatory cases. The first year the new service took care of 437 patients; the second year, 15,000. Both Paris and London already had such services, but Bellevue's was first in the United States.

The children's clinic, another important outpatient service, was established by Stephen Smith's brother, J. Lewis Smith. Dr. Lewis Smith and the famed Dr. Abraham Jacobi share the distinction of originating pediatrics in this country.

Anxious parents from as far away as Albany—and these were times when a railroad journey was a grave affair for poor people—brought their ailing children to the Bellevue Clinic. Dr. Lewis Smith was a quiet, unassuming man who carefully avoided the limelight and shared his brother's charitable bent. He had a prodigious practice among the poor, and one of his principal concerns was the foundlings of the city.

At that time abandoned babies and orphans were taken to the Almshouse, now removed to Blackwell's Island. As Dr. Smith said, "Better that they should be drowned like some pitiful and unwanted kittens—for to send them to the island is to assure their deaths within two months." Through Smith's efforts the Foundling Hospital was put up, and thereafter New York's orphaned babies had a much better chance of survival.

Lewis Albert Sayre, founder of orthopedic surgery at Bellevue, was another friend of the young and helpless. When challenged by a malformation of the bones, Dr. Sayre's ingenuity was limitless. He devised countless new splints and braces, and new and radical methods of treatment by repeated exercise and manipulation.

Sayre was particularly clever at improvising with whatever materials lay at hand. Once he ran out of dressings while treating a serious stab wound in an East Side tenement. The sofa on which the patient lay was so dilapidated that the oakum stuffing was sticking out. Sayre grabbed a few handfuls of the oakum and dampened it with balsam of Peru, then used as an expectorant and soothing agent for ulcers. The dressing worked so well that in the future he used nothing else, and soon oakum had supplanted all other dressings generally.

When his student John Ridlon asked him to what he atributed his great success as a surgeon, Sayre explained:

> More to what I don't know than to what I do know; I've never been much of a reader and so I haven't known what other men have tried to do and failed in doing. If a problem presented itself, I did what I thought it best to do and I was usually successful, but if I had known good men had tried to do the thing and failed, I probably would not have made the attempt or would have failed myself from lack of self-confidence.

In 1853 Dr. Sayre was appointed surgeon to Bellevue Hospital, and in 1859, surgeon to the Charity Hospital on Blackwell's Island. He, too, along with Drs. Jimmy Wood, Stephen Smith, and Alonzo Clark, was one of the prime movers in the organization of the Bellevue Hospital Medical College, and in 1861 was made professor of orthopedics, surgery, and fractures. The Bellevue chair of orthopedics was the first of its kind in this country.

In 1876 he was appointed by the American Medical Association as a delegate to the International Medical Convention at Philadelphia. There he performed an operation for hip-joint disease which he had been the first American surgeon to complete successfully. Lord Lister said of it, "I feel that this demonstration would of itself have been sufficient reason for my voyage across the Atlantic."

Dr. Sayre's great contribution was to substitute simple and practical methods within the reach of every practitioner, for costly, complicated mechanical devices which only imperfectly or occasionally accomplished their purpose. His inquiring mind made him a superior diagnostician as well as an original surgeon. He constantly impressed the critical importance of exact diagnosis on his students. Without diagnostic precision, he claimed, the value of surgical skill was reduced by one half. In this connection he often cited the case of a girl who came to him in a spinal brace with her forearms completely paralyzed. A thorough examination convinced him that there was nothing wrong with the young woman's spine. It suddenly dawned on him that the limpness of the hands, which could be extended but not flexed, was symptomatic of lead poisoning. But it still remained for him to prove this. Long questioning revealed that the girl had not drunk water from lead pipes. Dr. Sayre suggested champagne from a bottle that had been washed with lead shot. But the patient assured him that never in her life had she tasted champagne at all. Nor had her house been recently painted. But finally the girl brought Sayre a bottle of liquid face powder labeled "Bloom of Youth." Analysis showed that it contained compounds of lead. Dr. Sayre not only cured the girl of her paralysis by giving her an antidote, but he headed a vigorous campaign to prevent cosmetics manufacturers from using the poison in their balms and lotions.

A case which perfectly demonstrates Sayre's flair for detection and his insistence on getting at the root of things was played up in the newspapers as "The Case of the Girl with the Charcoal Scales." It was one of the most fantastic hoaxes in Bellevue annals.

A Miss Perry of Oneida, according to an article in the *Transactions of the Medical Society of New York,* had not urinated for fourteen years! Also, the skin of her face, left arm, and left leg had become covered with black scales. From time to time, the report said, she coughed up a black substance that looked like charcoal. Dr. Sayre was amused. "If this woman truly has not urinated for fourteen years," he said, "then Noah himself should attend her when the dam breaks."

Eventually, having admitted his curiosity, Sayre was invited to visit Miss Perry and her physician, a Dr. Perkins. First he was shown an enormous book containing a record of the case, and endorsements by lawyers, businessmen, ministers—and, strangely enough, a few doctors. Dr. Perkins produced a prune jar filled with black pellets. His patient, he said, had coughed them up. He also showed Dr. Sayre a boxful of pieces of charcoal which he said had scaled off his remarkable patient, leaving the skin beneath unharmed.

Dr. Sayre asked to see the patient. He reports:

> I found a young woman with good muscular tone, whose face appeared to have over it a black mask, leaving only eyes and mouth exposed. This black substance disappeared under a bandage which covered her head. As I held out my hand to begin the examination, the patient screamed in apprehension so that I was forced to desist.
>
> I proceeded to examine the left arm and leg, similarly encased in the same black substance. At this time the attention of Dr. Perkins was diverted and I managed to snip off a small piece, which proved to be nothing but cotton and gum, covered by a black substance.
>
> The agitation of the patient would permit no further examination and I retired to the drawing room, determined

to make known my findings to Miss Perry's niece and her minister.

The minister and the niece were convinced of the fraud and wanted to expose Dr. Perkins, but the other relatives, when they heard of Sayre's opinion, wouldn't believe it. They insisted that the woman was no fraud and asked him to call in on the case another important medical man of the city.

The following day Sayre returned with Drs. Wood, Fordyce Barker, Austin Flint, Abraham Jacobi, and other Bellevue notables. This time the woman, though still in bed, had no "charcoal exudation." It had peeled off during the night, her physician said. Dr. Sayre called the good doctor a swindling rascal. Over Perkins' frantic objections and notwithstanding Miss Perry's struggles, he inserted a catheter into her bladder and readily drew off a quart of urine. Perkins, meanwhile, decamped, taking with him his testimonials and his prune jar and box of specimens. Dr. Sayre had the woman removed to Bellevue, where she was isolated, put on a vegetable diet, and given castor oil. The next day the woman, it was obvious, was urinating with perfect normality. Beaten, she permitted the doctors to remove the sticky black coating from her limbs.

Dr. Sayre flattered himself that he had rid the medical profession of at least one impostor, until his house surgeon repeated to him the woman's parting remark: "What would you think if this singular disease should return when I get home?" And so Sayre was not too much surprised when he heard later that the woman was once more afflicted with the strange disease, was in charge of another doctor, and attended by a committee of ladies who lectured on the phenomenon.

Another outstanding Bellevue doctor contemporary with Dr. Sayre was Edward Janeway, pathologist and anatomist. As silent in manner as the corpses which he so expertly dissected and subjected to microscopic examination, he was at a complete loss in social gatherings. He could remain mute for an hour at a stretch if he had nothing pertinent to contribute to the conversation. Then, when he did speak out, he said what he had to say bluntly and succinctly. At the same time he was a highly cultured and well-read man, thoroughly acquainted with the latest developments of the French school of medicine, then enjoying a creative surge. But in the sickroom this silent man became a different person. He was utterly kind, alert, intense, eager, and completely at his ease.

From abroad Janeway brought with him a quasi-homeopathic conviction that doctors, by excessive medication to relieve symptoms, often did more harm than good. It was his belief that nature alone was the great healer and that the doctor would do well to understand disease so thoroughly that he could furnish co-operation. Enormously erudite, possessed of a photographic memory, his experience all convinced him that drugs, as then known, were in great measure useless. His highest commendation for a medicine was: "I would take that myself; I don't think it will hurt you."

His pupil Dr. John Bayard Clark once remarked:

> Some of us heard Janeway say that a certain doctor wouldn't do a patient any harm. I didn't understand his meaning then, but the thing got stuck in my mind, and I remembered it. It was some years, I think, before that saying commenced to make its real impression. Then, as time and experience went on, clearer and clearer became its significance, 'til I've come to see it as an expression of that deeper wisdom of the man whose simple words often reveal such subtle truths.

Janeway's ability as an internist was so brilliant that he soon had the wealthiest practice in the city. But success did not raise his fees. All his life he charged rich and poor alike at the same nominal rate. "The condition of my patients," he said, "is of first importance. The condition of my pocketbook is as God wills it."

Dr. Janeway's wife, who had to manage a substantial household on his at best uncertain income, was philosophical about the family's chronic lack of funds. The only thing that amazed her was her husband's refusal even to discuss the subject of fees. In this regard, Dr. Alonzo Clark reported a conversation he overheard between Dr. Janeway and his wife. Mrs. Janeway had inquired about a wealthy patient to whose bedside her husband had been summoned in the middle of the night.

"Very sick man," said Janeway. "Pneumonia, very unusual type."

"But that long trip," urged Mrs. Janeway. "You must have spent hours getting there. It should be a very good fee."

"It was in the upper lobe, right side," mused Janeway. "Quite unusual, very rare thing to see in these cases."

"Did you remember to keep his address?"

"Well, no," said Janeway absently, "but I have my notes on the case."

"But his name," Mrs. Janeway said desperately. "At least you have his name so you can send a bill?"

"His name?" repeated the doctor, surprised and put out by this interruption of his train of thought. "Why on earth should I ask his name? The man was sick!"

Dr. Janeway carried his belief in the impotence of drugs and the superiority of natural healing to a point where he applied it in the most literal fashion, to himself. Having fallen ill with pneumonia, he shut himself in a room at Bellevue and asked the young doctor from his staff who was attending him to give him nothing but frequent doses of old brandy. "Time," he said, "will heal me if I can last long enough. And what better way to assist Time than with old brandy?"

Many of the surgeons and physicians of the day were slipshod about attending post-mortems. Dr. Janeway never missed a single one. He carried an enormous caseload at Bellevue and checked each diagnosis by careful post-mortem. He could be found in the deadhouse at almost any hour, patiently, meticulously dissecting.

His constant inquiry into the primary lesions of disease,

plus almost total recall, in time gave him an uncanny diagnostic insight. Dr. Reginald Sayre, the son of Lewis Sayre, who studied under Janeway, tells a story of the doctor's remarkable powers:

> One day as he passed through the admitting office, he said, "Who's been through here?" The attendant replied that no one had been admitted, but finally remembered that a case of measles had been sent to the erysipelas pavilion. Janeway insisted on visiting the pavilion, and there found that the patient in question had smallpox, not measles. He remarked with some impatience to the house physician who was with him, "Could you not smell the smallpox in the admitting room? Measles smell like mice. This was altogether different."

Dr. John Clark also said:

> There were three things Dr. Janeway didn't like. One was a newspaper reporter who tried to get inside information when some especially prominent person happened to be a patient in Bellevue. The other two things were a dislike of writing medical papers, and speaking in public. Anything, in short, which might by any chance give an impression of putting himself forward was distasteful to him.

In spite of his reticence and his dislike for writing up his findings, Dr. Janeway's reputation grew year by year, until he was considered the leading New York diagnostician of his day. He left his impress on a whole generation of Bellevue medical students, above all in respect to pathology and internal medicine.

XII

A LONG—AND REVEALING—
QUOTATION

In 1870 the *New York Evening Post* came out with a scare story which aired a brand new medical theory, and once again focused public attention on the wretched condition of the Bellevue plant. An enterprising reporter claimed that since Bellevue was so drenched by disease, the old walls were crawling with effluvia. The buildings should be torn down at once, and replaced. Other newspapers took up the cry, and finally a committee was formed which duly examined the walls for "effluvia." Finding none, they recommended that Bellevue be permitted to stand.

But the Medical Board, seizing this golden opportunity for betterment, pointedly reminded the city of its promises to replace the plumbing system. They also demanded that something be done about the high death rate in the surgical department. On this point they were grimly insistent.

At this time the general mortality rate in Bellevue was higher, though not much higher, than in other large city hospitals. In 1871 Bellevue's death ratio was 14.2 per hundred, while in the general hospitals in London it ranged from 7.2 in the Royal Free Hospital to 12.7 in Kings College. In the Edinburgh Royal Infirmary it was 9.2 and in the Glasgow Infirmary it was 11.8. However, in Bellevue's surgical wards the death rate had soared to 24.9 and showed every indication of going higher. This was inevitable where the patients were desperately poor and ill fed, and where they were freely used as experimental material. Dr. Henry Mann Silver has left a graphic picture of surgical procedure in Bellevue at this time.

> Leg fractures: The larger number of fractures of the leg were of the compound comminuted variety caused by the wheel of a horsecar over the leg. These cases were carefully explored with the finger, and usually condemned to amputation. In less serious injuries, if the wound was small, it was sealed with a cotton and collodion dressing, and the leg placed in a fracture box well padded with oakum. The simple fractures were also placed in a fracture box. When all signs of inflammatory swelling had disappeared, they were put in plaster of Paris casts extending from the toe to the knee.
>
> Bellevue figures for 1870 show that of 26 cases admitted, one died within two hours; 15 of the 25 which remained were treated by amputation. Of this number 10 recovered and five died. Of the 10 treated without amputation, three were fractures of the thigh and all of these died. The other seven patients recovered.
>
> Abdominal surgery: Surgery of the abdomen was a closed book. Dr. Jimmy Wood was busily opposed to operations for pistol shot wounds of the abdomen, preferring to use the Clark or opium treatment. It was not until the evening of November 2, 1894, when Dr. William T. Bull opened the abdomen for a pistol shot wound and successfully closed eleven perforations of the intestines, that surgery of the abdomen for pistol shot wounds became possible.
>
> Stab wounds: In stab wounds, three or four feet of intestines generally protruded, covered not infrequently with bar-room sawdust. These were washed, if necessary, and replaced, the wound being carefully closed. The patient was placed under the influence of opium at once and the quantity of food reduced to a minimum. Occasionally hypodermic injections of whiskey were given. A hot air bath was used, and if the shock was severe the extremities were rubbed with tincture of Capsicum. If the intestines escaped injury, this treatment was usually successful.

A committee composed of Drs. Sands, Janeway, Crane, and Gouley was appointed to study the surgical death rate problem.

They came to the conclusion that the main factor was infection. They recommended less crowding in the wards, improved ventilation, and better nursing. They also urged the general adoption of antiseptic treatment of wounds.

The committee's final report said, "In the present state of surgical science, the hope of completely eradicating these damning figures is vain and illusory." Just how true these words were is superbly told by Dr. Charles Fox Gardiner, a native New Yorker. Surely no more vivid account has ever been penned than this astonishing firsthand description of Bellevue and its Blackwell's Island outpost of last resort. Dr. Gardiner deserves to be quoted at length. He gives an inimitable picture of New York in the latter half of the nineteenth century, as well as an intimate account of a doctor's early years.

> At the age of eighteen I became a clerk in Mr. Charles M. Hinman's silk importing business in Worth Street, New York. So far my life had been a pleasant one, divided chiefly between outdoor sports, canoeing, sailing, tramping the Adirondacks, and the woods around Lake George, which I knew as well as the streets of New York, and training at Wood's gymnasium on Twenty-eighth Street near Fifth Avenue, where for two hours daily for many years I worked at boxing, tumbling, running, in an effort to build up a frail physique. I had lived abroad for some time and saw the fighting in the streets of Paris at the time of the Prussian victory. My Father believed every gentleman should know how to dance, to fence, and to ride, so at Dodworth's Select Dancing Academy on Twentieth and Fifth Avenue I was taught to dance, to walk, to bow, and to behave in correct Victorian manner; at Dickel's Riding Academy on Forty-third Street I learned correct seat, how to ride bareback over hurdles, and how to keep proper form and place in line when we rode to music; at Senack's famous Salon of Fencing I became familiar with the rapier manual, the broadsword and single stick. Of my own volition, I had studied drawing at the Broadway studio of an impatient Frenchman named Ronderl. But of formal education I had received less than one year!
>
> Now suddenly my Father's affairs were not prosperous, and I must become a wage earner. At Mr. Hinman's I was office

boy and bill collector. He was a pleasant gentleman, but I hated the work, and this, my first venture in the business world, came abruptly to an end. I was deeply interested in comparative anatomy and in my spare time read all the books I could find on the subject and then began to dissect cats. I dissected out the muscles, nerves, and blood vessels and drew colored charts of them. One Saturday in August I was careless and left a cat inside my desk. Monday morning when I opened the door the smell almost choked me. My boss had just arrived and was opening the windows. "Charley," he demanded, "what the devil have you got in your desk to make such a smell?" Horribly embarrassed, I unlocked my desk, bundled a newspaper about the cat, and dashed down the stairs for the nearest ash can. Mr. Hinman was looking at my anatomy charts when I returned. I expected to be fired, but all he said was, "I want to show these charts to a friend of mine and I'll talk to you tomorrow." His friend was a well-known surgeon, who remarked after seeing the drawings, "Hinman, you are a fool trying to make a business-man out of the boy who drew these charts. Give him a chance. He's a born doctor."

My boss saw my Father, and it was all arranged. Father said he could manage somehow, and in a week I was sitting on the hard benches of the College of Physicians and Surgeons on Twenty-third Street and Fourth Avenue, and the hated business was left forever.

In those days, Dr. Gardiner goes on to say, no especial preparation was required of entering medical students. They simply attended lectures and at the end of two years took their first examinations, in anatomy, physiology, and chemistry. Dr. Gardiner confesses that he went to his first lecture filled with excitement. The lecture-room was in the form of a pit. The professor sat below at a table, facing tiers of wooden benches extending upward and backward nearly to the ceiling. The light was dim, the whole place dusty and littered with cigar stubs and matches. The air was so hot, Gardiner says, that students frequently fainted. Eight hours of this on hard benches reduced the brain to a muddle. The students lounged on the seats—rough, untidy, their feet on the backs of the benches in front.

The lecture was given in the precise and dull manner common at that time, a deadly monotony.

Gardiner found he could do better working alone, and gave up the lectures. He knew no Latin, and had to master this along with his other studies. Chemistry was especially difficult for him, but at the end of two years he passed an examination in toxicology and chemistry, and was licensed to gain his living as a chemist if he failed in medicine.

The dissecting room was in the shape of an "L," reached by a narrow, windowless hall, a relic of the time when it was unlawful to use dead bodies for dissection. A vile smell of decay hinted at even greater unpleasantness in the dissecting room proper, a long narrow room lit by skylights. Here the cadavers lay in rows on zinc-covered tables, wrapped in wet cloths. They came from the poorhouse, the river—the unclaimed human debris of the metropolis. Gardiner's first task was to dissect out the arteries in the arm of a husky longshoreman.

Gardiner goes on:

> At the end of the second year, I was greatly encouraged by passing all the examinations with high marks. Then, in order to study under Dr. Austin Flint, who was a famous scientist and a personal friend of mine, I transferred to Bellevue Medical School. There were still two years to go, but one could if he wished come up for the degree in one more year. This I decided to do. I told no one. I was scared half to death when examination time came a year later and so nervous I could scarcely write out my answers to the questions written on a big blackboard. That night I turned and tossed, sleepless, my brain busy with questions and answers. In the morning I was early at the college, my knees trembling. In a sort of dream, I took the big envelope the clerk handed me and opened it. In a dream I read the curt statement: "Number 120. C. F. Gardiner has passed his examinations and is entitled to practice as a Doctor of Medicine."

The next step now was to get some practical experience, on the staff of a hospital if possible. To obtain such a position in the seventies, it was necessary to take the competitive examina-

tions held in the spring and fall by a board appointed by the
hospital of application. Young Dr. Gardiner joined a cram
quiz conducted by Dr. Winters, on Thirty-eighth Street. Dr.
Winters' class was limited to twenty. The fee was $100 for six
months' coaching. After cramming, Dr. Gardiner was accepted
by Charity Hospital, the Bellevue adjunct on Blackwell's Island. He was one of four taken from among thirty-two applicants.

A small steamer ran as a ferry to Blackwell's Island in the
East River. This landed Dr. Gardiner at the hospital dock,
whence he walked up to the hospital, a huge building of gray
stone, plain and ugly. There were twenty-four doctors in all,
about a hundred nurses, ten male nurses, and fifty orderlies.
Downstairs at dinner he met the house surgeon, a Dr. Godhill,
reputed to speak twelve languages. He was told to report for
duty that afternoon at the receiving hospital on the dock and
to be prepared to vaccinate 150 new patients arriving on the
steamer from the city. He continued in this dismal assignment
for six long months. Other dirty jobs came his way, such as
hunting up the bodies in the morgue for the post-mortems
which were held nightly at the hospital.

Of this he writes:

> The morgue was an old barn-like building at the end of
> the dock, unlighted and full of cracks through which rats
> entered and swarmed all over the bodies. On both sides were
> rough board shelves seven feet wide. On these the dead were
> stacked up like cordwood, feet out, making a hedge as high
> as my head. Numbered tags were fastened to the arms, and I
> would climb among them trying to locate the particular num-
> bers wanted, then call the yard men, drunken obscene brutes,
> who came grumbling with their stretchers.
>
> It was not so bad summer evenings, for it was cool and
> pleasant on the dock, and often I would stand and watch a
> Fall River steamer go past on the river, a blaze of lights like
> a floating palace, the band playing and people laughing
> and dancing on deck. On cold and stormy nights it was
> another matter. . . . The old building would creak and shiver
> in the wind. Under my feet I could hear the slap of the

waves against the floor. In the flickering light shadows chased
one another, and long dusty cobwebs hanging from the roof
waved back and forth. When I found and pulled out the
bodies wanted, I would walk back along the wet boards of
the dock, guided through the yellow fog by lights from the
hospital windows. Such work, the house surgeon said, kept
us young cubs in our places.

Advancement depended on the pull one had with the ward
heelers and powerful bosses who then ruled Charity Hospital.
The shameless brutality of the hospital officials in neglecting
the patients shocked the young doctor. Accommodations were
primitive. Electric lights, telephones, elevators, and modern
plumbing fixtures were unknown. Cocaine to relieve pain
had not yet been discovered. The opening of the abdomen as
a surgical measure had never been attempted. It was not
known that malaria and yellow fever were caused by mosquitoes, or that tuberculosis was a germ disease. Childbed fever
killed thousands; the pathogens of typhoid fever were unknown.

Dr. Gardiner continues:

> But in spite of the overcrowding, despite misery, Charity
> Hospital at that time was a valuable field for a young medical
> student . . . Cases were constantly admitted from ships back
> from long voyages to the tropics, from the Guinea coast of
> Africa with yaws, malignant malaria, Malta fever, sleeping
> sickness. From South America came yellow fever, leprosy, rare
> skin infections, Barbados leg, cholera, swamp fever, all kinds
> of infections from insects, snakes, and poisonous plants.
> Smallpox was isolated in the pesthouse, and I sneaked over
> occasionally, gave the gate man some whiskey, and took a few
> notes. I was in turn assigned to these wards: surgical, medical,
> throat, maternity, syphilitic, and insane. . . .

Wanting more practice in surgery, after about a year in
Charity Hospital Dr. Gardiner got himself transferred to the
prison service. The prison was built on the banks of the river
on a stone retaining wall. It was old, damp, without comforts
of any kind. Gas jets were used for lighting, water was carried

in by buckets, and all refuse and drainage dumped into the
river. In winter the cells were as cold as outdoors. The hospital
was a makeshift affair of twenty beds under the roof on the
fifth floor, reached only by one narrow stairway. All water was
carried up the long flights of stairs, and all slops carried down
in buckets that sloshed over, making the stairs a mess. The
patients' beds were cots with straw mattresses. There were no
bedpans, oakum being pushed under the patients when necessary and dragged out after some hours. The heat under the roof
was intense during the summer, and the air at all times thick
and foul from wounds and dirty bodies. The nurses were
prisoners on parole, a lazy lot of cutthroats, as Dr. Gardiner
remembers them, who were often drunk on smuggled liquor,
but who had some pull with a Tammany boss and were given
soft jobs. There was an unending battle against bedbugs, lice,
and cockroaches.

> The first morning in that horrible little prison hospital
> I confess my stomach was in a bad way. I could eat no
> lunch. . . .
> I was very happy in the company of two other doctors
> on the staff. They were both splendid men whole-heartedly
> devoted to their work. . . . We had been eight months in the
> prison service when the typhoid epidemic broke out in New
> York. Charity Hospital was so crowded with patients that
> some had to be put in tents. There were not enough nurses,
> and things were in an awful mess. We hoped the prison
> might escape as we had a strict quarantine, but neither the
> cause nor prevention of typhoid was understood; so one day
> a guard came down and then case after case appeared among
> the prisoners, and the fever hit these poorly fed men very
> hard.
> Our little hospital was a bad enough place at best. Now,
> with twenty cases on cots and sixty on straw mattresses on the
> floor, we were so crowded we could get about only by stepping
> over the patients. Many were out of their heads, violent,
> crawling about, yelling. We tried to keep oakum under them,
> but the floor was soon covered with slime, the stench fearful,
> vermin swarmed all over. The nurses, ignorant paroled
> prisoners, were worse than useless; so, in self-defense, we three
> doctors rolled up our sleeves and did the nursing ourselves.

It was revolting in every sense, but we could not let these prisoners die from neglect. We tried to get help from anywhere, wrote frantic letters to the warden, the State Board, but everybody was too busy, and the old prison was left to boil in its own filthy juice. We three ate and slept in empty cells and worked day and night. The deaths were something awful. Hourly dead bodies were half carried, half dragged down the stairs and stacked up in a shed.

After six of Dr. Gardiner's colleagues had died of typhoid fever, he went back to New York to get a good rest, and later find a surgical clinic where he could get work. He had seen enough misery to last him a lifetime. Presently, he met Dr. Abbe, a well-known surgeon of the day who had charge of a surgical outpatient clinic at New York Hospital on Twenty-second Street. The clinic had all the newest equipment—tiled floors, operating room, private room and bath for each resident physician. Here Dr. Gardiner eventually became clinic chief. But his work among the poor and destitute left a mark on him which, as one can readily understand, was never erased.

· XIII ·

FEMALE PRINCIPLE AT WORK

Two years after the "effluvia" scare, a wealthy New York lady with charitable interests and a remarkable talent for organization became interested in Bellevue. This notable woman was to change the whole concept of hospitalization, not only at Bellevue, but throughout the United States.

Miss Louisa Schuyler, great-granddaughter of Alexander Hamilton, had joined Drs. Elizabeth and Emily Blackwell in founding the Women's Central Association for Relief during the Civil War. This organization had a far-reaching effect: it was the parent body of the American Red Cross; and its work in the war served as model and stimulus for the whole field of nursing. Louisa Schuyler was elected its president and was commended by Secretary of War Stanton for her organizational accomplishments.

When the war ended, Louisa Schuyler found herself unwilling to return to the social round of her class. She made up her mind to redeem a promise given to Dr. Willard Parker, like Dr. Stephen Smith a lifelong advocate of public health reform, to visit one of his pet projects, the Westchester County Poorhouse.

This institution was the fourth largest in the state, and was fortunate in having a kind and intelligent warden. But the warden was so handicapped by lack of funds and by political pressures that there was little he could do to relieve the misery of his charges. Among the hundreds of inmates there were sixty children under the care of one slovenly old woman. The woman's illegitimate daughter assisted her in the work, and "that daughter's own illegitimate child was one of the charges." Conditions in the rest of the poorhouse were so shocking that Miss Schuyler went away "heartsick and ashamed that such things could exist in our country."

Louisa Schuyler felt a fierce determination to change this abominable situation. She was hardheaded enough to realize that to get things done she would need the backing of influential people. And for this she needed incontrovertible factual proof of neglect and suffering. She set out to get it.

The climate of public opinion could not have been more favorable. New York had just been rocked (1871–72) by the exposure of the Tweed ring, and all thinking people were up in arms against municipal corruption.

William Marcy (Boss) Tweed had built the most powerful political machine in American history. The board of supervisors, the real governing body of the city, was composed of six Republicans and six Democrats. Tweed, who was street commissioner and leader of Tammany Hall, persuaded the supervisors to break down party lines so that they could control both party machines—and the attendant patronage.

The Tweed ring consisted of Tweed, who was successively school commissioner, state senator, and commissioner of public works; Mayor Oakey Hall; and Supervisors Peter B. Sweeney and Richard B. Connolly. From 1869 to 1871 these men controlled every public office in the city. They sold city jobs, tax rebates, controlled all city contracts, and issued bonds at extravagant rates of interest. During this short period, Boss Tweed and his friends mulcted the city treasury of almost $200,000,000.

When the reform movement put up a candidate for mayor who Tweed felt stood a good chance of winning, Tweed rammed through the state legislature a law which would keep appointees in office for the next eight years, no matter who won the mayoralty election. Then he proceeded to place his friends in the positions of street commissioner, park commissioner, police commissioner, and commissioner of charities, thus rounding out his control of the city government.

It was at this point that a disgruntled bookkeeper turned over to the *New York Times* complete evidence of Tweed's financial chicanery. The scandal rocked New York almost as badly as the Civil War draft riots. Posters bearing Thomas Nast cartoons of Tweed and his henchmen were hung on lampposts throughout the city.

Tweed was convicted of theft of public funds and was sentenced to twelve years in prison. He subsequently escaped and got as far as Spain, where he was arrested and returned to the United States. He died in Ludlow Street Gaol in 1878.

The exposure of the Tweed ring set off a wave of reforms, and investigations were launched into all city departments. Irate citizens demanded that their representatives give them a clean government.

It was at the height of this reform movement that Louisa Schuyler made her visit to Bellevue Hospital, accompanied by a friend, Mrs. David Lane. Later she wrote of this epochal visit in 1872:

> When I walked through the wards of Bellevue Hospital with Mrs. Lane and General Bowen [Commissioner of the Board of Charities] I saw at once that no permanent improvement in the condition of the hospital could be made until the nursing service was radically changed, and this could only be accomplished through the establishment of a training school for nurses. I determined then and there that this should be done.

On the evening of January 26, 1872, a small group of socially prominent New York women gathered in Miss Schuyler's drawing room. None of them had more than a vague idea of sociology or economics. Yet they had one thing in common:

they were the daughters and granddaughters of fighters—men who had carved a nation out of the wilderness. This heritage quickly asserted itself.

Mrs. Joseph Hobson has left an account of the meeting and its immediate outcome:

> It was in 1872 that my friend, Mrs. Virginia Osborn, invited me to accompany her to a meeting to be held at the house of Miss Louisa Lee Schuyler. She did not tell me its object, merely saying that she thought it might be interesting.
> I entered the room a perfect stranger. Mrs. Osborn introduced me and Miss Schuyler invited me to take a seat by her side. She stated the object of the meeting, then suddenly turning to me, she handed me a pencil and piece of paper, and asked me to take the minutes. I had never attended a meeting of this kind and knew no more about taking minutes than a baby. I protested but, smiling, she said, "Take note of what you hear as well as you can and I will help you afterward." Of course she had to rewrite those minutes.
> Thus commenced my education in philanthropy and, inspired by such a teacher, I soon became absorbed in the work. On the committee which was formed that day to visit and report on the condition of Bellevue Hospital, I found to my surprise and dismay that I was appointed chairman of the subcommittee to visit the surgical wards for women. I have never to this day understood why I was named chairman of that committee, for a woman more absolutely ignorant of the subject could not have been found in the Island of Manhattan.
> I soon found that the other members of the committee were almost as ignorant as myself. There were my friend Virginia (Mrs. William Henry Osborn), Mrs. Woodworth, and Mrs. Baldy Smith, wife of the well-known General who bore that nickname.

Mrs. Hobson may have been inexperienced as an organizer, but she had a bright curiosity and a clear and incisive mind. Her account of that first meeting at Louisa Schuyler's and its results continues:

> The whole committee was first to go in a body to the Hospital to be introduced to the authorities. On that day we were escorted through the wards by the Commissioner, General

Bowen, and by Mr. Brennan, the stalwart Irish Warden, who
was very polite. When I asked him years afterward how he
happened to treat us so well from the beginning, he replied,
"Oh, I saw you were all the real thing and would win out in
the end."

Typical of Louisa Schuyler's hurriedly improvised committee, Mrs. Hobson had never been in a hospital before. On her
first visit, the sight of the patients and the loathsome smells so
sickened her that she nearly fainted. But she persevered and
returned to her task the next day. She was looking about in
perplexity when a young doctor took pity on her. He suggested
she look at the beds and the bedding, the patients' clothing,
the bathroom.

Of what she saw then, she wrote in later years:

> The condition of the patients and of the beds was un-
> speakable. The one nurse slept in the bathroom and the tub
> was filled with filthy rubbish. To her was confided the care
> of 20 patients. Her only assistants were paupers, drafted from
> the workhouse, many of whom had been sent there from
> intemperance, and those convalescents who could leave their
> beds.
> It was Friday. The dinner of salt fish was brought in a bag
> to the ward and emptied on the table. The convalescents
> helped themselves and carried to the others their portions
> on a tin plate with a spoon.
> While I was watching this, my young doctor returned.
> Without speaking to him, I followed him out of the ward,
> down a steep staircase, across the yard filled with every kind
> of rubbish, into a large building which proved to be the
> laundry. Nauseate steam was rising from great cauldrons
> filled with filthy clothing, which one old pauper was stirring
> with a stick. I looked about, the hideous masses were piled
> up all around, but where were the laundresses? There were
> none. The old man was alone. "They've gone away," he told
> me. I asked him what soap he used. "I haven't had any for
> quite a while," he said. "How long a while?" said I. "Oh,
> I should say a matter of several weeks." In reply to my ex-
> clamation of horror, the doctor explained that it took the
> Commissioners a good while to supply all the requisitions.
> Meanwhile the hospital had to wait.
> Next we crossed to the kitchen. A huge Negro cook was

ladling out soup into great tin basins which the workhouse women were to take up into the wards. I learned that these same cauldrons were used for tea and coffee in the morning. Some pauper women were huddled together in a corner peeling potatoes. The whole place reeked with the smell of foul steam and food. I had to escape, it was too dreadful.

When I reached the outer air, my conductor said, "You've seen only the outside. It would take weeks for you to learn all the horrors of this place, but you must be very careful not to be seen with me or to quote me. It might cost me my position here."

"I'll come again tomorrow," I replied.

Mrs. Hobson did as she promised; likewise the other members of Miss Schuyler's committee, each to her task. Meanwhile, the leader herself was plotting daring innovations which would need unheard-of political and financial support for their realization. She had in mind an organization so influential and so powerful that it could enforce its demands for the health and welfare of all charity cases, not only in Bellevue but in all parts of the state of New York. To this end, after much spadework and wirepulling, she formed the State Charities Aid Association. This group still functions as a non-partisan, nonsectarian body. It exists entirely without state aid. The Ladies Visiting Committee at Bellevue became a subcommittee of the association.

From the very start the Ladies came back from their visits convinced that a nurses' training school was imperative before any lasting improvement in hospital care could be insured. A subcommittee was formed, headed by Mrs. Virginia Osborn, and Dr. W. Gil Wylie of Bellevue was asked to serve on it. Wylie was the same young doctor who had befriended Mrs. Hobson on her first visit to Bellevue.

The Ladies continued to make their weekly calls to Bellevue. They learned, among other things, that there were no night nurses. The wards were locked, and three night watchmen made the rounds of 600 patients. Not infrequently these

guardians drugged patients who were likely to demand attention, and drank the stimulants that had been prescribed.

An entry in Mrs. Hobson's notebook reads:

> If a watchman found a patient very ill or dying, he called
> a young doctor. Occasionally patients who had been over-
> looked were found dead in the morning. Rats scampered
> over the floors at night. In fact, it seemed hopeless to attempt
> to cleanse that Augean stable.
>
> One day on my way home, I stopped at a bookseller's and
> ordered Miss Florence Nightingale's works, and some theses
> on hospital management. These I studied and with the mem-
> bers of my committee visited the hospital constantly. We had
> learned a great deal in that first month. Miss Nightingale's
> papers had taught us what was required, and what ought not
> to exist in a hospital. But oh, how low our standards were.
> How much we had to learn—certainly in Bellevue, the only
> hospital I had ever seen, and which I was told was the largest
> pauper hospital in the city, with its 32 wards and over 800
> patients. Were all hospitals like this, I wondered . . .

It was a strict rule of the visiting committee that each
member keep an accurate, detailed account of all that she saw
and heard during her visits to the hospital. In the notebook
kept by Mrs. Osborn, we read:

> February 5th, 12th, and 19th, 1872: the number of patients,
> about 18 to a ward. All Irish Roman Catholics, most of them
> the most common class. We took books and papers to them
> and talked with them all.
>
> The nurse, whose wages are $16. a month, seemed kind,
> willing and obliging, having been six years in the city hos-
> pital, has the advantage of experience. From her and the
> physician of the ward, we learned the following: Diet: gen-
> eral breakfast between six and seven A.M., composed of coffee
> without milk and dry bread. The dinner is one day corned
> beef and cabbage, another day soup, another meat and pota-
> toes and so on. The supper at six of tea, which both nurses
> and patients pronounced nauseous, and bread with a little
> butter. The special diet for very sick patients is eggs, beef-
> steak, oysters, whisky, and port wine. But the physician said
> that, owing to the difficulty of obtaining any dish properly
> prepared, he rarely ordered it, contenting himself with eggs
> and wine.

We visited the kitchen which is across the open court, at
least 100 feet from the door of the hospital. All food must be
brought by hand this distance, in all weather, to all parts of
the hospital. There is one cook for all the patients, assisted
by some pauper women from Blackwell's Island. The kitchen
was dirty and lacking conveniences usually considered indispensable.

We were greatly impressed by the deficiency of night
nurses. The one who attends in Ward 18 had the charge of
five wards from 9 P.M. to 7 A.M., two of the wards being on
one floor, three on another. These nurses are supposed to
visit each ward every half-hour and to lay out patients who
die in the night. Our informant said she laid out three
patients the night before. Her wages were $10.00 a month.
The night service is so inadequate, the doctor informed us,
that whenever he had a very sick patient, he was obliged to
force the convalescents to act as nurses.

February 22: Doctor Wylie, the house surgeon, complained
of the lack of water at night, which was often required. Also,
the deficiency in lights for night operation; the necessity of
using candles—no gas. In the wards, no towels for the use of
the patients except roller in the bathroom. Sent some birds to
Annie Shay, ward 25, a patient who was specially recommended to us by Dr. Jimmie Wood.

April 11: One, if not the chief, difficulty to solve at Bellevue is that of labor. One hundred women taken from the
most degraded class are employed at Bellevue. We are convinced that thirty women at $10. a month would do the work
more efficiently than it is done today. Under an efficient matron there is no doubt but that the experiment would result
successfully.

There are about a hundred men hanging about Bellevue,
receiving no wages whatever, many of them having no positive work assigned to them, but faithful to their adopted
country at the polls twice a year, whose presence is a positive
injury to the morality of the establishment. There are many
others who receive such low salaries it is but natural to suppose that there must be valuable perquisites attached to the
post to induce them to accept it. From the payrolls we obtained the figures of $400. annually for an apothecary; his
assistants, $300. and $240. respectively.

May 11: At this visit, the visitors took up the question
with Mr. Brennan [the warden] of water coolers in the ward
and bedside pitchers for patients, etc. Found Annie Shay
crying for opium. . . . The night nurse, who had been em-

ployed to watch her after the operation, had given her large
doses at her own discretion to keep her quiet and had then
helped herself to Annie's brandy for her own gratification.
Proofs of the pernicious nursing in the hospital, that an ignorant woman has the power to dose a patient with opium,
and that the brandy should be left by the bedside to be taken
by whoever may choose. The dinner was merely boiled mut-
ton without any vegetables.

The following excerpts reporting on individual cases show
a recognition of the need for social service:

> Little Jimmie McGinnis is now the pet of the ward. We
> hope in time his father, who is intemperate, will consent to
> his being placed in some institution, where he can be edu-
> cated.
> One woman, who had her wrist dislocated, was crying
> quietly. She had left four children at home under seven. Her
> husband had been drunk ever since she left home. Mrs. Os-
> born arranged for someone to see that they were kept fed and
> kept warm. This woman found the children without shoes
> or stockings—no fire, nothing in the room but an old mattress
> and one covering. There the family of six slept. The mother
> had worked for nine years to keep them from starving. The
> children were bright and nice, and the mother looked respect-
> able.
> A bright girl, an orphan, not more than nineteen, looked
> like one to be watched over when she left the hospital.

From the start of their work at Bellevue, the lady visitors
became aware of the hospital's moral problems.

> The visitors are deeply impressed with an abuse which
> exists: the facilities which people of bad character enjoy for
> visiting the hospital. Keepers of houses of ill fame obtain
> access to the wards without difficulty, and thus not only watch
> their victims, sent there by them, but make the acquaintance
> of other patients whom they lure by specious promises into
> their toils. Men of the same dangerous class are constantly
> persuading these young girls, who are weak, lonely, and with-
> out financial security. The Visitors have seen as many as three
> men of decidedly vicious type sitting by one bedside at the
> same time. On several occasions the girls have besought the
> Visitors to rescue them, saying that unless the Ladies would
> help when they left the hospital, they had no way of escape.

Despite the thousand and one difficulties peculiar to an age in which the position of upper-class women was in great measure ornamental, the Ladies began to gain some measure of recognition. Mrs. Osborn records:

> May 7: Had a long talk with Doctor Mitchell. He confessed to me that there had existed at first among the physicians a great prejudice against our Association. They felt that we would find fault, make trouble, then get tired and summer would disperse us. Now, he said, they were not only reconciled to our visits, but felt that we had achieved a great many useful reforms, and that our visits had an excellent effect on the patients.

· XIV ·

THE LADIES PERSEVERE

Slowly the Ladies Visiting Committee began to introduce a semblance of order into the gloomy corridors and wards of old Bellevue. While chipping away at existing evils, they never lost sight of their original objective—a nursing school. This notation appeared in the minutes of a meeting held in 1872:

> We cannot but feel that this Association has effected all the reforms it can hope for until the nursing system is changed, but constant vigilance on our part is necessary to sustain the present improvements as, if the authorities of the hospital see that our labors are relaxed, they will immediately return to the former regime.

With her unerring sense of timing, Louisa Schuyler determined to strike again. Miss Schuyler broached the subject of a nursing school to Commissioner Bowen, who heard her out blankly. The idea of a nursing school had never come within his purview. Miss Schuyler filled him with stories of the great work of Florence Nightingale in establishing the St. Thomas's school in London and sent him off to beard the board of charities.

Though General Bowen was in favor of the idea of a nursing school, he found it difficult to persuade the hidebound members of the Bellevue Medical Board. The Board felt strongly about women in hospitals. To Bowen's plea that the

Ladies only wished to improve the nursing service in the wards, the good doctors replied that the kind of women the Ladies would introduce would undoubtedly be independent and self-assertive, and certainly ". . . not amenable to discipline. We prefer nurses who will do as they are told."

Fortunately not all the doctors on the staff embraced this arbitrary viewpoint. Drs. Stephen Smith, Jimmy Wood, Austin Flint, and Gil Wylie heartily and loudly embraced the plan. So, too, did several members of the house staff of Bellevue, who risked their positions by championing the visiting committee. Dr. Ernest W. Cushing of Boston was actually fired for his too vehement support of the training plan.

Never did a hospital have a more urgent need for topflight nursing technique. The only antiseptic in use at Bellevue was carbolic acid. Stephen Smith was in the midst of his uphill campaign for the adoption of Lister's antiseptic technique. Such simple operations as the amputation of a finger sometimes were followed by rapid infection and death. From 40 to 60 per cent of all limb amputations proved fatal. The house staff went from patient to patient, dressing wounds without bothering to wash their hands. Sponges used for washing wounds were not cotton, to be burned immediately after one use, but bits of real sea sponge used over and over.

Though conditions in private hospitals were superior to those in public institutions like Bellevue, a nurses' training program, even with them, was considered revolutionary. There was not a single trained nurse or nurses' training school in the whole United States. Nor did anyone have a clear idea of how to set up such a school.

In this crisis Dr. Gil Wylie went to England at his own expense to consult Florence Nightingale about her school at St. Thomas's Hospital. Wylie was unable to see Miss Nightingale because of her illness, but did make an extensive study of St. Thomas's school and of the nursing school attached to the University of Edinburgh. He returned in September, 1872, with copious notes and plans. Just before the board of charities met, a letter addressed to Dr. Wylie arrived from Florence Nightingale. This letter, one of the proudest possessions of the Bellevue Training School for Nurses—a framed copy of it hangs in the Washington headquarters of the American Red Cross—said in part:

London, September 18, 1872

Sir:

First, let me explain that your letter from Paris of August 26, was most unfortunately not forwarded to me 'til the day after that on which you proposed to leave England. When it reached me, I was overwhelmed with business and illness . . . (I should, perhaps, add that my medical advisors have warned me that if I have business interviews of more than half an hour, it is at the risk of my life.)

I wish your Association Godspeed with all my heart and soul in their task of reform. I will gladly if I can, answer any questions you may think it worthwhile to ask.

You say: "The great difficulty will be to define the instructions, the duties and the position of the nurses in distinction from those of medical men," and you are anxious to get my views in relation to this subject.

Is this a difficulty?

A nurse is not a medical man, nor is she a medical woman. Most carefully do we in our training avoid the confusion, both practically and theoretically, of letting women suppose that nursing duties and medical duties run into or overlap each other—so much that, though we have often been asked to allow ladies intending to be doctors to come in as nurses to St. Thomas' Hospital, in order to pick up, so they phrased it, professional medical knowledge, we have never consented even to admit such applicants in order to avoid even the semblance of encouraging such gross ignorance and dabbling in matters of life and death as this implies. . . .

On the contrary, the nurses are there, and solely there, to carry out the orders of the medical and surgical staff, including, of course, the whole practice of cleanliness, fresh air, disease . . . they must be, for discipline and internal management, entirely under a woman, a trained superintendent whose whole business it is to see that nursing duties are performed according to this standard.

For this purpose, may I say 1) that the nursing of hospitals, including the carrying out of medical officers' orders, must be done to the satisfaction of the medical officers whose orders regarding the sick are to be carried out (and we may depend upon it that the highly trained, intelligent nurse and cultivated, moral woman will do this better than the ignorant, stupid woman, for ignorance is always headstrong).

2) That all desired changes, reprimands, etc., in the nursing and for the nurses should be referred by medical officers to the superintendent; that rules which make the matron (superintendent) and nurses responsible to the house surgeons or medical and surgical staff, except in the sense of carrying out current medical orders, above insisted on, are always found fatal to nursing discipline; that, if the medical officers have fault to find, it is bad policy for them to reprimand the nurses themselves. The medical staff must carry all considerable complaints to the matron . . .

3) All discipline must be, of course, under the matron and ward Sisters. Otherwise, nursing is impossible, and here I should add that unless there is, so to speak, a hierarchy of women as thus: matron or superintendent; Sisters or head nurse; ward maids or scrubbers (or whatever other grades are locally considered more appropriate), discipline becomes impossible.

In this hierarchy, the higher grade ought always to know the duties of the lower better than the lower grade does itself, and so on to the head. Otherwise, how will they be able to train? Moral influence alone will not make a good trainer.

. . . You are doubtless aware that this is by no means a custom in Germany (in France the system much more nearly approaches our own). In Germany, generally, the ward nurse is immediately and for everything, under the ward doctor— and this led to consequences so disastrous that going into the opposite extreme, Kaiserswerth and other German, Protestant deaconesses' institutions were formed where the chaplain and the Vorsteherrine (female superintendent) were virtually masters of the hospital, which is, of course, absurd.

My friend, then, who has been for forty years medical officer of one of the largest hospitals in Germany, wrote to me that he had succeeded in placing a matron over his nurses —then, that after one and one-half years, she had been so persecuted that she had been compelled to resign. Then— that he had remained another year trying to have her replaced. Lastly, that failing, he had himself resigned his post of forty years, believing that he could better work for this reform outside the hospital than in it.

. . . I think I will venture to send you a copy of a paper—

the only one I have left (the original was written by order of the then Poor Law Board for their new Work House Infirmaries and printed in their reports). So many hospitals then wrote to me to give them a similar sketch for their special use, and it was so utterly impossible for me to write at all, that I abridged and altered my original paper for their use, and this, I fear, dirty copy is the last I have left. Pray excuse it. Again begging you to command me if I can be of any use to your great purpose, to which I wish every success and ever increasing progress, pray believe me, sir,

Ever your faithful servant,
(*Signed*) Florence Nightingale

P.S. You will find in the appendix to the printed paper all the steps of our training at St. Thomas' Hospital under our admirable matron, Mrs. Wardroper, but, as she may probably see this letter, I must abstain from praising her, as it were, to her face, which all noble creatures dislike.

(*Signed*) F.N.

Armed with Miss Nightingale's practical suggestions, the lady visitors began to line up for another assault on the board of charities, after already persuading the State Charities Aid Association, which Miss Louisa Schuyler had by this time molded into a powerful organization, to sponsor their project. Dr. Jimmy Wood and Dr. Stephen Smith dragooned the Medical Board into reluctant approval.

The Ladies next persuaded thirty-five leading physicians to ask for a public subscription of $20,000 to find a building for the nurses' training school. This fund was oversubscribed in a few days, and, armed with this public enthusiasm, the Ladies forced the reluctant board of charities to assign six Bellevue wards for the training of nurses: two women's medical wards, two women's surgical, one ward for the diseases of women, and one male surgical ward.

British nurses came from the upper servant class, but the lady visitors wanted women able to meet higher requirements. To attract superior young women, Mrs. Virginia Osborn bought and furnished a nurses' home on Twenty-sixth Street opposite the hospital. A circular was distributed in New York, inviting applications and stipulating that a prospective student must be well educated and have a real desire to become a nurse. The brochure concluded:

> We impose no vows. We say to all in the words of the holy founder of the Order of the Sisters of Charity, "Your convent must be the house of the sick, your cloister the streets of the city or the wards of the hospitals, the promise of obedience your sole enclosure, your grate, the fear of God, and womanly modesty your only veil."

The applications poured in, but most of them were so discouraging the Ladies almost lost heart. Finally six applicants were weeded out from the hundreds who had offered themselves. But the day of opening approached and the school still lacked the key figure so strongly stressed by Florence Nightingale—a trained superintendent. With sublime confidence, Virginia Osborn had the superintendent's bed made up anyway. A few days before the opening, May 1, 1873, a Sister of the All Saints Sisterhood of London called on Mrs. Osborn and was at once accepted.

Sister Helen (Miss Bowdin) soon proved that she was a gifted executive with a genius for handling officialdom. Her commanding presence, her beautiful voice with its clipped British accents, overawed all opposition. She ruled her wards, both hospital and students, with an iron hand.

Actually Sister Helen was almost more than the lady visitors bargained for. She saw no reason whatever why the members of the visiting committee should have any say in the management of the school. She demanded and got three women with hospital experience to act as night supervisor and night nurses, and calmly insisted that the board of charities pay them $20.00 and $16.00 a month respectively, as well as a $4.00 allowance for board.

One of these experienced women was Linda Richards, who had been trained in the care of obstetrical cases in the New

England Hospital for Women and Children. Later, she was
to establish training schools elsewhere in the United States,
then in Europe, and eventually in Japan. But of all her experiences, her first night at Bellevue remained the sharpest in
her memory.

I shall never forget my first experience on night duty. No
sooner had the day nurses left the wards than the gas was
turned so low that the faces of the patients could not be distinguished. One could see only the dim outlines of figures
wrapped in gray blankets lying upon the beds. If any work
was to be done, a candle must be lighted, and only two
candles a week were allowed each ward. If more were used
the nurse had to provide them. At midnight all the steam
was turned off; at three A.M. it was turned on again, and
the cracking of the pipes would waken everyone in the wards.
How cold and dismal were the hours between midnight and
three o'clock in the morning!

The captain of the night watch made several rounds of the
wards through the night, and at five A.M. he turned off all
the gas, leaving us in total darkness. Patients took advantage
of this condition to leave their beds and give trouble in many
ways. At the end of my first month I told Sister Helen I could
not be responsible for the patients unless I could have lights
in the wards. She said, "Go to the warden and tell him."
Under the solemn promise (always faithfully kept) to use no
more gas than would enable us to fulfill our duties, and to
turn off all gas as soon as it was light, we were allowed night
light. So one step in advance was taken.

Written night orders and reports were at that time unknown. Night nurses went on duty at eight P.M. I saw each
head day nurse as she left her ward, received orders and transmitted them to the night nurses. In the morning I gave reports to the head nurses as they began their day duty. All this
was verbal. When I had been on duty nearly a year, I kept
notes of one case to be written up by a nurse for Sister
Helen. Each nurse was required to write up a case. The doctor of the division saw the report and thought it was for him.
He was glad of it, as it helped him in his notes on the case,
and after that he asked me to write reports of all serious
cases. This was the beginning in Bellevue of a custom now
considered an elemental necessity in all hospitals, and in all
serious cases of illness under the care of trained nurses.

While the new nursing school was struggling toward success
the lady visitors kept on with their efforts at reform, some
times against almost impossible odds. In 1874 there was a
shocking mortality rate from puerperal fever. During the first
six months of the year Bellevue had 166 confinement cases
and of these 31 died of puerperal fever.

In her recollections, Mrs. Hobson tells of the maternity
wards situated on an upper floor of the hospital:

> We had no nurses there, and knew nothing about their
> management. We consulted Sister Helen, who said she could
> spare a head nurse and some pupils to take charge of those
> wards; and she also thought it very desirable that our pupils
> should have this additional training. Accordingly we made
> application to the Medical Board to allow this extension of
> the school, and received an invitation from the Board to
> confer on the subject. Mrs. Griffin, Mrs. Osborn, Mrs. Wood-
> worth and I were appointed to attend the conference.
> We found a number of the doctors present, among them
> Dr. X——, who acted as their spokesman, and our friend Dr.
> James Wood. The secretary read our letter, in which we
> offered to take charge of the obstetrical wards; and then Dr.
> X—— in the most vehement manner denounced us as spies,
> proposing to interfere with the management of the hospital,
> and declared that if we persisted in our plan we should have
> our training school closed. Dr. Wood, much agitated, walked
> up and down the room trying to speak for us and calm his
> colleague. But the others were evidently in sympathy with
> Dr. X—— and plied us with questions in regard to our plans
> and intentions, which bewildered us. . . .
> At last Mrs. Griffin, in her stately manner, rose and said,
> "Gentlemen, we will not prolong this interview; you will
> hear from us in a few days." I have never felt so indignant
> in my life. As Mrs. Osborn and I walked home, the tears
> rolled down my cheeks, I felt so humiliated by the insults we
> had received.
> A special meeting of the State Charities Aid Association
> was called, and we made our report. Immediately Mr.
> Howard Porter, Mr. Levi P. Morton, and General Barlow
> were appointed a committee to confer with the Medical
> Board without delay . . . they gave them to understand in no
> uncertain terms that New York City was behind us; and that
> they would not allow their wives and sisters to be insulted.

In fact, they made their view so plain that before long we received a communication from the Medical Board inviting the Training School to take charge of the obstetrical wards of the Bellevue Hospital. These three maternity wards were turned over to us in May, 1874, and we placed Miss Linda Richards in charge.

Miss Richards had scarcely been installed on this ward when a new epidemic of puerperal fever broke out, this time so violent that it accounted for thirty-one deaths between January and June. The Ladies were alarmed. They had been accused of criticizing and meddling in affairs which they did not understand; they could not face this situation which reflected on the competence of their nursing without doing something. They began to investigate in self-defense, and were told that puerperal infection was carried by the surgeons themselves from the surgical wards.

They set out directly for the hospital, and on the steps met several members of the Medical Board. Attacking the startled physicians without giving them time to organize a defense, the lady visitors gave them twenty-four hours in which to remove the lying-in wards from the surgical wards, on pain of exposure to the *Evening Post*.

The Board moved the ward to Blackwell's Island within the time limit, and the fever decreased. Unfortunately, there were no provisions for emergencies on Blackwell's Island. Many of the mothers who came to Bellevue waited until the last minute. An average of twelve women a month were taken in labor on the street. As a result, babies were born in the gloomy waiting room at the ferry landing, or on the boat itself as it thrashed through the chop on the East River. It began to look as if the chronic obstructionists on the Board would win out after all.

But once again the day was saved when the women badgered the Medical Board into moving the lying-in ward to an old firehouse between Second and Third Avenues. This dirty old building they scrubbed and fixed up themselves. Its death rate was soon the city's lowest.

Not until the second class was in training did the school adopt a distinctive cap and uniform. In 1876 Sister Helen consulted with the board of managers of the nursing school, who agreed that a uniform would help the service, provided it appealed to the nurses. Before that time the nurses had worn any kind of cap, as fancy dictated. But henceforth, the managers said, it "should be impressed on our nurses that the caps are intended to cover the hair and not to be merely coquettish ornaments; and that long dresses in the wards are most objectionable."

Miss Euphemia Van Rensselaer, a graduate of the first class and now Sister Helen's assistant, designed the first Bellevue uniform. She went home for a couple of days and returned in the "Stripes and Cap," looking so fetching that the class was delighted to adopt them. The style of the uniform has changed with the years, but never the material.

The board of managers of the nursing school soon came to believe that every woman patient should be accompanied to her operation by a nurse. The surgeons, however, feared such female intrusion might cause a disturbance, for some of the students were a rowdy lot.

Miss Van Rensselaer, a tall, serenely beautiful woman, volunteered to be the first nurse to make the trip to the operating room. She disappeared through the door of the amphitheater, with one of the board members anxiously waiting outside in the hall. After the operation was over, Miss Van Rensselaer returned safe and sound. There had been no horseplay or rude comment, the operating surgeon assured the much-relieved board member. The students, he said, had given one gasp and gape when they saw the nurse, and that was all.

Another graduate of the first 1876 class, Miss Frances Root, paved the way for the modern social service or community nurse. On her graduation, Miss Root decided that she wanted to devote herself to nursing the sick poor in their homes, under the auspices of the City Mission which, together with the Fruit and Flower Guild, occupied the house to the west of the Training School. A group from the mission who called themselves "Bible Readers" were already doing similar work, but Miss Root was convinced that the poor should have competent nursing and a knowledge of social hygiene, as well as material aid and sympathy.

As this was a volunteer organization, one of the members of the board of managers of the Training School agreed to be responsible for Miss Root's salary. Within the next few years several other nurses joined her. In a period of nine months in 1879, they made over 2,500 visits; the board of managers was well launched in social service nursing.

Another undertaking of the board was the publishing of a manual of nursing for the instruction of head nurses and students of the Training School. The book was compiled by Dr. Victoria White with the assistance of Dr. Emily Blackwell, and was revised by Dr. Mary Putnam Jacobi, wife of the illustrious pediatrician and an eminent doctor on her own account. G. P. Putnam's Sons published the book, which ran through many editions.

The school of nursing which opened on May 1, 1873 marked another first for Bellevue, but by a narrow margin. Five months later the New Haven school was opened, and six months later the Massachusetts General Hospital's school in Boston. Some claim that Dr. Valentine Seaman's nursing class in New York Hospital, for which he wrote *The Midwives' Monitor and Mothers' Mirror*, came first: other, the Philadelphia School for Midwives, or Dr. Maria Zakrezewska's school, which in 1860 trained six nurses at New England Female College in Boston. But the first permanent nurses' training program in this country was unquestionably started at Bellevue, a living monument to the power of womankind to change the world for the better.

· XV ·

GENIUS AND THE LESION

By the 1870's one great basic medical advance had already been accomplished: doctors had learned how to use deep anesthesia. This, in turn, made it possible for the surgeon to proceed slowly and carefully with his work. The time when John W. Francis would cut off a leg in twenty-six seconds was fast disappearing.

For countless centuries surgery had been a gruesome business, almost as harrowing psychologically for the operator as excruciating physically for the patient. All sorts of stratagems had been used to outwit pain—alcohol, opium, hashish, mandrake, pressure on the carotid artery, and the like. It was not until the eighteenth century when Sir Humphry Davy, inventor of the miner's lamp, discovered the anesthetic properties of nitrous oxide, or laughing gas, and Michael Faraday the same of ether, that the stage was set for the conquest of pain. Thereafter, it was only a question of time until practical minds turned this knowledge to medical use.

This momentous event came in the 1840's, when Dr. Riggs, on the suggestion of a fellow dentist, Dr. Wells, experimented with nitrous oxide as an anesthetic aid in pulling teeth. About the same time Drs. Jackson and Morton of Boston, the first a chemist, the second a dentist, rediscovered the value of ether as a means of inducing insensibility to pain, and proved its value to the staff of the Massachusetts General. Shortly after this a Dr. Simpson, gynecologist at Edinburgh, found that chloroform also could stupefy without causing death. Finally, in 1884, the Viennese surgeon, Dr. Koller, was able to use cocaine, an alkaloid derivative of the Peruvian coca leaf, to render his patients unconscious.

As we have said, the gradual perfection of anesthetics in the middle of the nineteenth century drastically changed surgical techniques. The cut and slash method went by the board. Henceforth careful preparation and a methodical, step-by-step operative procedure became possible. This in turn gave great impetus to the development of another field of medicine, pathology. For both preoperative and postoperative study demanded an intimate knowledge of the nature of the lesion— that is, the breakdown in cellular tissue which it was the surgeon's duty to relieve. At the same time, rapid advances in the knowledge of optics and microscopy, in chemistry, in histology, and the like, also enhanced the scope of pathological research.

In any event, the age of Virchow (leucocytosis), of Metchnikoff (phagocytes), of Schaudinn (spirochete of syphilis), of Wassermann (blood reaction of syphilis), of Ehrlich, Koch, Pasteur (study of microorganisms), of Finlay, Reed, Carroll, Noguchi (vectors of yellow fever transmission), and of other great pathfinders had arrived. With a realization that the roots of disease lay in the breakdown of the cell, either from external causes or inherent failure, a whole new medical vista opened up. Among the foremost disciples of the new science of pathology was a Bellevue man. His career is typical of the times and, as such, merits close attention.

In the fall of 1872 William Henry Welch, son of a Norfolk, Connecticut, family doctor, having been graduated from Yale, enrolled at the College of Physicians and Surgeons, oldest and most imperious of New York's three rival medical schools. Its competition were New York University Medical School, which bought diplomas from its parent university, and the Bellevue

Hospital School. Actually, none of this trio was a first-rate
school, but Physicians and Surgeons was the most pretentious.
In the main, like almost all medical schools of the day, Physicians and Surgeons was a business enterprise. It had no admission requirements, gave no grades, and asked only a single final
examination. Few students were failed, because the professors'
livelihood depended upon tuition fees. When the expenses of
the school were paid, the professors divided what was left
among themselves. The teachers were reluctant to raise their
standards for fear students would go elsewhere. (After young
Welch took his final exam he confided to his sister Emma in
a letter, "To tell the truth, it was the easiest examination I
ever entered since leaving boarding school.")

Welch found his chief interest in the clinic for nervous
diseases conducted by Dr. Edward C. Seguin, pioneer in the
use of the clinical thermometer. He was particularly attracted
to these clinics because Seguin offered a microscope as a prize
for the best notes taken by a student. Welch won the microscope—a Varick, with excellent French triplex lenses—but he
had no idea of microscopy, and there was no place he could
go for formal instruction.

In the fall of 1873 Welch's brilliant record earned him an
appointment as prosector—the assistant who did the actual
dissection—to the professor of anatomy. The prospect of end-
lessly dissecting the human body made him quail, but he
found to his surprise that after the initial shock, his new work
fascinated him. He later wrote of this period:

> We dissected night and day. You should have seen our
> dissections of radial plexus and the muscles of the back, etc.
> It was a work of art, and we had fresh beef blood brought in
> to smear over the muscles . . . I never felt so proud in my
> life.

At the urging of his professors Welch entered a competition
for the Thesis Prize, the highest honor Physicians and Surgeons
could bestow. His summary of the literature on goiter won

handily, but there was no money to publish it. Some time before, Welch had enrolled in courses at both the rival medical schools, New York University and Bellevue—a rare feat at the time. At Bellevue he drew the attention of Dr. Jimmy Wood, whose private cram quiz he joined but left when, halfway through the course, he heard that the rules had been changed so that only graduate doctors were eligible for internships. He was horrified to receive a telegram late in September notifying him that the rules had been changed back and that he was to report for the examination. As yet he had not studied surgery, but the examiner was to be Dr. Wood, and Welch thought he might get through because Wood had taken a liking to him. But, as it turned out, Dr. Frank Hamilton was the examiner. Then Welch had an extraordinary piece of luck. He was asked about goiter, a subject on which he was naturally expert.

William Henry Welch was appointed to Bellevue Hospital just six months before his graduation from Physicians and Surgeons. At Bellevue he came to know a remarkable man, the pathologist Francis Delafield, who also taught at Physicians and Surgeons. Delafield, although still a young man, was already one of the great "deadhouse men" of his time. He seemed very remote from his colleagues. Welch would watch him in his black skullcap and ticking apron, smoking a meerschaum pipe, as he cut and stained anatomical sections and stared fixedly at them under the microscope. In spite of his eagerness to follow Delafield's cryptic example, Welch merely looked on wistfully, never venturing to ask Delafield for instruction as to how to use the instrument.

In June, writing to his father, Welch reported:

> Yesterday Dr. Delafield asked me if I would not take his place as curator of the Wood Museum and Pathological Specimens, and be pathologist at the hospital for the summer. I accepted, of course, very gladly. It is the position which Dr. Delafield and Dr. Janeway have held as curators at the Bellevue Dead House that has given them their reputations

as pathologists, and it is as such that they rank among the first in the country.

Most young doctors would have gladly embraced the prospect of continuing to work at Bellevue under one of the nation's leading pathologists. But not Billy Welch. He realized that his one desire was to become a professor of pathological anatomy, to conduct research and teach for the rest of his life. In America this was impossible. Teaching and study were rewards given only to successful practitioners after years of work. Also, to qualify as a professor, he would need the superior training available only in such centers as Berlin and Leipzig.

It was here that Providence took a hand, in the person of Welch's old friend from prep school and Yale days, Frederick Dennis. Dennis had gone to boarding school with Welch in Connecticut and had followed him to Yale and the College of Physicians and Surgeons—and from there to Bellevue. Fred Dennis was everything that Welch was not: wealthy, socially prominent, facile, charming, and born to success. He determined to become kingmaker to his friend.

Welch took an indulgent view of Dennis' high-pressure tactics, convinced that they would do no good. When Dennis' father offered to pay half his fare to Europe if he would accompany his son, Welch jumped at the chance. He borrowed $500 from his sister Emma, but the elder Dennis ended up by paying his full fare. Welch's own father, who had been looking forward to a partnership with his only son, yielded without resistance and agreed to foot the bill for living abroad.

So, on April 19, 1876, William Henry Welch, accompanied by his omnipresent friend, embarked on the great adventure of his life. He would meet and study with Europe's greatest scientists, and try genuine research for the first time.

For two years, 1876–77, Dr. Billy Welch traveled in Europe from laboratory to laboratory and clinic to clinic, absorbing the new pathological techniques which were opening up an entirely new world in medical diagnosis. Before his eyes was unfolding definitive proof of the germ origin of disease. Marveling, impatient to emulate, he watched germs being cultured and identified.

In Europe more than ever Dennis' vocation became the advancement of his inimitably endowed, but always passive, friend. He secured Welch an opportunity to write on German universities for the *Lancet,* which Welch refused on the grounds that he did not know enough. He urged Welch to send his essay on lymphosarcoma to Daniel Coit Gilman, president of Johns Hopkins. Characteristically Welch refused. That would be pushing, he said.

It was at this time that Welch met T. Mitchell Prudden, who had also studied at the Sheffield school during Welch's stay in New Haven. These two became fast friends, and together they presented themselves to Robert Koch, *doyen* of nineteenth-century European bacteriology.

At this time cholera was making its fifth recorded migration around the world, and had reached southern France. In India, a prime source of the epidemic, Koch had isolated the cholera bacillus and analyzed its origin and methods of transmission. Then he had destroyed all his cultures for fear of spreading the disease. When cholera appeared in France, Koch hurried to Toulon, secured the germs from an autopsy, and smuggled them back to Germany in a test tube. The young American begged him for some of the deadly culture, but Koch refused. He kept the germs locked tight in his laboratory. Prudden and Welch, however, managed to obtain cholera bacteria from another source. Welch later recalled:

> Prudden and I both wondered whether Koch had found us out, for one evening when I had been looking at my cultures, Koch, as he sat and talked with us, remarked it would be better a man had never been born if he introduced a disease germ into a region where it previously had not existed . . .

Having meditated Koch's dictum, young Welch, who was always prone to be overscrupulous, suffered a change of heart:

> I rose at dawn, determined that it should not be I who unleashed this scourge on a defenseless people. I mixed a solution of bichloride of mercury and sadly poured it into my precious test tube of cholera germs, in the hope of destroying them. I then hurried through the early light to the river to rid myself of the deadly evidence.

As he was standing on the bridge about to drop his test tube into the river, he noticed a cloaked and muffled figure approaching through the deserted streets. He did his best to appear an innocent dawn wayfarer, and stared intently at the sluggish water. The muffled figure came up to him and laid a hand upon his arm. It was Prudden, bent on the same errand as his own. Solemnly, the young men dropped their cultures into the River Spree.

Fred Dennis, having been forced somewhat into the background after Prudden's advent, left for America before Welch had completed his studies. But he still nourished a determination to be Welch's tutelary spirit. When, a few months later, Welch also returned to New York, bringing with him an entirely new scientific concept of medicine, Dennis was at the dock, again ready to shower more favors. Presently he informed Welch that he had secured for him, through the influence of Dr. Jimmy Wood, an appointment at Bellevue to demonstrate pathological anatomy during the summer term. He had also persuaded the great Dr. Austin Flint, professor of medicine at Bellevue, to make Welch his assistant. But he neglected to say whether either position carried a salary, which was Welch's paramount need at the moment.

Welch balked at what for him had become a pressing and too personal interference with his life. He told Dennis he would first try to make his own way. But his initial attempts to interest his old professor, Dr. Francis Delafield, who was now pathologist at Physicians and Surgeons, in giving him a post there were unsuccessful. At the time, Delafield told him, there simply was no laboratory space available. And so he was forced back on the Bellevue proposal, and made up his mind to exploit it to the full, lack of facilities notwithstanding.

Straightway Welch began a carefully planned campaign to secure decent accommodations at Bellevue, fully aware of the intricate politics which plagued that institution. After weeks of discouraging negotiations, he got permission to establish a laboratory. He was given three small rooms under a stairway in a building since demolished. Scarred kitchen tables were the only furnishings. "The college," he said later, "generously spent fully $25.00 to equip the laboratory!"

He had been trying, he wrote his sister at the time, to get the laboratory in order, so as to organize a class that summer. But the material was so scanty that by rights he should have given up the whole idea of pathological innovation. "I do think," he wrote, "that the condition of medical education here is simply horrible."

From somewhere Welch procured six antique microscopes, the ubiquitous Dennis providing at last one, and in May, 1878, Welch addressed his first class of six students. Since his beginners were hopelessly unequal to the task of analyzing specimens from deadhouse autopsies, Welch appealed to his sister to comb the marshes of upstate New York for frogs, and persuaded his stepmother to send her servants out on the same errand. Welch and his students awaited impatiently the arrival of the frogs, bedded in damp grass and croaking placidly. Welch reported to his sister with some irritation that a friend in Bridgeport had sent ten large specimens in a bucket of water—all of which drowned. "It seems little enough to expect," he wrote, "that a man who has spent most of his boyhood near the water should have observed the childishly simple truth—that frogs breathe air."

Thus was begun the first laboratory course in pathology ever given in an American medical school. One of Welch's students during these early exciting days was Dr. Walter Lester Carr. In his reminiscences he recalls that Welch's bare rooms in old Bellevue were the scene of intense and dedicated intellectual activity.

> Microscopical studies were so unusual that the necessary equipment was not for sale. Teasers were made from darning needles and pieces of old wire. Sections were cut with razors brought from home. The slides, in the few stores that carried such oddities, were of varying sizes and thicknesses, and you had to take what you could find. Word of a new shipment received at one of the optical stores produced a stampede of young men from Welch's laboratory. Their microscopes were low powered and imperfect, but the forms seen through the weak lenses on the rickety tables were a vision of a new world.
>
> There were specimens in jars, rats in cages, and a few tanks with plant growths. . . . Frogs were stared at through the microscope and then connective tissue from a rat's tail was teased by a student and looked at by Dr. Welch as if he had never seen such a phenomenon. Sections were hardened, cut and stained and then examined under the microscope. Eventually the students worked up to making slides of simple pathological material in the dead house. More elaborate preparations were made by the professor himself.

All during this Bellevue period, despite the fact that he rapidly became a cynosure of the staff, Welch remained desperately poor. To piece out his earnings, with Dr. Henry Goldthwaite he organized a cram quiz designed for aspirants to army and navy medical appointments. Welch and his partner soon had twenty-five pupils at $100 a head, which gave him a respectable income, but Welch hated every minute of it.

Meanwhile, Welch's course in microscopy was so successful that Physicians and Surgeons got the alumni association to give funds for a pathological laboratory of its own, and to make pathology a required study for all students. Delafield promptly offered Welch $500 to head the histological department. "We've got to have you back here," Delafield said. "I have discovered that the ice cream parlor on the first floor will make an excellent laboratory. We must have pathology here."

Welch was overjoyed, until he found that Austin Flint, Dennis, and others felt that it would be treachery for him to leave the Bellevue Medical School. So he stayed on, though with grave misgivings, for he felt Bellevue's political entanglements would forever retard his professional advance. For the Physicians and Surgeons job he recommended T. Mitchell Prudden, his old friend from student days in Germany.

But the situation, in the broad, was much more propitious than Welch realized. The science of pathology actually was emerging as a widely recognized factor in medical training. A number of medical schools throughout the country added pathology to their curricula, thus furthering the new approach that Welch in New York, and others elsewhere, were so urgently recommending.

Great things were happening in Europe. Every day brought some new discovery. In 1879, one morning as Billy Welch lay in bed after a long night in the Bellevue deadhouse, Dr. Austin Flint burst through his door waving a newspaper.

Koch had discovered the tubercle bacillus.

In a few short weeks Welch was enthusiastically demonstrating Koch's momentous discovery before his laboratory class, and the word spread like wildfire. Welch's classes were crowded with visitors. Dr. Hermann Biggs wrote:

> In his most lucid and fascinating manner he showed us methods of obtaining sputum and how to isolate the tubercle bacilli. Even now I can see quite clearly the steam rising from the dish of carbol-fuschia in the sandbath containing the sputum, while Welch talked on, surrounded by fascinated students so silent one could almost hear their breathing.

Besides his work at Bellevue, in the cram quiz with Goldthwaite, and as Dr. Flint's assistant, Dr. Welch also dissected, as opportunity offered, in hospitals all over New York. With Dr. Dennis he shared the position of anatomy demonstrator

at Bellevue Medical, and as usual tackled most of the dirty
work. Once a week, as part of this job, he did an autopsy in
the deadhouse for the class. The colored janitor at Bellevue,
Alexander Dumas Watkins, watched Welch inject so many
cadavers that, until officially restrained, he sent off notices to
undertakers offering instruction in embalming in the manner
of Dr. Welch. Said Welch, "His technique on the whole was
admirable."

About this time he allowed himself to be persuaded by Dr.
Dennis to come and live with him in his apartment. This
move seems to have sealed his determination to strike out into
new fields, fields where pure research could be persued.

Welch was awed by the way Dennis lived, visiting his
patients in an elegant carriage, the while Welch himself was
using the recently constructed elevated railway, which he
found "really elegant, but inexcusably noisy." Some of Dennis'
extravagances took him aback. In order to attend a medical
society meeting in Cleveland, Dennis commandeered his
father's private railroad car and with him, at his own expense,
took a group of prominent doctors, including Austin Flint and
other luminaries. "It was furnished," Welch wrote his sister,
"with kitchen, dining room, staterooms, balcony and every
sort of luxury. They drank champagne, smoked, ate all the
delicacies which could be obtained at Delmonico's and apparently had a delightful time."

Suddenly Welch became fed up with living on sufferance
with Dennis, and with the lack of security and freedom for
research which clouded his professional situation at Bellevue.
He wanted to be free to think, and also to be fairly paid for
his thinking. Frustration began to depress him, and affect his
work. Then, when his spirits were at their lowest ebb, he
received a letter from President Daniel Gilman of Johns
Hopkins, requesting permission to place his name before the
trustees of the university for appointment to the chair of
pathology. The salary was to be $4,000 for the first two years,

$4,500 for the next two, and $5,000 thereafter. Gilman enclosed a personal note saying that "the action is hearty, unanimous . . . you must come."

But again Dennis intervened. He refused to hear of Welch's leaving New York, and set about making it impossible. In view of Welch's extraordinary laboratory work, it was not hard for Dennis to enlist Welch's Bellevue colleagues in this campaign. He finally inveigled Welch into staying at Bellevue if certain conditions were met. These were an adequate laboratory, and a salary of $4,000 for himself and $1,000 for a qualified assistant. Hereupon, Dennis persuaded Andrew Carnegie to pledge $50,000 for a separate research laboratory in pathology at Bellevue. In addition, he got the Bellevue trustees to appropriate $45,000 more for the purchase of a site for the new laboratory. He wrote old William Welch:

> . . . the choice lies between an income of $20,000 as the leading man in New York, and hence in America, and $10,000 as a scientific recluse buried in a provincial city among untried and inexperienced persons. His ideas, imbibed in Germany, are impractical in our form of government. He must not cut himself off from everything in the way of sacred associations and of true friendships and worldly emoluments—for an ideal which cannot ever be realized.

Dennis' persuasions convinced old William Welch, and he wrote his son, adding his arguments to Dennis'.

Welch was in a quandary. In the end it was Dennis himself who overbalanced the scales in favor of leaving the New York scene. By now Dennis considered that he had more than lived up to Welch's conditions, and when Welch asked him about the $1,000 salary which he had stipulated for an assistant and the $4,000 for himself, Dennis blandly said that Welch could make enough money from consultation and student fees to carry the salary of his assistant, and more than enough to earn $4,000 for himself.

This was the final straw for Welch. He accepted the appointment to Johns Hopkins without further ado. Then Dennis formally broke off their friendship and began to say some bitter things about Welch's lack of gratitude.

Welch wrote to his father:

> My eyes are opened to the fact that . . . I was not supposed to have control of my own life in my own hands. He [Dennis] evidently intends that our intercourse hereafter shall be merely formal.
>
> It hurts me to have him say that the conditions I made were fulfilled and that I could not honorably leave, for this is absolutely false and I do not believe that anyone who knows me will believe it. . . . It looks almost as if Dr. Dennis thought that he had a lien on my whole future life. When he appealed to what he had done for me I told him that that was a subject which I would in no way discuss with him, nor did I care to hint that perhaps my association with him may not have been altogether without benefit to him . . .

The year was now 1885, and Welch was thirty-five. He had already made a reputation beyond what most doctors could expect. In Baltimore he found a place in the world which could not have been more advantageous. At Johns Hopkins, Welch almost overnight became a different person—relaxed, friendly, and immensely productive. Release from the bureaucratic protocol and political interference inherent in the administration of a great city hospital like Bellevue caused him to expand and mellow into the image of the fatherly professor beloved by his students. Indeed, he became the "Popsy" of generations of Johns Hopkins men.

At Johns Hopkins Welch gathered about him men who were to become world-famous under his guidance. Sir William Osler, Harvey Cushing, Simon Flexner, William Councilman, William Stewart Halsted, Howard Kelly—all these sat at his feet. The medical historian Donald Fleming has said:

> Welch so firmly established the relationship between research, pure science, and medical practice that his influence is still felt wherever medicine is taught. Indeed, if it had not been for the lucky combination of great and stirring times and a great and inspired man, medicine would not be what it is today in America.

It is regrettable that Bellevue should have lost William Henry Welch. But this was inevitable. As a public hospital Bellevue's very structure made it impossible for Welch to realize his goal there. Welch gave only part of his genius to Bellevue. And in return Bellevue undoubtedly gave something to Welch—a sense of medicine's scope. In an address in 1930, a few years before his death, Welch said:

> I arrived in New York in 1878 when I became attached to Bellevue Medical College. Let me tell you, if I could not count on the good luck of getting a place at Bellevue as a young man just back from the other side and eager to teach pathology—I would not care to live my life over again. It was that start that I look upon as the germinal years of my professional life.

GENIUS AND THE SCALPEL

It is a truism that genius attracts its kind. Such was the case with Dr. Billy Welch. Many young doctors were launched on the road to fame at his makeshift Bellevue laboratory. One, Hermann Biggs, became the most famous public health man since Dr. Stephen Smith. Another, William Stewart Halsted, grew to be a giant among surgeons.

William Halsted came from a comfortably wealthy family with a town house on New York's Fifth Avenue and a summer home at Irvington-on-Hudson. Young Halsted was brought up by governesses until he was ten, then shipped off to Phillips Andover Academy and from there to Yale.

After his graduation from Yale in the summer of 1874, Halsted came home to New York and entered the College of Physicians and Surgeons. He very soon became first assistant to Dr. John C. Dalton of ambulance fame. While Welch was dreaming of science and pure research, Halsted was experimenting with local anesthesia and sending his excised tumors to Welch's laboratory for dissection and analysis. No two men could have been more unlike, but perhaps for this very reason they remained warm friends for a lifetime.

Halsted was a paradox who both intrigued and puzzled his associates by his contradictions. He was patient and kindly with his students, yet apt to be caustic and sometimes cruel to his colleagues. He was cold and austere, and yet he would play the most outrageous practical jokes. He was almost painfully exacting in his own work, and yet was always ready to admire the inspired guesses of his associates. He struck many as being an impossibly aristocratic perfectionist, but few men knew him well enough to judge him. He was completely misunderstood by almost all of his colleagues and feared by many of his resident surgeons. But to all he was a surgeon without equal.

At a time when operators were known for their speed and manual dexterity, Halsted would take hours to perform the simplest operation. His patients never suffered hemorrhage. His touch was unbelievably delicate: he handled tissue as if it were made of gossamer. He discovered ways of grafting glandular tissue, how to deaden nerves locally, and how to restore patients suffering shock from transfusion. His technique of handling breast tumors, aneurysms, hernias, glandular hypertrophy, fistulas, and the like established a new surgical norm. In his field Halsted made almost as deep an impression on American medicine as Welch.

This astonishing career very early took definitive shape—while Dr. Halsted was student and then a young visiting surgeon at Bellevue. A short autobiography which Halsted wrote in the form of a letter to Dr. Billy Welch gives us a remarkably clear sense of how the hospital had progressed in the comparatively short time since the period of reform under Drs. Jimmy Wood, Alonzo Clark, and Stephen Smith, and the Ladies Visiting Committee.

> As intern at Bellevue I followed the medical work with quite as much interest as the surgical, making rounds with Janeway, Loomis, and Jacobi, attending autopsies and spending much time in the medical wards. I assisted Jacobi at his surgical operations, which were very, very amusing, and became fairly well acquainted with Janeway.
>
> The surgical material was chiefly traumatic. Lister had just visited this country, and his methods were enthusias-

tically adopted by Stephen Smith and Sabine, not by any other of the surgeons at Bellevue. We had the opportunity to compare results, and you can imagine the difference. Fortunately, Frank Hamilton, Erskine, Mason, and Alexander Mott, the surgeons of our Division, made no objection to our attempts at antiseptic surgery. Hamilton's interest was almost solely in fractures, and naturally they became my main concern.

Halsted goes on to speak of his own work at that time, which, beyond establishing the fact that the left leg is usually longer than the right, consisted principally of his introduction of the hot bath in the treatment of infection, a method which has since been widely used with excellent results. He also devised a sliding apparatus to be used in the treatment of fracture of the neck of the thigh bone, and several other mechanical appliances for use in the treatment of fractures.

During the winter of 1877 Halsted acquired the additional position of house physician at New York Hospital. There he devised temperature charts still in use in many hospitals and in all the services in Johns Hopkins Hospital in Baltimore. It was during this already busy period that he performed a series of operations for acute appendicitis, finally evolving a successful and entirely original technique for this previously fatal condition.

He was at this time a brilliant and dashing operator, his technique admired and copied by his colleagues. Though a prodigious worker, he was at the same time a gay and delightful companion who was constantly in demand by New York's hostesses.

In the fall of 1878 Halsted set sail for Europe; his goal, Vienna. In Vienna he attended clinics supervised by Billroth and Braun, and for a brief period the lectures of Meynert, all leading figures of the then world-renowned Vienna school. He persuaded Meynert to give him a private course on the dissection of the brain, at 6:00 A.M., but as Meynert was always in bed on his arrival, and the lesson was given in Meynert's remarkably dirty bedroom, he soon released him from the contract. After Vienna, Halsted moved on to Leipzig. All told, he spent two years in Europe and, while this time was stimulating and broadening, he seems to have had very little of the dedicated concentration of William Welch during the latter's studies abroad. On his return to New York in September, 1880, Dr. Sands urged him to become his associate at Roosevelt Hospital, and he accepted.

It was about this time that Halsted organized a "quiz" which was to be a radical departure from the cramming quizzes so long popular in New York. Instead of anticipating examination questions and having his students memorize the answers, he used the functional approach and made his students learn by actual clinical contact. The great importance of Halsted's new approach is suggested by a description written by Dr. Arthur Purdy Stout, a contemporary of Halsted, of the medical education that previously existed.

> The catalog stated that "candidates for the degree of Doctor of Medicine must have attended two full courses of lectures—the latter in this college. They must have studied medicine three years under the direction of a regular physician or surgeon, have attained the age of twenty-one years and be of good moral character.
>
> They have also to write a thesis and pass a satisfactory examination before the college faculty on the seven branches of medical science taught in the lectures. These were— anatomy, physiology, and hygiene, chemistry and medical jurisprudence, materia medica and therapeutics, obstetrics and diseases of women and children, surgery, and, finally, pathology and practical medicine. . . ."
>
> This college work was more or less a farce. No student expected to get more than his M.D. from the Medical School. He got his real training from two sources, his preceptor and the private quiz. Every student had to be registered with a preceptor who must be a regular physician or surgeon— this practically amounted to an apprentice system and naturally much depended upon the ability of the preceptor as a teacher and inspirer . . . and the young graduate's future might be assured if his preceptor was a person of influence.

The private quiz was a peculiar institution and took the place of the conference and quizzes which exist today in the Medical School itself. From three to six doctors would associate themselves under the leadership of the most prominent member and invite the medical students to recite to them by heart the various subjects contained in the curriculum. It really amounted to an exploitation of the medical student, for the quiz masters were usually faculty members, and we have the strange picture of the faculty members of an institution advising their students not to pay any attention to the curriculum but to go outside to a private quiz— and usually the faculty member who gave the advice was running a private quiz himself.

Medical education was an expensive business even then for a student—he had to pay annually one hundred and forty dollars for his lectures, one hundred dollars for the private quiz, besides matriculation fees and incidentals.

But the quiz was only a part of Halsted's activity during this time, for he had his college duties at Bellevue as well, not to mention his surgical duties at several other New York hospitals. In 1881 or 1882 Halsted was appointed visiting physician to the Charity Hospital on Blackwell's Island, and the next year became surgeon-in-chief to the Emigrant Hospital on Ward's Island. There he helped reduce the mortality of childbearing from 25 or 30 per cent to 5 per cent.

Halsted was formally appointed visiting surgeon to Bellevue in 1883. He considered it impossible to operate successfully in Bellevue's antiquated amphitheater operating room, and so he asked the commissioners of charities and correction to put up an operating building for his sole use. When he was refused, he ended by putting up a tent, which cost him $10,000 out of his own pocket. It had large and numerous portholes which provided ample light. Water, hot and cold, and gas were piped in, and patients were rolled from the wards onto the platform floor.

Halsted also served one summer at the Chambers Street Hospital, where he carried out experiments in "refusion" of blood. There were many cases of illuminating gas poisoning, chiefly from the night boats on the Sound and the Hudson River. Halsted treated these patients by drawing out some of their own blood, shaking it with air to free it from the poisonous carbon monoxide, and then driving it back into an artery rather than a vein. By forcing the aerated blood upstream it mingled with and purified the poisoned blood, so preventing gangrene.

Halsted had occasion to practice real transfusion of blood in 1881, when he arrived by chance in Albany just as his sister, after the birth of her first child, was suffering a massive hemorrhage. He found her ghastly white, pulseless, and almost unconscious. "After checking the hemorrhage," Halsted says, "I transfused my sister with blood drawn into a syringe from one of my own veins, and injected immediately into one of hers. This was taking a great risk, but she was so nearly moribund that I ventured it, and with prompt result." A year later he operated on his own mother for gallstones.

During these years he shared with Dr. Thomas McBride a house on Twenty-fifth Street, between Madison and Fourth avenues. Dr. Billy Welch later remembered Halsted in this fashion:

> . . . a model of muscular strength and vigor, full of enthusiasm, of the joy of life. . . . With his intimates, who were few, Halsted was the most delightful of companions, full of original whimsical humor, matchless in sharpness and quickness of repartee, stimulating and interesting in conversation, more interested in intellectual and scientific subjects than in topics suggested by the current news of the daily papers . . .

In September, 1884, at the Heidelberg Ophthalmic Congress, Koller announced that he had anesthetized the conjunctiva and cornea of the eye by the local application of the drug cocaine.

Halsted was fascinated by the possibilities of local anesthesia. With two assistants, he began a series of experiments with cocaine. Halsted became so engrossed that he used his friends and his students to determine proper dosage for the blockage of various nerve trunks. One of his incidental observations was that if cocaine was snuffed up the nose, it would relieve the symptoms of a head cold and, in addition, produce exhilaration. The sniffing of cocaine meanwhile became fashionable at theaters, not only to prevent coughing and sniffling, but because its use seemed to add merit to the play.

Too late Halsted discovered the habit-forming characteristics of this highly poisonous drug. Little by little experimentation had become a secret pleasure, then a dreadful necessity. Halsted became a cocaine addict. He was but one of several doctors in his circle who were innocently betrayed by Koller's famous discovery. He ended up in a mental hospital in Rhode Island, where he remained for a year. In New York he had been a powerful, inquiring, and tireless worker, wasteful of his strength, performing countless operations. He came out a broken and discouraged man. He was so painfully shy that the most ordinary contacts with other people made him suffer acutely. Once he had been spectacularly sure in everything he did; now he was hesitant, meticulous, fussy, and petulant. He no longer laughed. In a final despairing effort to rehabilitate himself, he determined to take a trip to South America, taking less cocaine with him than his habit demanded. The experiment ended in near catastrophe. On the way back he exploded, broke into the ship's dispensary, and stole the entire supply of cocaine. Fortunately the captain was understanding enough to hush up the incident.

When Halsted returned, still shattered, to New York, Dr. Billy Welch had just taken up his new post at Johns Hopkins. Without hesitation, Welch made a momentous decision, though he knew full well that only three out of every hundred cocaine addicts ever shook the habit. He invited Halsted to work with him at Johns Hopkins, and installed him in his own laboratory where he could putter as he liked. He even took Halsted to live with him in his own quarters so that there would be no lonely hours of temptation. It was Billy Welch who saved William Stewart Halsted for posterity.

Under Welch's care Halsted slowly recovered, after one lapse requiring further hospitalization in Providence at his own request. When he came back this time he was much improved, but he was never entirely able to conquer his addiction.

His mind again became clear and sharp, and he could operate with phenomenal skill. However, his addiction had drastically changed his personality and appearance. Once a handsome figure, now he was bald, stooped, and extremely shortsighted. His thick glasses gave him a remote and vaguely sinister air. He became what the psychiatrist would call a compulsive neurotic. He had dozens of suits made in London, each with carefully hand-sewn irregular seams, which he would wear only once or twice. For years he clung to the glistening, high silk hat, long after it had ceased to be generally worn. He insisted that Charvet do his laundry, and each week sent off a big package of linen to Paris. When a well-groomed Baltimorean told him that he used a local laundry, Halsted listened politely and walked away murmuring, "How extraordinary!"

Gradually his surgical genius came up and out of the deeps. Dr. William Councilman, a famous contemporary, said of him:

> There was no basis of comparison between Halsted and the other surgeons of Baltimore. It was perhaps natural that, when he first came to the city, he should have had but little sympathy for its people. . . . At one time I found him in his rooms in a state of great indignation because his landlady had just sent him a bill for the cost of having his cannel coal, which he had been at great pains to procure in large lumps, broken into fine pieces. . . . Afterwards, Halsted became greatly loved by both the medical profession and the laity.

In the spring of 1889, a Miss Caroline Hampton of North Carolina came to Johns Hopkins as head nurse in the new surgical division. Instantly Halsted was fascinated. He saw to it that she was made head nurse in the surgical operating room, where he could see her daily.

Caroline Hampton was an aristocrat, niece of General Wade Hampton, a Civil War hero, and came from a family of almost feudal position in the Carolina country.

Halsted could never quite believe that this lovely lady would condescend to be his wife. He said to Welch, "When I look at her, I never cease to wonder that she should care for one as unworthy as myself." To which Welch answered, "Excellent. That is the only proper attitude for a husband."

So diffident was Halsted about expressing his deeper feelings that, even in distant retrospect, when he spoke of his Caroline he hid behind clinical irrelevancies. Speaking of the winter of 1889, when he was getting to know the woman he married, he refers to her as "the nurse in charge of my operating room," and then goes on to tell how, to preserve her arms from the irritant effect of mercuric chloride, he had the Goodyear Company make "two pairs of thin rubber gloves with gauntlets," one for her, one for himself. True enough, this marked the beginning of the use of rubber gloves in surgery. But at the time this was only of secondary import to the smitten Halsted.

Mrs. Halsted adapted herself amazingly well to the domestic eccentricities which Halsted, still secretly an occasional user of cocaine, increasingly exhibited with the passing years. She bore without complaint his extraordinary attention to detail, as, say, when they gave a dinner. It was he who had to supervise everything, even to the selection of flowers. He particularly objected to any sign of wrinkles in the tablecloth and had it ironed on the table. Coffee was to him something to be approached with the utmost refinement of the connoisseur. He insisted on picking out each coffee bean, which he ground to the exact degree of fineness. For his open fires nothing but the best lignum vitae would do.

Of one of these dinners, the great brain surgeon, Dr. Harvey Cushing, wrote his mother in detail:

The meal started with caviar, and then on to bouillon, roast oysters, and terrapin stew. Halsted had made the stew himself with turtles he had carefully chosen from a stock of live ones he kept in the cellar. The stew was followed by an asparagus course, then quail in blocks of jelly, and pâté de foie gras, omelet soufflé, ice, cheese, and, finally, fruit.

There were many kinds of wine, and the coffee was made in the library by Halsted with his freshly roasted beans. The party drank this coffee while gathered around an open fire made from a special kind of rare wood laid there during the day by Halsted, who would trust no one else to do it.

Halsted's loneliness and isolation were pitiable, but he never learned the art of getting on with people. He mellowed a little with time. He gave up the shiny silk hat, which made him so conspicuous a figure on the streets of Baltimore, in favor of an immaculate black derby. And, although he continued to be something of a recluse, he managed gradually to overcome some of his intense shyness and to see more people. He was particularly fond of Dr. and Mrs. Howland who lived nearby, and for such good friends he reserved his gentle practical jokes. During the First World War both Dr. and Mrs. Howland, who were violently anti-German, were outraged when all through the gloomiest days of the war they received weekly the newspaper *Fiegunde Blätter,* apparently direct from Germany. It was years before they discovered this was Halsted's doing.

In the operating room the personality changes in Halsted became particularly noticeable. Completely gone was the dashing style of the old Bellevue days. His deliberateness with the scalpel drove his assistants to distraction. "Halsted operation" became a Johns Hopkins byword. His concentration during an operation was so intense that once, as he completed the closure of a wound, he rested his hand gently on the shoulder of his assistant and said, "Would you mind moving a little? You've been standing on my foot for the last half-hour."

When Halsted worked on one of Dr. Harvey Cushing's cases shortly after Cushing arrived at Johns Hopkins, Cushing could not imagine why the operation was lasting for several hours. Fearing the worst, he prepared for postoperative resuscitation methods, and was astonished to find, when the patient was wheeled out, he had labored in vain. For Halsted's operations were rarely, if ever, complicated by shock. His operations were as nearly bloodless as could be. He avoided catgut because certain problems of infection at that time had not been solved. His probings were infinitely gentle; he closed his incisions systematically, matching layer on layer of muscle and skin.

Dr. Councilman, who worked closely with him at Hopkins, said of Halsted: "It is difficult to think of surgery more carefully conducted than was Halsted's experimental surgery. The dog, he treated as a human patient. There was the same care in anesthesia, the same technique in operation, and in the closure of wounds." About human beings, however, he was ultra-fastidious. A lady who came to him for examination with a dirty umbilicus got short shrift. "I do not," he said, "condone that nasty sort of thing."

Halsted's innumerable contributions to the technique of surgery covered every phase of wound-healing and repair, but his greatest service to medicine was in his approach to the larger problems of surgery, such as shock and the control of bleeding.

Of Bellevue, which he always loved, Halsted had this to say: "Only once in my life was I kept awake by great happiness—and this was the night I passed successfully the examination for Bellevue Hospital in 1876, for from that day I date whatever success I may have achieved in later life."

· XVII ·

PUBLIC HEALTH AGAIN ADVANCED

On the façade of the fine building of the London School of Hygiene and Tropical Medicine are carved the names of twenty-one sanitarians, physicians, and men of science who, by their contributions and works since the seventeenth century, have done most to advance public health and the prevention of disease. Here, in the company of Sydenham, Pringle, Jenner, Farr, Chadwick, Simon, Pettenkofer, Pasteur, Koch, Lister, Laveran, Reed, Gorgas, and other great names is inscribed the name of Hermann M. Biggs. If Bellevue had graduated no other student than Hermann Biggs it would still have a claim to fame.

Hermann Biggs (1859–1923), among other things, changed the spitting habit of the nation, though the impulse to expectorate was one of the most cherished features of American life. More broadly, he brought public health into line with the discoveries, by Koch, Pasteur and others, concerning the nature and spread of infectious diseases.

For about a quarter of a century he was connected with the New York City Department of Health, and for the last decade of his life, the New York State Health Department. By example and by public addresses he also had a great influence on the country as a whole in matters of public health.

In 1872, when Biggs was twelve years of age, he wrote a

school composition which proved to be his life's credo. "Rich
and poor must be employed to be happy," the boy said. "We
have active minds, which cannot rest. They must be occupied
and interested in some way. . . . To be perfectly idle is to be
perfectly miserable."

Biggs entered the Bellevue Hospital Medical College in the
fall of 1881. In one of his first student essays he coined his
famous phrase: Public health is purchasable. Within natural
limitations, he said, a community could determine its own
death rate. This was to be the guiding principle of his life.

Dr. Welch recalls Biggs as perhaps the most active and
interested of his pathology students, though at that time pathology was not a required course. He stayed over-hours and
helped prepare stains and specimens. Dr. Welch gave him a
key to the laboratory and often assigned him special problems
to work out. Pathology was already taking a central place in
Biggs's mind. Through it, his passion for research found a
satisfying vent. His professor-student relation with Welch to
some degree continued all through his life. Whenever a new
discovery or a new health idea was brought to Biggs's attention,
his first question was likely to be: "What does Welch think
about this?"

T. Mitchell Prudden, Welch's old friend at the College of
Physicians and Surgeons, was also close to Biggs. Their friendship solidified into a lifelong alliance in the cause of public
health. Prudden was a shy man, and had none of Biggs's ability
to deal with politicians and bureaucrats. He remained a silent
but influential partner in all Biggs's monumental undertakings.

In industriousness and energy, Biggs rivaled the Halsted of
Bellevue days. At any one time he had a dozen jobs on his
hands. As early as 1885 he ran Bellevue's new Carnegie
Laboratory, the one originally intended for Dr. Welch, although Dr. Janeway and Dr. Fred Dennis were its nominal
heads. In addition, Biggs served as city pathologist and filled
the same post at Bellevue Hospital. At the Bellevue Medical

School he taught pathology, anatomy, and anatomy and practice of medicine. He was also visiting physician at the Workhouse and Almshouse and at Bellevue Hospital. Beyond all this he had a sizable private practice and conducted quiz classes.

Biggs's life at this early period is described in a letter by a student friend:

> He and a number of other Cornell men had rooms in the same house, and I naturally was taken in with them. There were six or seven of us, and after dinner we usually gathered in one of the rooms to smoke and talk for an hour or so as we had in our college days. But, though Hermann loved to sit around and talk, he limited himself, as I remember, to half an hour and a very small, mild cigar. The rest of us often sat up 'til all hours, if we had a particularly hard subject the next day. But Hermann wouldn't. Whether he had mastered his subject or not, when the hour he had set to go to bed came, to bed he went. Hermann was one of the most normal men I ever knew—a clean, sane mind and a clean, sane body.

It was in 1887 that Dr. Biggs, with Dr. Prudden's backing, first put his knowledge of bacteriology to serious use in the cause of public health. He had just returned from a stay in Paris, and was interested in problems of disinfection at the New York Quarantine Station. At that time cholera was taking a great toll of human life in Egypt, Italy, and India, and large quantities of Egyptian rags were being imported into the United States. The possible danger of the introduction of Asiatic cholera through these rags was much emphasized by Dr. Joseph B. Bryant, then New York's commissioner of health. Later, cholera did appear among Italian immigrants in quarantine. Dr. Biggs used bacteriological techniques to spot a case of cholera, and on the strength of this suggested that Bryant establish a division of bacteriology and disinfection in the city health department. This innovation proved to be a valuable control. It consisted of examining the feces for the cholera spirillum. Previously, ship surgeons had been vaguely diagnosing incipient cholera cases as eclampsia, tubercular enteritis, pneumonia, and the like.

Such was the beginning of a new and sure technique of cholera detection. Very rapidly it replaced vague speculation as to the receptive soils and favoring atmospheres so often cited as causes of cholera by the doctors of that day. Very shortly afterward, the value of the new bacteriological approach was again proved when a correct diagnosis of Asiatic cholera was made at the quarantine station, resulting in the isolation of the victim and the prevention of an epidemic.

In 1889 Dr. Biggs, with Drs. Prudden and H. P. Loomis, wrote a report which became a landmark in the tuberculosis control movement, which began in New York City, spread through the United States, and then through the whole civilized world. Night after night at the health department office on East Twenty-fifth Street, Biggs and Prudden had talked far into the small hours about the contagiousness of consumption and the backwardness of the profession in realizing its dire possibilities. Out of these discussions, after Health Commissioner Bryant had been prevailed on formally to request it, came the famous Biggs-Loomis report. Its historical value lay in its self-evident practicality and truth. It concluded that tuberculosis is a preventable disease, not directly inherited, and acquired by direct transmission of the bacillus from the sick to the healthy, usually by means of the dried and pulverized sputum floating as dust in the air. As preventive measures it recommended a rigid inspection system to insure against tubercular meat or milk, an educational campaign, and the disinfection of wards and rooms housing tubercular patients. Excepting its emphasis on dust infection, the report could scarcely be improved upon today. Soon the Health Department was putting out educational leaflets, and the long campaign against TB was under way.

As repeatedly demonstrated in the history of Bellevue and of the metropolis whose moods and experience it reflects, only a striking and dramatic catastrophe will persuade the public to take systematic precautions for their own safety. In the year 1891 the death rate from all causes was 26 per 1,000. The specific death rates for certain diseases were as follows: typhoid fever, 23; diphtheria, 81; pulmonary tuberculosis, 307. Such rates as these should have been sufficient to stimulate vigorous action, but they were habitual occurrences and therefore ignored. It was only the new menace of Asiatic cholera in 1892 which actually made progress possible.

In that year a situation arose which did scare people into action and incidentally realized Dr. Biggs's dream of a division of bacteriology and disinfection in the New York Health Department. In February, typhus was brought to the city by the steamship *Massilia*. There were 145 cases and 13 deaths on board the quarantined vessel, and 114 cases and 32 deaths ashore among the general population. Smallpox deaths also jumped to 81. But it was the menace of cholera which loomed most threateningly. The disease had been raging in Persia and in Russia; in the summer of 1892 it made its way westward to ports where it was potentially in direct contact with the United States.

Meanwhile, Biggs had received assurances from the Hamburg-American Line, one of the principal means of transport for immigrants from areas where Asiatic cholera was virtually endemic, that the German government was making every effort to screen out suspected carriers. But even as this letter was being written an epidemic was about to strike Hamburg. By the end of that September this German port on the Elbe had 7,427 cases, and by the end of the following winter, 9,341 more.

Meanwhile, ships of the Hamburg-American Line bearing immigrants were approaching America. New York woke up in earnest to its imminent danger. An advisory committee on cholera was formed, with Dr. Biggs its leading spirit. Biggs wasted no time.

First, the city water supply was intensively inspected. Then the streets were thoroughly cleaned, and food and milk inspectors warned to be especially vigilant. Some 39,000 tenements were cleaned up in order to "strike at the breeding places of the allies of cholera, as well as of cholera itself." A circular of instructions on the prevention and treatment of cholera (emphasizing the danger from unboiled water and uncooked or spoiled foods) was issued in English, German, French, Spanish, Italian, and Yiddish. But, most important, under Dr. Biggs's prodding the New York Board of Health created a new administrative division of pathology, bacteriology, and disinfection, with Biggs in charge. Thus the battle lines were drawn when a whole series of German immigrant vessels arrived in New York, all carrying Asiatic cholera. The threat of an epidemic was summarily contained.

Two small rooms on Bleecker Street, near the headquarters of the health department, were fitted up for a laboratory. As no trained bacteriologists were available, an intelligent and well-educated chemist, who knew something about bacteriology and was already engaged in work at the Department of Health, was assigned to the laboratory with some technical assistants and, under Dr. Biggs's direction, commenced work on the diagnosis of cases of Asiatic cholera.

Although 76 deaths occurred on ships at sea, almost all from cholera, and there were 44 deaths from cholera among immigrants at Swinburne Island and at other places in the port, among residents of New York there were but 10 clearly defined cases of cholera between September 5 and September 23 of which 8 proved fatal. The precautions taken prevented a single instance of secondary infection on shore.

Dr. Biggs was particularly proud of the Health Department' disinfecting plant on Sixteenth Street, originally designed by himself and Prudden, and completed under his own vigorou direction. He believed it to be "the most efficient plant of it kind in this country." One feature of Biggs's plan was a pro

The Publick Workhouse and House of Correction of the City of New York. Erected in 1736, it stood on the present site of City Hall. The Infirmary, which is the forerunner of Bellevue Hospital, was on the second floor on the Broadway side of the building.

Entrance to the old Administration building, about 1860. President Washington was inaugurated on this balcony.

View from the East River of Bellevue about 1816.

There were few changes in 1848, except that some fill had been added to Bellevue's front lawn.

By 1879 the old hospital had grown enormously trying to keep pace with the city around it.

In 1954 these new buildings were completed, extending four blocks to the north of the

(*Top*) These spanking new Ambulances were added in 1870. (*Bottom*) In the late 1920's the automobile had taken over. Each car was assigned a doctor.

These early Supervisors of Bellevue nurses were trained by Florence Nightingale. This picture, taken about 1872, shows the ubiquitous "Black Bottle."

Hermann Michael Biggs
1859–1923

Frederic Shepard Dennis
1850–1934

John Wakefield Francis
1769–1861

William Stewart Halsted
1852–1922

David Hosack 1769–1835

Valentine Mott 1785–1865

Charles Norris 1867–1935

Stephen Smith 1823–1922

George David Stewart
1862–1933

William Henry Welch
1850–1934

James Rushmore Wood
1817–1882

Walker Gill Wylie
1848–1923

Early Bellevue amphitheatre, built in 1871.

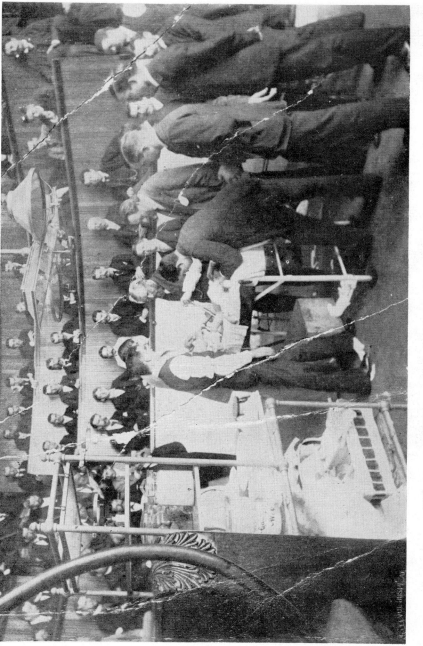

The new amphitheatre, built in 1890—the most modern of its time.

About 1885—Dr. Fred Dennis, facing camera, has his hand on the patient's chin.

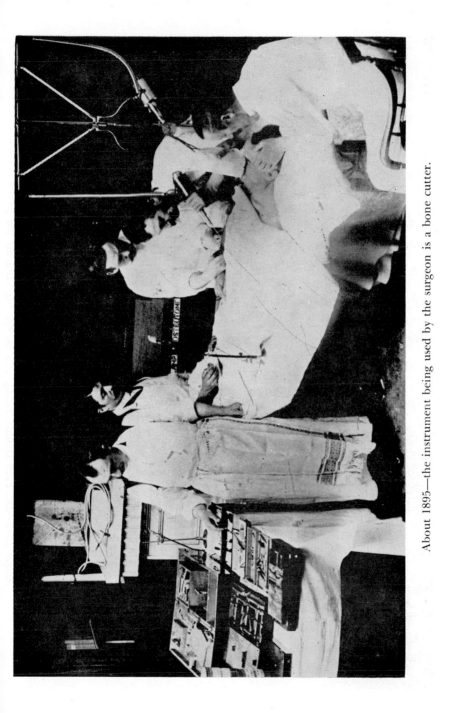

About 1895—the instrument being used by the surgeon is a bone cutter.

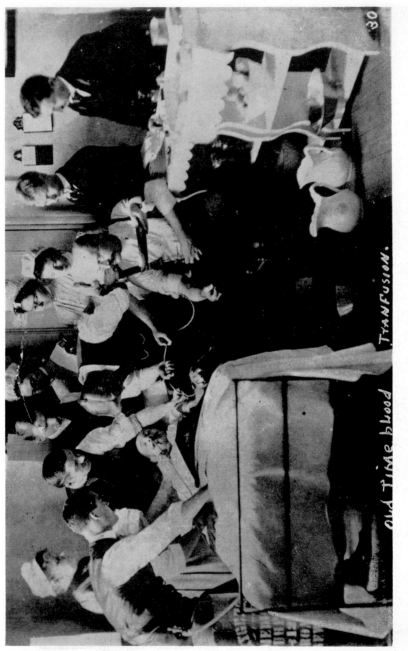

This early blood transfusion necessitated giving the patient oxygen as well.

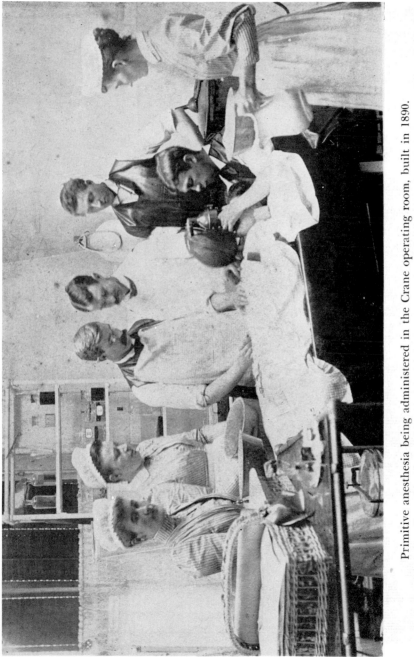

Primitive anesthesia being administered in the Crane operating room, built in 1890.

Each year the Circus comes to Bellevue. This picture was taken in the late 1920's.

vision that drivers and workmen at the disinfection plant should wear special overall suits and have them frequently disinfected. Workers on the receiving end were given uniforms of brown duck; those on the outlet side, white duck. This provision was characteristic of Dr. Biggs's grasp of detail. Nothing escaped him.

The next big step in Dr. Biggs's health program for New York, a program now beginning to attract national attention, was his introduction, 1893, of new culture methods of his own devising for the diagnosis of diphtheria. Simultaneously he recruited Drs. William H. Park and Anna Williams to carry out his plans for extending the use, in public health, of bacteriology and pathology. In these recruitments Dr. Biggs's right-hand man, Prudden, heartily concurred.

William Halleck Park, who was to become one of America's leading public health authorities, had studied in Vienna, and had also worked for two years on diphtheria in Prudden's laboratory in the Willard Parker Hospital. At this time Biggs and Park had not met. But it so happened that Biggs had sent a patient to the Willard Parker Hospital with a diagnosis of diphtheria. Park disagreed. In his opinion the patient was suffering from syphilis. When the staff jeered at him, Park hotly inquired who this Biggs might be anyway. Only the best bacteriologist in the United States, he was told, and the main board of health man. But as it turned out, Park was right. The young doctor, during the luncheon discussion of his prospective post, was much relieved when Dr. Biggs refrained from mentioning this incident.

Without delay, Dr. Park and Dr. Anna Williams, whose name is also inseparably connected with the laboratory, moved into their first quarters, two upper floors of a tenement house near 42 Bleecker Street. There they began to breed pure cultures of the diphtheria bacillus in peptone sugar broth, and to test the toxin on guinea pigs. This work progressed rapidly, and only four months after Park's appointment, Biggs recom-

mended bacteriological procedures for the diagnosis of diphtheria. Such diagnosis by clinical observation alone, he argued,
is frequently impossible. He pointed out that from 30 to 50
per cent of the cases sent to the Willard Parker Hospital as
diphtheria had been erroneously diagnosed. Bacteriological
tests would save the city a lot of money. This typically canny
argument sealed the board of health's resolve to go along
with Biggs's ideas.

With the laboratory safely installed, and in possession of the
public confidence after Parks had scotched a rumor that dead
fish in the park reservoir caused diphtheria, Dr. Biggs
journeyed to Europe to see what success Koch was having in
Vienna and Roux in the Pasteur Institute in Paris. Both Koch
and Roux had made a workable diphtheria antitoxin by injecting animals with the toxin from their cultures until
sufficient antitoxin had been manufactured to neutralize the
poison. Dr. Park had emulated this procedure and had only
waited, for its practical application, until his superior surveyed
the Paris inoculation experience. When Roux reported that
three out of four inoculated children recovered from diphtheria, Biggs cabled Park to start producing the antitoxin on
a large scale. After some preliminary differences of opinion
over whether goats (Koch) or horses (Roux) were better
sources of the antitoxin, the laboratory bought forty horses on
Prudden's responsibility, and then stabled them at a nearby
veterinary college. Soon after Dr. Biggs's return, an outbreak
of diphtheria in a children's home in Mount Vernon was
checked without fatality by the new antitoxin, and the public
was well on the way to being convinced of its invaluable
merits. By means of newspaper campaigns as well as political
pressure Biggs eventually got enough money to produce the
precious antitoxin on a scale large enough, until private enterprise took over, for the city's current needs.

For a time all went swimmingly with the Biggs program of
using antitoxin to combat diphtheria. But, unseen, a ground-

swell of opposition was building up in the profession—that seemingly inevitable repudiation of a novelty after its first spectacular success. Biggs's chief critic was Dr. Joseph E. Winters, attending physician at the Health Department Hospital, a most overbearing and opinionated man.

At a medical meeting before which Dr. Biggs cited statistics to prove the value of his serum, Dr. Winters rose to the attack. He denounced the Biggs antitoxin as a fraud. There was not the least evidence that it inhibited the formation of a membrane in the throat. It had no effect on temperature or pulse. Diphtheria patients recovered much better if promptly put to bed and left to cure themselves.

Actually, the statistics were not completely reassuring. But the real trouble lay in the as yet unperfected methods of preparing the antitoxin, and an understandable timidity about giving what later turned out to be the proper dosage. However, as for Dr. Winters' contention that the antitoxin was harmful because "it would dissolve the human blood corpuscles and produce an antitoxin septicemia with subsequent pneumonia," this was nonsense.

The newspapers seized upon the argument, and for a year or more public confidence in the new anti-diphtheria serum from horses was dented, if not broken. Then a second battle of words was fought over the issue, at a meeting of the Bellevue alumni. Dr. J. W. Brannan, who had carefully prepared a rebuttal of Dr. Winters' charges, and who was able to quote at length in favor of the antitoxin from statistics compiled at Bellevue and Willard Parker, utterly demolished Briggs's recalcitrant opponent. Thereafter the health department program against diphtheria was left to develop in peace.

Testing for typhoid fever was the next program introduced by the laboratory. Here the carrier problem was even more serious than in diphtheria or tuberculosis.

"Typhoid Mary," most famous carrier in medical history, was examined at the laboratory in 1907. Her reaction was highly positive, but she felt perfectly healthy. Also, her only way of earning her living was by cooking—a kind of work in which she would be an especially lethal menace. On the laboratory's recommendation, she was confined to Willard Parker Hospital for nearly three years. Meanwhile, the board of health worked out methods of safeguarding foods served to the public. Mary was still a menace, for it was impossible to rid her of the disease. But finally she was let out of Willard Parker with a stern warning to report every three months for a checkup.

Once free, Mary simply disappeared. For years the health department was out of touch with her. Then suddenly Sloane Hospital for Women reported an epidemic of twenty cases. Health department inspectors traced the infection to the kitchen. And there, who should they find but Typhoid Mary, calmly mixing a batch of dough. This time they took her to North Brother Island and kept her there for twenty-three years, until she died. It was a harsh thing to do, but there was no other way to control the menace of the toxins in Mary's bloodstream.

When Seth Low was elected mayor of New York on a reform ticket, Dr. Biggs turned down the job of commissioner of health, but accepted the policy-making post of general medical officer. One of his first moves was to accelerate his campaign against tuberculosis. It was his belief that legal measures should be taken to ensure the compulsory reporting of TB cases by the profession, the better to control infection and follow through on the cure. Doctors themselves at first resisted this innovation, in part on the grounds that it was an unwarranted interference, and in part because their fees were threatened. This latter objection arose from the fact that in the 1890's it was insurance company practice to refuse to allow death claims if the insured person had died of tuberculosis. The patient with TB often warned the doctor that if he let the cat out of the bag his bill would never be paid.

However, four years later, in 1906, with the now powerful backing of Biggs and Prudden, the health department made it compulsory to report all cases of TB. By this time Biggs was recognized as an international authority on public health. His methods of controlling diphtheria had been widely adopted in the British Isles and on the Continent. But this time he barely pulled through to victory. The New York County Medical Society came out against the new ruling, deeming it "unnecessary, inexpedient, and unwise." Fortunately Biggs had the press firing on his side, and in the end saw the profession not only acquiescent but actively won over to his view. More and more he was coming to represent, as one writer had said of him, "an impersonal force of nature."

In addition to his Health Department duties, Dr. Biggs led the reorganization of medical education in the city, this in the middle of his strenuous campaign for diphtheria and TB controls. The time seemed ripe, he felt, to combine the Bellevue Medical College and the medical school of New York University into a single institution, thus avoiding inefficient duplication. Biggs, now professor of both therapeutics and clinical medicine at Bellevue, was the decisive influence in bringing this to pass. In the spring of 1897 the Bellevue property was transferred to the University. Chancellor McCracken announced the establishment of the University and Bellevue Hospital Medical College. It would, he said, be "the largest and most thoroughly equipped medical institution of learning in the country." Thanks to Biggs's foresight, land had already been purchased at Twenty-sixth Street and First Avenue. Here a six-story building was erected to house the new school. The committee which had been appointed by Chancellor McCracken of New York University to form a new faculty for the merged medical school named only one Bellevue man among seven openings. This evoked passionate protest at the East River establishment. After all, by common knowledge the Bellevue school had been clearly superior to its rival. Dr.

Austin Flint was particularly enraged, and in riposte persuaded Cornell University to set up a clinic in the city, an outpost of the medical school then located in Ithaca. Gradually the teaching program at this clinic was integrated with the Bellevue intern system, and came to dominate the hospital's Second Division.

Dr. Biggs, this while, kept apart from the turbulence and progress which he had innocently set in motion. Among other things, he met and married Frances Richardson from Cornell, who had been playfully recommended by a Mrs. Ruggles, sentimental wife of a health department colleague, as an ideal partner for him all of ten years earlier. This marriage, as predicted, proved to be an unusually happy one, though Dr. Biggs was already beginning to show signs of diabetic failure, which he vainly tried to control by a dietary regime. Mrs. Biggs did everything in her power to make her frail husband conserve his strength, and succeeded in signally prolonging his career, at least until he had been chosen, together with Drs. Hester, Holy, Prudden, and Welch, as one of the organizers and directors of the Rockefeller Institute for Medical Research.

Hermann Biggs was a great and tireless physician, a servant of humankind, the kind of doctor who ennobles the medical profession. He stimulated and enlightened generations of students. From him they gained a vision of scientific penetration tempered by sympathy. Yet it was as a public health genius that he contributed most. In this field he towered far above the rest.

XVIII

SMALL WAR, GREAT PROGRESS

The brief conflict with Spain in 1898 was unquestionably the least justified and the most enthusiastically fought war in American history. Fomented in good measure by jingoistic newspapers in search of circulation and power, it was the kind of war in which victory is assured and practically nobody gets hurt. Its casualty statistics, compared with those of most wars, make unusual reading: 274,717 enrolled, 290 killed, and 2,565 dead of disease.

But for the epidemics of typhoid and malaria and yellow fever which swept the Florida and other camps, the Spanish War would be remembered as not much more than a comic opera in which T.R.'s buck teeth flashed resolutely and very briefly in the Cuban sun. In actual fact, the hurriedly recruited army did suffer quite intensively, from disease if not from gunfire. And these sufferings were not entirely useless. Quite soon they brought into being countermeasures that were to prove of lasting benefit to epidemiological control the world over.

When the McKinley administration broke relations with Spain in the spring of 1898, again Bellevue doctors and interns rushed to the recruiting offices to offer their services. They did not have to wait long for opportunity to exercise their skills. At Chickamauga the soldiers died like flies, even before they were through training. At Tampa conditions were still more deplorable. The doctors badgered the troops about hygiene, but in vain. The men would not drink boiled water. Too flat for their taste, they said. Also, a minority of the doctors supported the cause of ignorance. Boiled water, they declared, was quite unnecessary; Army beans and Armour's canned beef were to blame for the Army's troubles.

Returning troops, crowded into Camp Wyckoff at Montauk Point, were in an even more parlous state. Most of them were so weakened by bouts of dysentery and fever that they had to be carried on stretchers from ship to shore. Had the Army really been faced with a fight, it would have had to shoot at the enemy from the hospital bed or the latrine. The afflictions that had taken grim toll of armies all the way from Hannibal crossing the Alps to Napoleon in Moscow struck hard at the bewildered heroes of Daiquiri and Siboney. It was, very literally, an army with its pants down. A troubling and sobering sight, on-the-spot observers said, was to see rows upon rows of sick and delirious young men laid in blankets on the bare sand of the Long Island beach.

Bellevue was packed to the roof with soldiers picked up from the streets in a state of collapse, or taken from the Long Island trains unconscious. New York hospitals were so jammed that some of the dischargees were shipped off to Boston and Newport. Doctors and nurses worked around the clock, until they were red-eyed and faint. Presently the incursion had run its course, and the profession began to take stock of the whole experience. It was obvious that military hygiene was in great and immediate need of improvement.

The doctors who had served in the camps were teeming with new ideas about both surgery and medicine. The campaign was for them a tremendous object lesson pointing to the need of more bacteriological knowledge and better means of hygienic control. In surgery there had been some notable advances. Whereas in the Civil War soldiers with abdominal wounds had been written off, with the new antiseptic techniques used in the Spanish-American War, hundreds of such abdominal cases were able to make a good recovery.

Another thing was accomplished by medicine during the year of war. The War Department, which had previously been unshakable in its determination not to use woman nurses, finally backed down. The Bellevue Nurses' Registry had been asked to help supply nurses for the Army. Only a year earlier the new registry had broken away from the board of managers of the nursing school, because it would not permit the installation of a telephone in the school's registry in the hospital. Thereafter, any doctors who wanted a Bellevue nurse either had to send a note by messenger or go over to Bellevue themselves. The doctors naturally took the course of least resistance and began getting their nurses from other registries which could be reached by phone. Faced with this situation, fifty Bellevue alumnae opened their own registry on East Forty-second Street. It was this new Bellevue registry that acted as recruiting agent for the Army and gathered into New York groups of graduate nurses from all over the United States.

Nurses from Bellevue, Roosevelt, Presbyterian, and other New York hospitals, as well as numbers from out of town, and a group of nuns, had served as surgical nurses at Camp Wyckoff at Montauk. They arrived in tens, then twenties, then fifties. They toiled under unspeakable conditions in hastily improvised shelters. In fact, the carpenters were just finishing the tent hospital when, late in the fall of 1898, the last patient was moved out of Wyckoff.

For the first time, too, nurses had actually traveled with an army. Bellevue nurse Annie Turner was one of the leaders. An article in a Pennsylvania newspaper describes some of her adventures. It tells how, during Miss Turner's tour of duty in Havana, Army doctors were experimenting with inoculation to fight yellow fever. The experiments were soon abandoned after seven persons had been infected by mosquitoes, and of these, three had contracted the disease in such violent form that they died. The fact that one of the deaths was that of Miss Maas, a close friend of Miss Turner's, a 26-year-old American nurse who had volunteered for the experiment, cast a gloom over the whole project. It was decided at this time that the only possible hope in the fight against yellow jack was the destruction of the mosquitoes themselves, which carried the disease.

During the Spanish-American War, the article relates, Miss Turner was at Santiago when nine nurses dropped with yellow fever, and at Port-au-Prince, scene of another epidemic. Malaria added to the nurses' worries, and in the rainy season a nurse on duty at least fifteen hours a day had to fight ankle-deep mud and never ending downpours as well as disease. Miss Turner stayed on after the war, heeding a plea from Major William Crawford Gorgas, Army sanitation expert and later Surgeon General, for more nurses.

Miss Turner wrote later of her nursing career in public health and in the military service:

> In those days conditions were very bad. We had no sanitation whatever. There was smallpox later in the hospital where I was stationed on the Pacific side. We'd have 1100 to 1200 patients at one time, not counting the insane. But none of it was as bad as the yellow fever in Cuba—the year that they got the big epidemic, when they discovered the cause. That was terrific. I had never worked in my life as I did there.

Dr. William Gorgas, one of the conquerors of yellow jack and himself a Bellevue man, keenly remembered the Ancon Hospital where Miss Turner served in the Canal Zone. Gorgas reports:

> The corps of American trained nurses brought from the United States took the place of the French Sisters, who, although devoted and self-sacrificing, did not possess the technical knowledge necessary for this work. These American nurses, in the charge of a Miss Hibbard, struggled valiantly

through those trying days. They added not only to the efficiency of the department, but to its charm and even its romance. It is true that one of our more cynical doctors once said that "some were with the Army in the Philippines, some were with Doctor Gorgas in Cuba and some were with Washington at Valley Forge." Yet the rapidity with which they were snapped up by the young doctors at the hospital was a matter of common comment.

One case in particular, I recall vividly. Miss M—— unfortunately violated the rules to the extent of making short trips to the city of Panama, while the epidemic was in full swing. Another case of yellow fever was the result—an extremely severe one. Doctor Carter told me the story: "I had been away for a few days," he said, "and when I got back, I was rushed in a cab to the nurses' quarters at Anconcita. I found Nurse M—— tossing from one side of the bed to the other. Neither morphine nor cocaine quieted her. Finally I said—Now, child, you have a fine constitution and you ought to do well, but if you don't lie still in that bed you are going to die—She insisted that she couldn't keep still, but suggested if Major J—— (calling the name of one of the younger doctors on duty) would hold her hand, she would try. I gave Major J—— a call and stationed him at his post. She quieted down immediately and the major sat by her all night. The girl got well and it wasn't long after that when I got cards to their wedding."

In 1903 Miss Turner returned to the States for a year and a half, only to head back into the hard work department— duty in the Panama Canal Zone—where the big ditch was being hewed out of the jungle. Miss Turner stayed in the tropics for twenty-four years. During one period in Cuba, Miss Turner wrote a letter to one of her friends at Bellevue. At this time she was superintendent of the Training School for Nurses in Remedios. The simplicity and matter-of-factness of this letter make the whole experience seem a lark, hiding the very real dangers of her job.

> Remedios is a town of 5,000 inhabitants, 200 miles from Havana and a 12-hour journey by rail. The town is one of the oldest on the island, resembling all other Cuban towns, only a little more antique and dirty.
> The training school was founded July 1900 with Miss

Edith A. Sampson as Superintendent. It was the outcome of an industrial school founded here by the Cuban Orphan Society and our home was furnished from the things they had had here in the asylum.

The school is preparatory. The girls are supposed to stay here one year learning something of hospital work, housekeeping, cooking and sewing and then go to the larger schools in Havana for two years. They have very little education so it is necessary to have a teacher to teach them the common branches. I began with four young, new and ignorant girls and 90 patients in the hospital. Half of the beds were old canvas cots, put in the wards in any shape and all were filled with vermin. The pillow ticks dirty and ragged and not enough pillow cases to change one ward at a time. There was so little clothing that the patients were often obliged to stay in bed. There were no tables or chairs for the nurses, and only one thermometer for the whole hospital. The patients had not bathed in a long time and were afraid of water.

I began to scald beds and bathe patients. The latter meant lots of fighting as a Cuban believes water is sure death to a sick man and it takes persuasion of the strongest sort to make him take a bath the same day he takes a cathartic. I wrote to Havana for a few things to work with. In the meantime tore strips from four of the wider sheets and had them made into pillow cases. I cut 52 pairs of pajamas out of material I had in the house and got them made in the women's ward.

Our floors are of rough brick. Old and broken and had not been scrubbed for some time. All the patients spit on the floor although each one has a cuspidor by his bedside.

The hospital is still bad and I had to look back over my six months' work and make comparisons in order to keep myself from getting completely discouraged.

Since I came we have had forty new bedsprings and have painted some old iron beds to put them on. Each ward has a certain number of beds and they are kept there. Formerly they were carried out into the yard when a patient went out and brought in again when a new one came. I oblige all patients to bathe or leave the hospital. Each one has a towel and clothes enough so that they can get out of bed. The floors are a little cleaner. They do not spit on the floor much any more. Each patient has an old "black bottle"* for water. Now

* The "black-bottle" was a leather-covered receptacle used for water by the early attendants and "ten-day drunks" who served as nurses. This bottle was entirely innocent, but to Bellevue patients, who were mostly drawn from the ignorant and illiterate in New York's slums, it became somehow linked with

we have water coolers so it is not necessary to pump water from the well each time. I have sheets, pillow cases, gowns, thermometers, scissors, watches, rubber sheets, tables for the wards, and wash basins.

I have been promised some new chairs and bedside tables, and, best of all, a force of men will soon come from Havana and put down new cement floors.

When I came, the surgical dressings were done all over the hospitals and the basins were never washed between cases. Now every patient that can walk comes to a certain place in the inside courts to be dressed, and one girl does nothing else but wash basins. I have the medicines given by the nurses American style, although I am obliged to write all the lists. Formerly each patient had his own medicine on his stand and took it when and how he liked.

One of the achievements of which I am proudest is getting the large inside patio cleaned up, the stones out and planted with Bermuda grass. This is the dry season. We have no way of watering it, but fortunately have had two good rains lately and most of the plants are beginning to show a little green.

The director of the hospital is a fine physician, a good surgeon and, best of all, a man of sterling common sense and has stood by me nobly. He speaks English and wants American improvements. He has aided me in every way. But even then it has been a constant struggle to make these few changes.

We have a very comfortable house some distance from the hospital and at present I have nine girls, a housekeeper who also makes the girls' uniforms, and a cook. I keep three girls in the house to help sew, cook, clean, etc. All have washed dishes and they take turns in waiting on the tables. I told one to fold linen and help in the drug store and the others in the wards, changing them from one place to another about once a month.

These girls are young and do not know how to do any sort of work well. So one could only hope to make them a little bit better now and hope for greater things in the future. I do not know enough Spanish to give them theoretical instructions. I do give them an English lesson each day and give lessons to other people in the evening, so I have little time for dissipation. The great event of the day for me is the com-

---

the staggering death rate in the old hospital, and became a thing to inspire terror and fear of imminent death. Many of the superstitious thought the "black bottle" contained deadly poison which the nurses used as a practical means of relieving the overcrowding of the wards.

ing of the train which I always hope will bring me letters and news of the world I have drifted away from.

An order has just been issued by the military governor which says that no hospital less than a hundred beds can have a training school, so no doubt this will be closed in a short time. Whether I shall stay in Cuba then or come home, I do not know. I've now been three years in Cuba and feel it's about time to return to my own country. To all my fellow nurses I send wishes for prosperity and happiness wherever they may be. We are widely scattered, as I believe we should be, but we can be, and I am sure are, loyal to each other and to the old school which has done so much for us.

Out of her experience, Miss Turner developed a strong case of hero worship for three great men: Doctor William Gorgas; George Washington Goethals, the Canal engineer; and Teddy Roosevelt.

Gorgas she admired because of his battle with disease; Goethals, "gifted, unselfish, clean and straight," because "anybody could talk to him" despite his staggering burden of work; Roosevelt because he came to the men and women in the ranks, not their superiors, to learn what he wanted to know. Miss Turner received a treasured service award from the Canal Zone years, bearing Teddy Roosevelt's likeness. She and her sisters in white did yeoman work in putting into use the epidemic controls which came into being in reaction to the disastrous experience of the Spanish-American War. Thus, the great movement initiated by Hermann Biggs, Stephen Smith, and others was carried far afield from New York.

XIX

IMPROVEMENTS AT THE
CENTURY'S TURN

On the morning of December 15, 1900, the *New York World* carried an eyewitness story of a hideous killing in the hospital which became a legal *cause célèbre*, and lent great impetus to a recent and belated awareness of the gross neglect of psychotic patients and mental hospitals. Thomas J. Minnock, a *World* reporter, by feigning insanity got himself committed to the Bellevue pavilion for the insane, the same stunt pulled four years before by Nellie Bly, a woman reporter from the *Post*. Unlike Miss Bly, Minnock had neither integrity of purpose nor accuracy. He was quickly discovered to be a fraud, and kicked out with the warning that he might be brought to book. Undeterred, the next day he gave the following story to the *World*, which duly printed it.

On the evening of Tuesday, December 11, according to reporter Minnock, a Frenchman named Hilliard was admitted to the pavilion suffering from alcoholic mania. Hilliard was recalcitrant and refused to eat. Hereupon, a male head nurse named Davis, with the help of two other nurses, twisted a sheet around the Frenchman's neck, and garroted him to death. Then they threw the body into a bathtub full of cold water, in a vain effort to bring him to consciousness. The next morning, according to Minnock, the nurses made a number of hurried calls to the morgue to make sure the murder was hushed up.

This wild story evoked a storm of indignation. Davis was indicted, and later brought to trial for manslaughter. The Court of General Sessions was jammed with sensation-seekers on the opening day.

Feeling was running high against Davis, and as the trial got under way, even the judge seemed rather cool toward the defense lawyers. The prosecution obviously had an excellent case. There was much damning evidence against Davis besides Minnock's testimony. The autopsy report had disclosed several bruises on the dead man's forearm, forehead, arm, hand, and shoulder, three broken ribs and a broken bone in the neck, as well as a suffusion of blood on both sides of the windpipe. Cause of death was reported as strangulation.

The prosecution called to the witness stand two inmates of the psychiatric pavilion, one a paranoiac, and the other a patient suffering from general paresis. For the first time in New York history a court admitted the testimony of an insane person.

Such civic leaders as Ogden Mills, afraid that a conviction would ruin the already none too savory reputation of the Bellevue Training School for Male Nurses, hurriedly shored up the defense by hiring Francis L. Wellman, a lawyer noted for his skill at cross-examination. The ensuing attack on the credibility of the prosecution's chief witness was so clever and devastating that Wellman used it as an exemplar in his famous *Art of Cross-Examination*.

Minnock, an attractive, traveled young college graduate, had a pleasing, assuring manner on the stand. He had told his story of the garroting well, dwelling with just the right amount of emphasis on each gruesome detail. Wellman began by quizzing him about a signed story of his life which had appeared a few days before in the *Bridgeport Sunday Herald*. This story told about his studies with the French scientist

Charcot, who had purportedly taught him hypnotism. Under pressure, Minnock reluctantly admitted that he had never actually met Charcot, that his closest association with the scientist was an acquaintance with a woman who had said she was Madame Charcot. He did not really know anything about hypnotism at all. In sum, the story was mostly fable, with a few facts. The court refused to allow Minnock to be interrogated at length about the article, but the defense now had a foot in the door. A reporter who had once palmed off fiction as fact, he might try the same trick again. This thought did not escape the jury.

By this time Minnock himself was flushed and pugnacious. He finally admitted, however, that after he had been exposed as a faker by one of the Bellevue staff doctors, and had been taken for a hearing before a police magistrate, he had at this time sworn on his oath that he had found nothing to criticize during his stay at Bellevue. Apparently the story about the alcoholic Frenchman had not occurred to him until after he had read the report of the autopsy in the morning paper. (It will be observed that death through violence actually had occurred through someone's hands.) At any rate, he wrote his story of the garroting and took it to the *World*. The editor, who it would seem was suspicious of Minnock's dependability, bought it only when he had obtained Minnock's affidavit.

Luckily for the defendant, too, when Minnock appeared before the coroner, he again embroidered his tale. For example, he said that Davis anxiously phoned the morgue the morning after the patient's death. But in fact there was no direct phone connection between the insane pavilion and the morgue. And morgue attendants swore they had received no inquiries about the body.

The testimony of the insane witnesses, which had promised to be the most interesting aspect of the case, proved to be anti-climactic. The defense was able to show that they were merely repeating lurid newspaper accounts which had made a detailed impression on them. As the trial wore to an end, defense attorney Wellman had the upper hand. The court was now as strongly in favor of the nurse as it had previously been hostile. Davis was acquitted, the press approved, and the fickle public nodded its satisfaction. Thus Bellevue escaped an unpleasant scandal. Whether or not Davis was actually guilty has, of course, never been settled.

The department of charities and corrections, under which Bellevue functioned, heaved a sigh of relief. They were well aware that, quite outside of the Davis incident, many things could have been said about the hospital that would have made ugly listening. Hardly a day passed but that there were rumors of brutalities and violent deaths—from the legendary "black bottle" or means less arcane. Not only the insane pavilion but the entire institution had so far outgrown its facilities that the care of the patients was, to put it mildly, anything but adequate.

Neither the hospital staff nor the department of charities was entirely to blame. The plant was inadequate, and public opinion was only halfheartedly in favor of improvements. After all, Bellevue was for the poor and destitute. Nonetheless, to avert future disasters, the mayor and the board of aldermen came out with a plan to separate Bellevue from the department of charities and corrections and place it under a new board of trustees who were to have management of all city hospitals.

The new governing board of Bellevue and allied hospitals, consisting of people prominent in civic affairs, with Dr. J. W. Brannan at their head, began, in 1902, to survey Bellevue's current situation and needs. Dr. Brannan came out of retirement to give his entire time to reorganizing Bellevue. He strove to attract young doctors with enthusiasm and ideas; he bludgeoned the city government until it reluctantly handed out the funds for some brand-new facilities. His return to activity lasted for twenty years, and all this time Bellevue

Hospital was Dr. Brannan's first interest. From then on, Bellevue pretty much ceased to be a political football. New York was not only growing; it was growing up a little as well.

Very soon the new board had assembled a Bellevue staff that was second to none. Serving under Dr. Alexander Lambert as consulting physicians were Drs. Austin Flint, Jr., Francis Delafield, Edward Janeway, and Abraham Jacobi; as chief surgeons, Drs. Dennis and George David Stewart. Dr. Stewart, who had been superintendent of the hospital, was made chief of the board of health. To succeed him as superintendent, the board chose Dr. William Mabon, a graduate of Bellevue Hospital Medical College, who had made a reputation as a psychiatrist, among other places at the St. Lawrence Hospital for the Insane, whence he was called to Bellevue. A psychiatrist (then called an "alienist") and neurologist were appointed to each division. Among these newcomers were Drs. Bernard Sachs and Joseph Frankel. Chosen for the insane pavilion was Dr. Flattius Packer, first assistant physician of Kings Park State Hospital. Packer brought with him two assistants, one being Dr. Menas Gregory, who was to have a great influence on Bellevue psychiatry for the next forty years.

The trustees now gave their attention to the plant. They found the insane pavilion to be incredibly inadequate, worst of all the buildings. For example, it had no ventilation system at all. However, the rest of the hospital was almost as bad, and so they continued their survey to the bitter end. The total picture was depressing, even by the standards of a half-century ago. The board saw that nothing could be accomplished by shifting wards from one decrepit wing to another, piecing out with a new pavilion here and there.

The main building—that is, the old Almshouse—contained 718 of Bellevue's 946 beds. This hideous structure was now more than eighty-five years old. The plumbing leaked; the electric wiring system, the result of constant aimless extension, was a glaring fire hazard. Wires hung in festoons between the buildings and disappeared, like ivy run mad, right through the stone masonry.

The receiving and examining quarters, the board found, contributed greatly to the popular impression that going to Bellevue was like entering the jaws of death. One dim and airless basement room was used to process eighty to a hundred patients daily: people struck down in the streets, the insane, the acutely ill. The trustees were moved at once to put in bathing facilities so that the patients could be stripped and cleaned before they added their bit of infection to the already purulent wards. They also required that the house physician or surgeon should himself examine the patient during the day. Formerly the arrangement had been quite haphazard. By day young interns, by night assistants, had languidly carried out this preliminary work. Bellevue as a surgical and medical experimental center using as material the human wreckage of the city was one thing. As a hospital it was a disgrace, even by city hospital standards of the day. For good reason the unfortunates who found themselves being carried within its portals felt that dread which Dante describes as peculiar to the gates of hell.

The trustees—and why they did not know before is a mystery—solemnly reported that the staff's quarters were abominably crowded. Forty-three interns, they observed, were snuggled into the sixteen rooms. But their digs were palatial compared to the slavey precincts in the basement. Bellevue's maids, who gathered and disposed of the hospital's vast production of slops, lived in a Stygian dormitory containing, within its space of 45 by 36 feet, no less than thirty-one beds, together with concomitant commodes. These poor souls even lacked chairs to sit on. Off duty, they sat on their beds and stared hard at their chamber pots, or reached for the pint of gin tucked beneath the mattress. Their wages: $10.00 a month.

Moved, the trustees gave them chairs. Hard ones, to be sure, but chairs. They also, in a fit of generosity, transferred some of the maids—we imagine them as being the younger and prettier ones—to the carpenter shop on the second floor of the old boilerhouse. Meanwhile, they overhauled the medical college building and eventually converted it into dormitories. They also asked the board of estimate for an appropriation to increase the wages of the employees and thus improve the type of worker. Turnover of personnel in this era of cheap labor ran from 40 to 50 per cent a month. Then, as today, all types of hospital work were underpaid, only more drastically so. Either the poor creatures quit of their own accord, or were kicked out for incompetence or drunkenness.

The prison wards were even worse than the pavilion for the insane, which rivaled Bedlam. The trustees described the men's prison ward as "indecent." A low, basement room with little windows on one side, it measured only 20 by 40 feet but contained thirteen beds, with more mattresses on the floor as business required. An iron fence running down the middle of the ward separated prisoners held on more serious charges from the drunks. These two factions stared at each other through the pales. There was one toilet for all, an ancient and rusty bowl with the wooden seat long gone. When the gas was lit, the air became heavy and fetid. In the women's ward, the toilet was in the pantry, where the cooking utensils were kept. The nurses had to dodge about patients enthroned, while preparing sparse snacks for those recumbent.

The trustees declared that henceforth ambulance duty should be assigned only to interns with at least six months' hospital experience. Formerly, the youngest and newest men on the staff had drawn this important task. A female head nurse was assigned to every ward except those where prisoners, drunks, and venereal cases were kept.

But four years passed before one of the trustees' most important recommendations was carried out: the affiliation of the nursing school with University-Bellevue Medical College or, to use its present name, New York University College of Medicine. From this time on, the college took over the teaching and awarding of diplomas to students, although both student and graduate nurses continued on the city payroll.

Another change much appreciated both by the patients and their families was inaugurated by Dr. Mabon. The families of the moribund were given notice of this fact by telegram. Before, word had been sent by letter, which characteristically arrived after the principal was in the morgue.

With the new trustees' blistering report shoved under their noses, the board of estimate appropriated a sum for the preparation of plans and specifications for a new Bellevue. This was to cost $3,000,000. McKim, Mead and White, at that time perhaps the best known architects in the country, were engaged. They were assisted in arriving at their design by a committee of physicians and surgeons selected from the Medical Board. The entire north block of Bellevue was to be condemned, and the hospital grounds to be increased 75 per cent by the erection of a bulkhead extending two feet into the river. The commissioner of docks planned to build a new commercial pier at the foot of Thirtieth Street, and donate the old one at Twenty-eighth Street to the hospital.

While all these physical changes were in progress, the new members of the staff, a younger group, quickly gave old Bellevue a fresh lease on life. Bernard Sachs, psychiatrist-neurologist, had been educated in Strasbourg, Paris, and Vienna. After returning to America, he had made a name for himself as a specialist in mental and nervous diseases. Charles Norris, the new head of the department of pathology at Bellevue, had studied in Germany. His interest in toxicology stemmed from studies he made in Dr. Prudden's laboratory, of wood-alcohol and tetraethyl-lead poisoning. Subsequently he had become professor of pathological anatomy in the new Cornell clinic, but gave up teaching for active research and clinical work at Bellevue. He and Dr. Prudden planned the fine pathological laboratory that was to be a part of the new Bellevue.

An outstanding member from the old staff was Dr. Alexander Lambert, son of a prominent physician and the second of three brothers, all doctors and all connected with Bellevue. Sam, the oldest, who became a leading internist remembered not only for his skill but for his keen wit and ribald stories, interned at Bellevue. Adrian, the youngest, did early work in chest surgery and the tuberculosis service. Alexander was on the staff for more than forty years, much of this time as chief of the Fourth Division.

Dr. Alexander Lambert, childless himself, was very fond of younger people and always showed a sympathetic interest in the affairs of the interns under him. He was not only a first-class practitioner of medicine, but a driving force in getting things done. Forever up in arms against inefficiency, he kept both himself and everyone in his entourage on the jump. It was a typical Bellevue sight—Dr. Lambert racing up and down the aisles of the "A & B" building, his interns panting after him, never quite able to keep pace with their hyperactive and explosive mentor.

With him, humor followed anger as sun the rain. One day he heard a loud bang in a laboratory where one of his assistants was making some urology tests. He looked in from the door. The young man before the Bunsen burner had the jagged remains of a flask in his hand. Glass was all over the floor. Dr. Lambert sniffed the air, and burst into laughter. "Good heavens, man," he exclaimed, "you've been testing my brother Sam's Napoleon brandy!"

Though short, thick, and inclined to stoutness, Dr. Lambert was fond of hunting and riding. Astride a horse, he bounced in the saddle like a jumping jack. He sometimes went duck-hunting with Theodore Roosevelt, a patient of his, though this meant squatting at the rainy break of day under an upturned boat at Lloyd's Neck. He was warm friends with Roosevelt. On one occasion when Roosevelt, then in the White House, consulted him about the value of the experiment in mosquito control at the Panama Canal, he was instrumental in persuading the President to continue it. Lambert had the eccentric habit of using a bicycle to make his calls, and would appear at staff conferences in plus fours.

Though not a specialist, as a pathologist Dr. Lambert did fine work on tetanus and diphtheria in the Physicians and Surgeons laboratory, where he collaborated with Dr. Prudden and Dr. Park. He was one of the first systematically to study alcoholism, and was also active in early heart research. His cardiac clinic at Bellevue attracted not only doctors from other divisions but many men from Presbyterian, New York, and Roosevelt hospitals who were interested in the subject.

Another impressive member of the old staff was Dr. George David Stewart, chief surgeon of the Third Division. Dr. Stewart, a large, good-looking man of Scottish descent from the Maritime Provinces, had trained at Bellevue, and he became a leading figure in the so-called Golden Age of Surgery between the turn of the century and World War I. Dr. Stewart's Friday morning clinics at Bellevue were always crowded with visiting surgeons, and the post-clinic discussions were invariably stimulating and informative.

Dr. Stewart was a lifelong student of the Bible, like his equally famous colleague, Dr. Menas Gregory. He had been brought up very strictly in the Presbyterian style, with Sunday fishing, swimming, and whistling prohibited by his stern mother. Yet he always felt, in later life, that the belief in God she had instilled into him was his greatest asset. He felt that the younger agnostic generation missed a great deal of life's essence. Prayer, for example, to him was as natural as breathing.

"The finest arterial remedy I know," he used to tell his students, "is the peace of God which passeth all understanding." Needless to say, psychosomatic medicine has borne out this insight.

Dr. Stewart, though no writer, was an excellent conversationalist and after-dinner speaker. Often he was called on for this purpose three or four times a week. At one gathering he enchanted his dinner partner so much the man forgot to ask his name until later.

"That was Dr. George Stewart, the surgeon," his host explained.

"Surgeon!" exclaimed the man in amazement. "Why, he talked about nothing but the Bible all evening. He knew so so much about it I thought he was a bishop."

Despite Stewart's piety, he loved a good joke—that is, on the other fellow. As chief of surgery at St. Vincent's Hospital, he was treated there like a king. When he entered the hospital, bells rang, assistants, interns, and nurses dashed about, and like a shot the surgical staff assembled to follow him on his rounds. It was standard practice to station one of the Sisters at the admitting desk to warn the hospital of Stewart's visits.

On one particular day a new Sister was in charge of the admitting desk and when Dr. Stewart walked in, all he got was a polite look of inquiry.

"Nurse," he said in his broad Scottish brogue, "wad ye hae the guidness to inform the staff of my presence?"

"Who are you?" the nurse asked. Stewart drew himself to his impressive height. Making his eyes flash, he replied: "In this hospital, I am Jesus H. Christ, good woman. And see that ye never forget it!"

One of Dr. Stewart's oldest and warmest friends was George F. Baker, the banker, who gave a million dollars to the creation of a George David Stewart Endowment Fund to promote the teaching of surgery at New York University College of Medicine.

Among Stewart's hobbies was versifying. Occasionally he read his jingles before the Chakara Club, a group of doctors with literary tastes. Still remembered is "A Tired Doctor's Prayer," in which he pictured himself as longing for the day when he would be planted under a white oak tree, deaf to telephone bells and doorbells, and no longer responsible to mama when baby swallowed carbolic salve.

In all respects Dr. Stewart was the prototype of the successful, gregarious, socially aspirant and yet responsible, medical man of the Golden Age. On him science had left no sobering mark; he comes to us straight out of Veblen's revealing pages. But he was a believer, a man with a scale of values, who behaved as he believed. Since his heyday, giant strides have been made in medicine, thanks to the steady mergence of the art of healing with the sciences of chemistry and physics. But on the medical scene, men of Dr. Stewart's sanguine and immensely reassuring character no longer loom.

In the early 1900's, too, nursing standards improved in step with improvements in physical plant and medical understanding and technique. Vast changes had taken place since Florence Nightingale's letter and Bellevue's first attempt to make nursing a true profession. The rise of a feminist movement, culminating in the fight for women's suffrage, gave impetus to progress in nursing. Typical of the dedicated woman of the bloomer years was a most remarkable person called Lavinia L. Dock, who made herself a leader and spokesman of the nursing vocation.

Miss Dock was a mature woman, who had been well educated in private schools, when an article in the *Century Magazine* convinced her that she should enter the Bellevue Training School for Nurses. When her decision became known, it appeared so revolutionary that the social leader of her small New Jersey town exclaimed, "But I always thought the Dock girls were ladies!"

Following graduation, Miss Dock was the first nurse to be engaged by the United Workers, a pioneer social organization in Norwich, Connecticut, which voted to "try the experiment of employing a trained nurse for three months to attend cases of illness in all parts of the town." According to an early report,

Miss Dock "entered upon her duties with enthusiasm and soon proved of value in such work."

Miss Dock left Norwich and volunteered for service in a yellow fever epidemic in New York, and later became one of the pioneers in the Visiting Nurses of the New York City Mission. She had returned to Bellevue as night supervisor when Isabel Hampton (Robb) invited her to become her assistant in the new school at Johns Hopkins Hospital in Baltimore. Miss Dock was the first instructor in a school which was setting new standards for nursing education. Hopkins' nurses of the period never forgot the superb quality of her teaching or the forthrightness with which she praised or blamed as the occasion arose. For three years Miss Hampton and Miss Dock enjoyed the exciting interplay of mind on mind in a new and stimulating situation. Then, since Bellevue graduates were in great demand, Miss Dock accepted the position of principal of the already well-established Illinois Training School for Nurses in Chicago.

Of her brief tenure there, Miss Dock wrote with revealing candor: "I can confidently assert that my principal aims and endeavors were right and sound, but I showed no diplomatic skill whatever in personal relationships." Actually, as it proved, had she stayed at Illinois, she might have missed what was called by her the most rewarding experience of her life. This was the privilege of working and living at the Henry Street Settlement with Lillian D. Wald. Among the first to join this brave and intelligent little band of visiting nurses and pioneer social workers, she was "daily to share the tragedies, the victories, the hopes, the practical problems, and the jokes of Henry Street."

There, amid the misery and squalor of New York's teeming East Side, they "dwelt together, finding fellowship in common hopes and faith in democracy." Their methods of dealing with the intolerable social conditions which surrounded them attracted people from all over the world who were probing deeply into the causes of poverty, disease, and social unrest.

"It was at Henry Street," says Miss Dock, "that I really began to think." Deeply compassionate, intellectually forthright and farseeing, happily and often amusingly unconventional, she became socialistic in political outlook, ardently pacifistic, and militantly suffragist.

Of this halcyon period she relates:

> One of my proceedings amused the charitable, for it was not according to the books. One of those altogether lovable Irishmen who can't help drinking was to go to Bellevue to be treated for alcoholism. I was deputized to take him there. On the way to the street car we passed a saloon. He stood still and vowed he could go no farther without a drink. Persuasion was useless, and, although we had never then heard of psychiatry, I went into the saloon with him, saw that he had only a small drink, and he was then quite willing to go the rest of the way. I landed him safely into the hospital, but I fear I shocked my associates.

Miss Dock became convinced, quite early in her years at Henry Street, that the social evils pullulating about her could not be effectively dealt with without universal suffrage. By 1912 she was writing to her friend Mrs. Bedford-Fenwich, editor of the *British Journal of Nursing*:

> I am really passing through a period that seems actually like a sort of intoxication with the work for women's suffrage. . . . Do what I will, I can't make anything else seem really important just now. I only live for the work in meetings, propaganda, headquarters and the reading of suffrage news. It's the most fascinating and exhilarating work I ever did.

Miss Dock once appeared at a meeting of the National League of Nursing Education wearing across her chest the conspicuous slogan "Votes for Women." She ignored the topic assigned her, and proceeded to make an impassioned suffrage speech to her woefully unresponsive audience.

Of all the varied experiences in her energetically zestful life, Miss Dock has said that she derived the greatest satisfaction from two things: going to jail for suffrage, and collaborating with Miss Adelaide Nutting on a history of nursing. She went to jail on three separate occasions. On a fourth, she went to the polls to insist on voting, and demanded that she be arrested for her offense. Theodore Roosevelt, then police commissioner of New York City, refused to put her in jail.

The preparation of a materia medica for nurses, one of the earliest textbooks for nurses, while she was night superintendent at Bellevue, was her most important work; 100,000 copies in several editions were sold. As the publisher—G. P. Putnam's Sons—had been unwilling to make the initial investment, Miss Dock's father, although believing that he was "gambling on a gold brick," advanced the funds required to launch this famous best seller. Massive, often dangerous, dosages of medicine were the order of the day. Nurses, Miss Dock felt, needed more specific information, not readily available in ponderous medical tomes. The project involved intensive correspondence with the authors of those works, most of whom fortunately proved to be co-operative. Her methods of making nauseous doses more palatable became an important feature in the success of her book.

Another little volume called *Hygiene and Morality*, published many years before venereal disease could be mentioned in polite society, gave significant evidence of Miss Dock's social vision and moral courage. But her four-volume *History of Nursing* written in collaboration with Miss Adelaide Nutting was a landmark. Two years were spent gathering material, chiefly abroad. Again a publisher failed to recognize the potentialities of the book. The dauntless pair secured a bank loan, and so successful was their venture that the loan was repaid within a few months. These four volumes provided a foundation for the widely used *Short History of Nursing* on which Isabel M. Stewart collaborated with Miss Dock.

Miss Dock was also one of the collaborators on the *History of the Red Cross Nursing Service*, which through World War I and the postwar period exerted such a powerfully constructive influence on the development of nursing in this country. She had become interested in disaster work during the Johnstown Flood, at which time she met Clara Barton, founder of the American Red Cross.

Throughout her life Lavinia Dock carried on a relentless fight for the prestige of the nursing profession. Her vast correspondence embraced the civilized world. Her writings were reprinted in nineteen languages. It is largely due to the efforts of this one courageous woman that nursing is so firmly established as a scientific profession today. She died on April 18, 1956, in her ninety-ninth year.

XX

DAWN OF SOCIAL SERVICE

The beginning of the twentieth century also ushered in the age of specialization which continues to this day. Characteristic of this trend was the development of special techniques and facilities for handling TB.

Among the young doctors attracted to Bellevue during the 1910–15 period was James Alexander Miller. At the time, Dr. Miller was slated to become the chief of the Vanderbilt Clinic at Presbyterian Hospital and was content with his work there. But when he discovered what a remarkable opportunity there was at Bellevue for research in TB, he accepted an appointment on the medical staff of the First Division, saying that he "might as well go down and see how the other half lives." For at this time Presbyterian was perhaps the best hospital in New York, and long remained so.

Although Dr. Miller's appointment to Bellevue was in general medicine, already he had a special interest in tuberculosis—an interest awakened during a summer spent helping the famous Dr. Trudeau in his practice at a fashionable resort in the Adirondacks.

The tuberculosis wards at Bellevue, Dr. Miller presently realized, were a mine of pathological material. Nobody paid any attention to the TB cases. They belonged to no division, but were dumped, with the prison, alcoholic, and insane wards, into what were known as the outlying services. Every six weeks there was a staff change, the interns of one division rotating with another, which meant that one intern from the division was responsible, pro tem, for the wards. There were no trained nurses to help preserve order. The visiting physicians seldom showed up as they were supposed to do, and as a result these patients were hardly ever examined. No records were kept of the cases, not even of deaths. Most of the patients received "standing order" medication, consisting of one-half ounce of whisky per diem, one-quarter grain of morphine if the patient hemorrhaged, and another dose of whisky if he was being transferred. The outlying services wards were openly deemed the last stop before the sanitorium or the grave. Where such an attitude prevailed, there was little use trying to cure anybody. Dr. Miller, however, was to change this sorry state of affairs.

With backing from Dr. Brannan, who himself had been cured of tuberculosis and was keenly interested in the disease, Dr. Miller got the wards transferred to the First Division. This brought them within an orderly system of control, and insured better medical attention.

Miller next established a TB clinic in the outpatient department, open from one to four every weekday afternoon. There he examined patients, advised them about diet and the dangers of infection, and taught them how to live at home. He minimized drugs, and recommended fresh air and a weekly checkup on each patient's case. He also moved twelve of the patients who were in the early stages of the disease to a tent on the grounds, and then transferred them again to a shack where the old tennis court used to be. This improvised shelter held twenty-five beds. Though dismally cold in winter, it was an improvement over the dark and crowded wards. Now that all the tuberculosis wards were under the aegis of First Division, doctors in the other divisions saw to it that whatever TB cases they turned up were shifted into Dr. Miller's care.

This expansion, trivial though in fact it was, cost money

which the board of estimate was loath to provide. Dr. Miller
became much engrossed in the problem. At this time, in private
practice he was an assistant to A. Alexander Smith, professor
of medicine at New York University College of Medicine and
for many years head of the Third Medical Division at Bellevue.
In line of duty he attended many of Dr. Smith's wealthy
patients. Among them were the Misses Blanche and Martha
Potter, who lived in Ossining.

Often, as the young doctor waited for his train after paying
the Potter girls a visit, he would tell them about the clinic and
the shack on the Bellevue lawn. To them he confided his plan
for anchoring an old ferryboat at the foot of Twenty-sixth
Street for use as a day camp where clinic patients could rest
every day in the open air. He wanted to provide milk and fresh
eggs for indigent victims of TB. Also, he told the Potters, he
hoped sometime to educate his patients in the desirability of
not coughing in people's faces and not spitting on the floor.

The Potter sisters naturally became interested in the persuasive young doctor's charitable impulses. Miss Martha gave
several thousand dollars toward the ferryboat and, after Miss
Martha's death in 1910, Miss Blanche became chairman of a
women's auxiliary to aid the tuberculosis service. During the
years in which she served with the auxiliary, Miss Blanche's
interests branched out into the Nurses' Training School and
other activities. She became, in fact, one of the most efficient
and influential volunteer service workers in New York, with a
particular devotion to Bellevue and TB services.

In 1910 the old ferryboat *Southfield* was tied to the landing,
and the day camp was set up, and that same year the first
pavilion of the new hospital—the "A & B" building—was completed. The TB wards finally came up out of the basement of
the old administration building.

At the same time, Dr. Miller secured the services of a nurse
half-time from the recently established social service department. Miss Anne Morgan, of the banking family, was keenly

interested in the social service venture, and herself paid the nurse's salary, since no provision had been made in the budget. Presently the tuberculosis auxiliary subsidized full time another graduate nurse and also a student nurse. These workers did some badly needed educational work in the homes of out-patients. They explained about ventilation and diet, and showed how to utilize roofs and fire escapes for rest cures. They also brought back reports about conditions which were useful in directing public attention to the general need.

The next step in the Miller reforms was to help provide poor TB patients with some semblance of proper diet. The auxiliary raised many thousands of dollars a year for the clinic, the day camp, extra nurses, and services. But that was not enough—not nearly enough. For about fifteen years the TB service existed almost solely on contributions and the interest of a few people. At last Dr. Miller was persuaded by Dr. Charles Norris to take a leaf from Hermann Biggs's book—and go to the politicians for help.

With Dr. Brannan's aid, in 1926 Dr. Miller got the tuberculosis service listed on the proposed city budget! Thereafter it was a question of lining up political influence to guarantee its acceptance. Dr. Miller determined to solicit the help of Mayor Jimmy Walker, whose brother he had treated for TB. He telephoned the mayor's secretary, a Miss Wagner, sister of the Senator and aunt of the present mayor of New York. Miss Wagner put him down for 2:30 the following day. Right on time, Dr. Miller pushed through a milling throng at City Hall, all waiting to see the dapper mayor.

Jimmy Walker was beginning his day. He sat at a table swinging his leg and listened while Doctor Miller told him about the service. On and on they talked. Miller became a trifle nervous, remembering the people waiting outside. But Jimmy Walker brushed them off with a smile; he was enjoying himself and didn't intend to be hurried.

"I'm with you, Doc," he said at last. "You can have whatever you want."

From that day on, Miller's department was showered with favors so lavishly that other heads wondered how he could get so much and they so little. Within fifteen years a pattern had been set. The TB service was well organized and well staffed. From pariah status it rose to be one of the most popular services in Bellevue. The medical clinic especially, a small room with a shoulder-high partition, was always crowded with doctors from the other services looking over the fence.

Side by side with the tuberculosis service grew the social service department, originally set up at Bellevue in 1907, with one nurse who had a vaguely defined job and unlimited opportunity to relieve human suffering. The idea of such a department had first occurred to Dr. T. F. Armstrong, a Bellevue medical superintendent, after reading an article by Dr. Richard Cabot describing an experiment with a social service nurse in Massachusetts General Hospital. Armstrong instantly saw how much such a service might mean to Bellevue.

He interested Mrs. John L. Wilkie, a member of the board of managers of the Nurses' Training School, in social service work, and prevailed on her to go to Boston to learn firsthand what Dr. Cabot was doing. She came back completely won over and on fire to do something of the same sort for Bellevue. From the trustees she wrung the promise of a salary for a nurse, if one could be found with adequately exceptional qualities. Mrs. Wilkie now began a search for the right nurse. At first she got nowhere at all. There were any number of good nurses with plenty of hospital experience, but few, if any, of them had been trained in social service. Nursing schools paid little attention to this new branch of the profession. Actually, there were few opportunities anywhere for a nurse to gain experience.

And so Mrs. Wilkie was moved to seek the advice of Miss Lillian Wald, founder of the famous Henry Street Settlement. She, in turn, suggested Miss Mary E. Wadley, a graduate of the

Bellevue Training School and one of Dr. Hermann Biggs's public school nurses. Mrs. Wilkie invited Miss Wadley to tea, told her about the new experiment, and left her eager to try her hand. She would have to chart out a new field, for there were no landmarks, no methods of procedure, to go by. It was a formidable prospect, but she had been taking care of 1,300 school children in the Italian section, and was confident she would not fail. Certainly her new working arrangement would not be entirely strange, since she had trained at Bellevue.

Miss Wadley began by making herself known at charity organizations with which she would have to co-operate. The second day of her new job, she made the rounds of Bellevue's TB wards to meet doctors and nurses and explain to them what she hoped to do. That very afternoon the house physician of Old Ward 20 gave her her first case, a young immigrant girl who had been in the country only two months and was now being discharged without friends, money, or a home to go to. Further complicating her situation was an irresponsible nature. The house physician did not want to turn the helpless girl out into the New York streets with no protection. Did Miss Wadley think she could do something for her? Miss Wadley nodded her head. Questioning revealed that the girl had a sister in the suburbs who was willing to come for her.

No sooner had Miss Wadley begun work than she found she required an assistant. So many desperate cases were turned over to her or discovered by her on her rounds that within a month she had 110 patients in her charge. The trustees voted a second salary and employed an assistant, but almost as soon as the new nurse was familiar with the work, she was snatched away to fill a vacancy in the regular nursing service. Social service was still looked on as a "frill," and subject to pre-emptions by other services. Miss Wadley was again given an assistant, and again robbed of her services. Thereafter she worked on as best she could, unaided except by devoted volunteer help.

The next year the Free Synagogue offered a group of volunteers, who proved to be a godsend in that they relieved Miss Wadley of the work with Yiddish-speaking patients whose needs were difficult to understand. She next set about creating a staff that would include a nurse, or nurses, able on daily rounds to talk with Italians, Greeks, Poles, and other immigrants in the wards. These people were quite unable to explain their symptoms and home situation except through the eager but often highly colored translations of other patients. Miss Wadley believed that a nurse who could get the firsthand stories from patients would be a great help. She also thought that the social service department should have someone to check on patients as they were admitted, perhaps by talking with the relatives in the waiting room in the admittance hall. This, she felt, would not only relieve a patient's anxiety, but permit social service to find out whether he would need help when discharged.

Miss Wadley lived to see many of her ideas take concrete and effective shape. Before her retirement a social service worker in her department had been assigned full time to the admitting office. Her job was to reassure the frightened patients, and try to establish the identity of amnesia patients or accident victims brought in unconscious. This latter task was one that often required the gifts of a Sherlock Holmes. She also saw the whole program so carefully organized that today no Bellevue patient is discharged without an investigation of the environment to which he is returning. But in 1907 all this, of course, was nebulous. For eighteen months Miss Wadley carried on her work almost unassisted. After this probationary period, slowly the service began to grow. In 1908 a committee of influential volunteers, with Mrs. William Osborne as their chairman, organized to advise and give financial support to the Bellevue Social Service Department. Subcommittees were formed to develop special services. The work of the department was extended to include children and mental patients. One of the first to use a special social service nurse was Dr. Miller's tuberculosis service.

Thus, social service gradually became an integral part of the Bellevue scheme. In 1926 Miss Wadley looked back on the first twenty years of social service at Bellevue, and herself was amazed at so much progress against such great odds. The hospital had built the largest social service department in the United States or, indeed, in the world, and had given assistance to 225,000 patients. Miss Wadley's system had been adopted by fifty other hospitals throughout the United States. She had the satisfaction of knowing that her objective of doing for each case "the common sense thing in the common sense way" had widely influenced the character of social service work throughout the country.

In spite of her heavy responsibilities all these years, time had dealt gently with Miss Wadley. A plump, small, humorous, clear-sighted woman, to the end of her career she liked her fellow human beings and never flagged in her determination to see their problems realistically and in the round. Her personal life had been emotionally enriched by the adoption of a son and daughter. By personal example she had kept her staff's *esprit de corps* at high pitch. After twenty-five years the service had fifty-one graduate nurses on its roster, an elite group that scorned the bureaucratic and perfunctory.

Miss Wadley's portrait, which hangs in the outer office of the Bellevue Social Service Department, is a reminder to all interested in her work of the enormous improvements which she set in motion. Today, in most cities, every big hospital has a social service, and many hospital and nurses' training schools now train their students in the basics of this field of endeavor.

Even back in 1926 when Miss Wadley took careful stock of her achievements, great changes had occurred, not merely in public care of the poor and weak, but in the very social conditions which had given rise to so much misery. Contemplating the scene, Miss Wadley wondered whether, after all, she might not be seeing things through rose-colored glasses, and even went so far as to call a staff meeting to check on her observations. The nurses convinced her that the change was not with them, but with conditions.

Within fifteen years the desperate poverty that had at first occupied them had almost disappeared. The whole character of their work had changed. Social misfits rather than the economically distressed were the main concern. The staff tried to formulate the reasons for this betterment and listed them in this order: advances in medical service; welfare legislation, including workmen's compensation; widows' pensions and rent laws; safety devices in factories; clinics and industrial plants in which workers' cuts and bruises are attended to before they become infected; the rise in the economic level of labor; employment bureaus for the handicapped; the increase in the number of convalescent homes; the educational and preventive work done by the board of health; visiting nurse organizations, and hospital service workers.

To be sure, the millennium has not yet arrived. No social service worker has ever deceived herself about this, not even the oldtimers who remember the bitter early days at Bellevue. But in the spring especially, when contagions used to flourish, they are keenly aware of the human benefactions they have so largely helped to bring about.

XXI

WOMEN AGAIN SCORE

During the period immediately before World War I, Bellevue was also physically expanding as fast as new buildings could go up, some on land still in process of being reclaimed from the river. When digging started on the foundations for pavilions "A" and "B" beside the erysipelas and alcoholic wards, tidewater flowed in so fast that large pumps had to be installed. All day and night their throbbing reverberated through the wards. Trucks roared all day long on the river's edge; concrete mixers added to the din as they prepared material for the new breakwater. Gray dust drifted through the wards. It was like being sick in the midst of a construction camp. Even the cripples who for generations had sunned themselves on riverside benches fled indoors. But in good time this pervasive feeling of disorder passed, and soon proved that passing discomfort was a small price to pay for permanent benefits.

At any rate, in keeping with the general atmosphere of dislocation peculiar to the times, in 1912 the first woman doctor in Bellevue's history was added to the staff. This spectacular innovation came about through Dr. Alexander Lambert's interest in electrocardiography. At an American Medical Association convention Dr. Lambert had seen an electrocardiograph exhibited by Dr. MacKenzie of London, who had done much toward stabilizing knowledge of the heart. Wanting one to use in his own clinic, but knowing that it would be practically impossible to get the board of estimate to hand out the necessary $4,000, he paid for the apparatus himself, with the proviso that Bellevue would give him space to work with it. Then he engaged Dr. Catherine R. Kelley, a slim, quiet New Hampshire girl, as his clinical assistant to operate the machine.

When Dr. Kelley came to Bellevue in the spring of 1912, she was hardly aware of the feeling there against her sex. Her object was research, and here was the opportunity. And so she simply plumped ahead, looking neither to right nor left. As the electro-cardiograph was the first machine in the city for purely clinical investigative work, the clinic rapidly developed a busy service. Doctors, both from the other divisions in Bellevue and from outside hospitals, came to see the machine work and study its findings. Because this was a brand-new field, there was always a feeling of excitement about the place.

After having worked in the clinic a few months, Dr. Kelley asked Dr. Alexander Miller if she might serve part time in his TB clinic. He said he would like to have her, but he explained frankly that, although he personally had no prejudice against women, he did not feel he could get her a regular staff appointment. Bellevue was a city hospital with a rugged tradition in which women were not easily accepted. Nonetheless, if she would take a courtesy appointment, the work was hers.

Dr. Kelley told her chief that being on the staff was not her main concern. All she wanted was an opportunity to work. But later that same year, Dr. Miller was able to offer her a regular staff position. Now Dr. Kelley was not sure. Whereas her courtesy appointment had restricted her to the outpatient department, henceforth she would be in the regular wards, where the patients were either moribund or awaiting transfer to a sanitorium. In the outpatient department she had managed to show results, and find gratification in this.

Nevertheless, Dr. Kelley took the appointment. Like the men, she made the rounds in the morning at seven o'clock and at night at eleven. She was deeply moved by the way the nurses kept the dreary old wards and the helpless patients clean. Equipment was either worn out or nonexistent. Everybody was trying to make things hang together until the completion of the projected pavilions "F" and "G," then in noisy process of construction. Dr. Kelley's fortitude came to be admired by the whole staff. This favorable impression quickly bore fruit.

During the next summer, four women doctors passed the examinations and were given positions on the Bellevue staff. These young women were made of stern pioneer stuff. Merely to achieve internship they had to overcome endless obstacles laid in their path by stodgy tradition. All had been graduated from Cornell University Medical College in the class of 1914. Early realizing how hard it was for a woman to get an internship at a good hospital, they had determined to make student grades that simply could not be disregarded. One took top honors in her class; none of them fell below eighty.

During their senior year the girls planned their attack on the citadel of putative male superiority. The father of one of them, a lawyer, drew up a petition which pointed out in dry legal terms that since women were admitted to the college, it naturally followed that the college, as in the case of male students, was responsible for providing them, if they qualified, with internships. The girls debated whether they should present this document to the Cornell Medical Board of the University, but finally did not, in fear that the board would look upon it with only academic interest and leave a major talking point pigeonholed.

The first outside help for their case came from Cornell women doctors already out in practice. These people had teas and dinner parties to which they invited members of the boards of various hospitals, influential politicians, physicians, visiting doctors, in fact, everybody and anybody who might help. With a following established, the girls then made personal calls on the doctors in charge of the various divisions at Bellevue. For they all wanted to get into Bellevue, and had been told that a great deal would depend on the personal impression they made. The doctors at Bellevue were cautious. There were no quarters, they said, for women doctors. The girls retorted they would sleep in the corridors. Then other specious excuses were offered. The charity sort of work at Bellevue was too hard and grim. They were unsuited for ambulance calls, and so on.

Meanwhile, the first examination due at Bellevue was in the Fourth Division, and they had at any rate gained the sympathy of a young doctor who knew the chiefs of the various departments. He coached the girls in his office, and briefed them on the personalities of all the Fourth Division doctors, also on what questions to expect in the exams. Two of the girls, Helen L. Palliser and Anna Tjomsland, finally took the examinations. Aware that there were only nine openings for the fifty-nine applicants, they strove mightily and came well out on top. Then, shortly afterward, Geraldine B. Watson, whose father had penned the eloquent legal appeal, and May E. Walker, also took examinations, in their case for the Second Division. They too came through with flying colors.

Drs. Watson and Tjomsland entered Bellevue triumphantly but a little uneasily in July, 1914. During the first six months, fingers were pointed at them from all sides. They responded to this vulgar pressure by being rigorously circumspect. They smoked no cigarettes in the hospital grounds, received no men callers, and only emergency phone calls. Their only diversion was an occasional dip, during the warm months, in the East River at night when its excrementious flotsam was invisible. Occasionally on a week end, too, they canoed on the Hudson, always by themselves.

They had no time, however, to lament their self-enforced nun-like regime. Each day was crowded with tense experiences—operations to watch, the responsibility of their own first cases, the thrill of having patients completely trust and depend on them, the emotional stress of wanting very much to help while knowing nothing could be done.

When, after the first six months, Dr. Palliser came on duty, to be followed soon after by Dr. Walker, their sternly self-disciplined classmates felt that they could relax a bit, although they never forgot for a moment that if they did not make good no other women could get into Bellevue Hospital. The women doctors, feeling that there was some safety in numbers, permitted themselves to smoke cigarettes and enliven their hours off duty by playing chess or singing to the accompaniment of Dr. Palliser's mandolin, then a mildly *avant-garde* symbol. The room in which they slept was large, but not large enough to keep all four of them from being awakened when any one was called at night. Rats of heroic East River dimension came up through the floor at night and playfully scampered across their faces. Midnight searches with a flashlight for bedbugs were part of their regime. But they were not shaken.

In due course Dr. Watson became the first woman house physician at Bellevue, and Dr. Tjomsland, the first resident in the Children's Surgical Division. Dr. Tjomsland also made history as the first woman doctor to ride a Bellevue ambulance. A very tall and beautiful Norwegian blonde, she looked like a stirring Valkyrie as she perched above the beautiful, high-spirited bay that drew the old-fashioned Black Maria.

The new women doctors at Bellevue became the butt of stupid newspaper quips and cartoons. Although they did everything they could to avoid newsmen for fear of losing their jobs, they made good and frequent copy for idle reporters. In spite of her best endeavors to avoid publicity, Dr. Tjomsland saw her picture in the *Police Gazette*, snapped when she was dashing, in a delightfully ruffled state, to a fire. Anxious at first, she found there were to be no repercussions. Her male colleagues smiled, and took off their hats. Presently everybody was for the women, and soon they were being asked, like the men, to stand the staff a beer every time they brought in a corpse. In time no one thought it at all strange when they sat on a drunk to hold him down, or delivered twins in the ambulance en route to the hospital.

This was the carefree era before the United States entered the First World War, when the chief topic of conversation at Bellevue was the scramble for space in the new buildings and the chief excitement was the failure of the city to pay its employees for two whole months. Soon, however, this optimistic, burgeoning time of change was lost in a rush of greater events, and in retrospect took on a roseate, nostalgic glamour. After World War I, when they thought back on the good old days, the staff even had fond memories of the nasty old deadhouse and of the street-cleaners' dump at the foot of Thirtieth Street.

In 1912, shortly before World War I revolutionized the world picture, Dr. Biggs and others fought a climactic battle of their own on this side of the water. Pulled to office this year on the coattails of Woodrow Wilson, a curious fellow named William Sulzer became governor of New York. After many years in the state legislature, Sulzer had served in Congress as representative from a New York City district. He was erratic, egotistic, and a demagogue, but nonetheless a demagogue with a real desire to render public service. His besetting weakness was an almost total absence of horse sense. Sulzer's brief and otherwise politically disastrous nine months of gubernatorial service were marked by two of the most notable social advances in the history of the state. These were the reorganization of the Health Service and the Labor Department on sound and progressive lines.

New York State prior to 1913 had a fairly good health setup according to then-existing standards. But measured by the standards developed by Biggs in New York City, the state's health program was hopelessly archaic.

Shortly after Sulzer's election, the liberal social forces of the state sensed an opening and seized on it. At a dinner given by Mr. Henry Morgenthau, Governor Sulzer met with executives of eight or ten health and social agencies. Each was given ten minutes to present his idea of one particular phase of an improved state health service.

Sulzer, asked about his plans for the health commissionership, replied that he wanted "the best health man in the United States." When it was pointed out to him that under the existing law this would be far from easy, he calmly said, "Well, let's change the law!" The suggestion was then made that a commission might be created to revise the entire scheme of health organization. To this idea Sulzer responded with astonishing alacrity.

On January 10, 1913, Governor Sulzer appointed a special commission for "receiving suggestions and making such recommendations as may seem fitting with regard to what changes, if any, are at this time advisable in the laws of this state, relating to and affecting public health, and in public health administration." Hermann Biggs of Bellevue was naturally made chairman of the commission. This report, presented to the Governor on February 15, urged a complete overhaul of the state department of health. Such were the forces abroad that novelty instanter was embraced.

The commission's bill was transmitted with blinding speed to the legislature and enacted into law. A health council was appointed in a flash. Inevitably, Dr. Biggs was made a member, and, at its meeting, chairman.

This bill marked the most important advance in the history of state health administration in the United States since the first state health department had been established by Massachusetts in 1860. The legislation was signed with a flourish by the Governor on May 17, 1915, and the appropriation of the department was increased from $180,000 to $298,000 to make its execution possible.

Feeling that he had accomplished a tremendous amount, Dr. Biggs escaped with Mrs. Biggs early in the summer to Europe for a vacation. Returning to New York in the fall, they found, to their dismay, that things had been going very ill with poor Governor Sulzer. Brought up for years as a Tammany man and elected as a Tammany man, once in the governor's chair he became swollen with self-importance and in his heady state unfortunately broke with the machine. Not only that, he removed the superintendent of prisons, a man with strong Tammany backing, vetoed rigged election bills already passed by the legislature, and demanded a real direct primary law. In all ways he allied himself, as he had done in the case of the health and labor laws, with the most progressive and constructive forces of the state!

The machine that had cordially accepted the health legislation refused to swallow such a thing as direct primaries. Tammany began countermaneuvers. A special session of the legislature was called for June 16. Instead of passing Sulzer's direct primary law, the lawmakers appointed a committee to investigate the Governor's campaign expenditures' record during the recent election battle. Tammany saw to it that strong evidence was brought forward indicating he had concealed contributions to his personal campaign fund, in violation of state law. They also showed that he had used some of his campaign funds for stock speculation; that he had attempted to tamper with witnesses and influence the course of the legislative investigation in improper ways. All this was common Tammany practice. Alas, Sulzer had broken the gang law.

On August 13 he was impeached, and in October a Court of Impeachment removed the poor chap from office. His was one of the most pathetic stories in the history of New York politics—the story of a man with a shady background, who rose to real stature in office, and in vain tried to use his powers for good. His past proved his undoing, once again proving that he who dabbles in pitch will surely be defiled.

Lieutenant-Governor Martin H. Glynn now became governor, and in due course himself came to face the problem of health department reorganization. He arrived at the same con-

clusion reached by Sulzer, that Biggs was the only man to undertake the job.

The issue was placed squarely in Biggs's lap. If he refused
the position, Commissioner Porter, a minion of reaction, would
surely be reappointed. Since Dr. Porter had publicly avowed his
opposition to civil service for sanitary supervisors and had
officially recommended the abolition of the public health council, it was clear that without Biggs in charge the whole program
would be in jeopardy. And so he took the job, with the qualification that he was to maintain his residence in New York
City and give only part of his time to the state. Assured of an
absolutely free hand, he yielded. On January 1, 1914, Biggs
became state commissioner of health. New York State's excellent
health record dates almost from the day of his appointment.

· XXII ·

BELLEVUE GOES TO WAR

On July 27, 1914, Dr. William Welch wrote from Munich:

> We have arrived in the midst of a great war excitement.
> The German masses are apparently eager for war. . . . The air
> everywhere echoes with shouts of *Deutschland über alles*. It
> is all quite thrilling, but a general European war is too hor-
> rible to contemplate, and it seems impossible that it will
> occur . . .

But by the autumn of 1916, Bellevue was frantically preparing for American's impending entry into the holocaust. By
November, Dr. George Stewart had formed the Bellevue unit.
Miss Carrie J. Brink chose the nurses from the alumnae of the
Bellevue Training School, calling them in from hospitals in
Philadelphia, Pittsburgh, Boston, and other cities all over the
country. Experience, endurance, judgment, and the ability to
co-operate were the qualities sought. It was Miss Brink's strongest wish to lead the unit overseas, but hospital authorities
pleaded that she was needed at home—among other reasons, to
help the overworked staff get through the worst epidemic of
infantile paralysis the country had yet seen. Besides, the Bellevue doctors felt that Miss Brink was too old to stand the strain
of directing a field unit under battle conditions. In the end,
Miss Beatrice M. Bamber, who was superintendent of nurses
at Harlem Hospital, was assigned the job.

The board of the Bellevue Training School collected $125,000 to equip the unit, largely contributed by Mrs. William Church Osborne and Mrs. E. H. Harriman. A great many other New York citizens and private organizations also pitched in.

The women of a Presbyterian church donated two motor-cycles, and Mrs. John B. Hartwell presented every nurse with a service watch. Drs. Carl G. Burdick and Arthur Mullin Wright handled the purchase of instruments, ambulance, trucks, everything from handbags to kitchen equipment. By the middle of the following summer, an officer from the Quartermaster Corps was crating the unit's materiel at the Bush Terminal across the river in Brooklyn.

When final arrangements had been made to turn over the Bellevue unit to the U. S. Army, it included 32 officers, 65 nurses, 6 civilians, 106 enlisted men, 1 dietitian, 3 secretaries, and 2 technicians. Most of the enlisted men were from Yale, Harvard, and Princeton; a smaller number from Wesleyan. All these college boys had signed up in the enthusiastic hope of seeing service at the front. Fortunately for them, this never came to pass. The unit was used throughout the war as a base hospital. The boys carried stretchers, unloaded supplies, and moved beds industriously. But at a safe distance behind the lines, where medals were not won.

As the officers of the unit one by one entrained for camps in various parts of the country, behind them they left Bellevue in a furore of activity. Strange medical reserve officers by the dozen were attending demonstrations of the preparation and use of the new Carrel-Dakin dressings and Thomas splints, taking Dr. Hirsch's course in X-ray practice, or perhaps one of the courses in military surgery conducted by Drs. Stewart and Hartwell.

In November, 1916, the Bellevue unit was mobilized in the Twelfth Regiment Armory, and its officers began as best they could to teach their men close order drill to march time played on the grand piano in the corner. Excitement mounted. Everyone felt that the day was near when they would move.

But for four months orders were delayed; the men drilled, and fidgeted, repeating the latest rumors and killing time at the Armory. By the time embarkation orders came, the fine edge of expectation had been blunted. One cold bright morning early in 1917, the Bellevue unit sailed out of empty New York harbor. Not a single tugboat gave them a toot. So quiet was the bay that they could hear the slap of waves on the shores of Governors Island. Nothing was moving except a single camouflaged freighter, heading south rather than east.

The Bellevue unit regretted that it was not the first to go overseas. The unit from Cleveland's Lakeside Hospital, as well as the Harvard unit and one from Presbyterian Hospital in New York, was already in France serving with the British Army. But since Bellevue had been first to organize, it won the honor of being designated American Base Hospital Unit Number 1.

When the unit looked over their transport, the *Olympic*, to their surprise they found that there was another outfit just like their own among the six thousand troops aboard. Both units were kept busy en route treating flu, measles, mumps, pneumonia, and just plain seasickness among the troops packed so tightly that they scarcely had room to light a cigarette.

The skipper, Sir Bertram Hayes, according to scuttlebutt, had a price of 20,000 reichsmarks on his head. At any rate, Sir Bertram proved to be a nimble dodger. The *Olympic* landed in England, having sighted only one periscope and dropped only a few depth bombs. A few days later the unit crossed to France, the doctors going with the Army on cattle boats, the nurses and civilians traveling de luxe on an English hospital ship.

On a black spring night of 1918, the unit now known as Base Hospital Number 1 reached Vichy and there, in a blacked-out station, was met by the mayor and representatives of the French Army. Shortly after, members of the Army Medical

Staff arrived and began to raid the Bellevue unit. Within a few days Dr. Wright was transferred to the front; Dr. John McCoy a couple of weeks later.

The two largest luxury hotels in Vichy were transformed into hospitals. The Hôtel Carlton was designated the surgical department, Hôtel l'Amiraute the medical department. No French maids or porters being available, the nurses themselves turned to, scrubbed the walls and floors with soap and water. They made up 316 beds, and set up a ward for the seriously wounded in the Carlton's ornate dining room. Unfortunately their crated supplies had yet to appear, but as it turned out this made little serious difference. The first batch of patients proved to be ambulatory poilus from the French military hospital a few blocks away. These people hobbled in under their own power, all laughing and excited about the prospect of getting American food, chewing gum, cigarettes, and the like. The staff had no dressing trucks, or stands. But they put the men to bed and borrowed boards from the French, on which they carried about their drugs and instruments. Two days later the poilus were moved out to make room for American wounded. However, they like the army chow so well that they kept coming back to the hospital mess line again and again.

Soon the equipment arrived, in the nick of time for what became a flood of American casualties from the Second and Third Divisions, who had fought successively at Cantigny, Château-Thierry, and Belleau Wood. They were brought over the road to Vichy in trucks and there divided between the two hotels. The medical and gassed cases went to l'Amiraute, the wounded to the Carlton. From then on, they arrived in waves, rolling up day after day. No sooner had the doctors and nurses read the tags and labels on one case, got him cleaned and operated on, than another rolled in. Endless rows of clay-colored bodies under khaki army blankets lay still on stretchers in the halls, asking only that they not be moved.

Within a few weeks, the Vichy base hospital was also acting

as an evacuation hospital. Everyone who could be transported was moved even farther from the front. Other units arrived, and ten other hotels were converted to hospitals. On the hot summer nights, these elegant hotels de luxe reeked with the smell of antiseptics.

By August, 1917, the Vichy hospital center was one of the largest in France. Base Hospital Number 1 now occupied space in eighteen buildings, able to accommodate five to six thousand wounded and sick. Some of the convalescent soldiers made such good medical orderlies, and the need for them was so great, that the doctors and nurses hid them in the cellar when Major John Wyckoff, the evacuation officer, made his rounds. The American zeal for antisepsis caught on among them and they contributed greatly toward maintaining the Vichy hospital's high standard despite the rush of work.

During this interim other Bellevue people of high and humble professional estate had been drawn into the vortex of the Great War. On March 5, 1917, the *New York Times* quoted Dr. William Welch as saying: "Germany has flung down the gauntlet to the United States and there is no honorable course open for us other than to fight; and since war is inevitable, let it begin at once." Reading this erroneous report, Welch and his friends professed surprise, but took no action publicly to set the case to rights. Welch wrote to a friend:

> Did you see in the *New York Times* that I have declared war against Germany? I assure you I did not say that, for I was trying to tell a reporter something about the Research Council, but all he seems to have seized on were some rather hot remarks which I made about the filibuster.

All such demurs notwithstanding, on July 16, 1917, Welch was commissioned a major in the Medical Section. A less military figure than the rotund Bellevue-Johns Hopkins medico would have been hard to find. "I do not like at all the idea of being commissioned a medical officer in the Army," he wrote to his niece. "If I have to put on a Major's uniform I think

I shall drop out." Much later, he was to tell his Yale classmates at his fiftieth reunion:

> It was lucky that I knew young Billy Gorgas. [General William Gorgas, U. S. Surgeon General and yellow fever hero.] He had been a pupil of mine when I first started out in New York running that very demoralizing thing called a cram quiz. . . . I knew him well enough to go over there right after the war started and tell him to put me to work, if he thought he had anything I could do. From that time until the end of the war . . . I was actively at work there in the Surgeon General's office.

For all his genius, Welch must have taxed headquarters protocol to the breaking point. In another letter to his niece, he confided:

> It seems I have been a kind of privileged person all this time, and they have let me infringe regulations about a number of things. For months I did not even get into a uniform, which I realize now was the most irregular thing imaginable, and I wonder how they winked at it.

Of Welch's change into uniform, Dr. Simon Flexner says:

> How successful was this military masquerade is open to question. Even after he had his eagles the stout old man [Welch was over seventy], who somehow looked even stouter in uniform, never gave off a martial aura. When he walked the streets in all the majesty of his high rank, he replied to the crisp salutes of his inferior officers by lifting his hand vaguely in the direction of his cap and gently wiggling his fingers . . .

Hermann Biggs, the great public health man, was busy both home and overseas, as a member of the Medical Section of the Council of National Defense and on the Medical Advisory Committee of the American Red Cross. It is typical of Biggs's absolute preoccupation with the subject of mass health that he should still have time in the midst of war to complain to the New York State Board of Health about the growing menace of automobile accidents. He sharply reminded them:

Among the preventable causes of death showing an increase during the year are those due to injuries caused by
automobiles, which were responsible in 1917 for over 1,000
deaths—three times as many as in 1912—and far more deaths
than typhoid fever, scarlet fever, and poliomyelitis combined. I earnestly recommend that educative and regulative
measures for both pedestrians and drivers be introduced at
the earliest possible moment as a means of reducing this
unnecessary waste of life.

What Dr. Biggs would have thought of the current automobile accident death rate, and the popular follies which it so
strongly reflects, can only be imagined.

The overseas experience of the nurses who served in the base
hospitals had a broadening and maturing effect on the whole
profession. The women came into contact with a different
world, psychologically and medically, from which they returned
with vivid impressions. Letters sent home by nurses of the
Bellevue unit give some impression of how American women
reacted to their first big-scale war away from home.

Wrote Miss Beatrice Hosken:

There were 1,500 patients at Vichy when I returned and
only 1,000 now, so you can see how rapidly men are being
returned to America. . . . Miss Ulmer and I have received
citations from headquarters for heroic conduct under enemy
artillery fire. This came as a great surprise to us as we did not
expect any recognition at all.

In 1918, after the armistice, Miss Ethel Randall wrote:

We got to Mayen, Germany, on December 19th, and I
must confess that it was a great disappointment to most of us
to be ordered here instead of back to the States. This country
is a very great contrast to the desolate hillside near Verdun,
where we had our hospital during the drives at St. Mihiel
and in the Argonne. In our journey here, it was a great shock
to us to wake one morning to see well tilled land, trim neat
houses in fields green with winter crops, after having passed
through the battle-scarred country near Verdun the evening
before. It did not make us feel any more kindly toward the
Germans.

It took more than three days to bring us here, and they were not days of happiness. We could get only third class French cars, each compartment being intended to seat 8 people on very hard seats. When I tell you that for three nights, five of us slept in these compartments, you will understand that we had to be quite some managers. Stretchers were arranged, one above the other, the top one being a very few inches from the ceiling. So, one passenger was on the floor and two reclined on the benches, and two on the stretchers. Of course it was no one's fault that the lavatory was out of commission, and water flowed into the compartments on either side, so that we got somewhat wet and had moreover a most unpleasant odor about us. Some of our party will never, I think, be on pleasant terms with others—even should we be over here months longer—and that journey is to blame.

We have taken over the largest German hospital in the town—a beautiful building it is, too—and have also fitted up three schoolhouses as hospitals. I am now on night duty on the top floor of the largest, and have care of a regular Bellevue ward—nephritis, rheumatics, bronchitis, tuberculosis, mixed in with everything else, mental cases, etc. But they all cough, and as my largest ward was evidently the auditorium and has excellent acoustic properties, sometimes I am nearly crazy. These men are all so homesick and talk of nothing else but going home.

You said in your letter that you hoped I would not have to wear so many pairs of stockings all winter. Well, I wear even more clothes now. The furnace in our hotel is broken, and the proprietor claims that he would have to spend 4,000 marks to put it in order, which he can't do. Most of the rooms have coal stoves, but mine is not one of them. As it is always cold, and as I keep the wards cold at night, I feel the need of many clothes. The German woman who washes my hair (with yellow laundry soap, if you please) says Americans wear too many clothes. I showed her what I had on, and she nearly had a fit; but she takes a cold bath every morning and wears only a muslin undergarment.

There is a certain scarcity of certain articles here. The people will do almost anything for a piece of American soap. Two of the nurses who were out walking were quite astounded when a couple of privates stepped up and asked whether they would like some soap. Strange to say, the privates who have not been stationed near any hospital unit often fail to recognize our uniform, and in France the requests *"Mademoiselle, voulez-vous promenade?"* were quite frequent. Army French is a mixture. A man will be told to carry out an order "Tout suite" and to it will be added, "The touter the sweeter."

Every day a new rumor reaches us. One day it will be that we are to go to Russia, another to Palestine and today that we will go back to the States with the Third Division at Bellevue. I never pay any attention to them.

Miss Marion Rottman wrote:

Last week we received a convoy of repatriots from Strasbourg. One, a flying lieutenant, had a fractured femur, and when we operated we found a machine gun bullet, a piece of clothing and some upholstery and tacks from his own flying machine, a compound fracture that had healed and five inches of shortening. Nothing had been done for it, while in the enemy camp, and for three months he carried all these things imbedded in his thigh. We have him up in a Thomas splint with traction and the officers say he will have a fairly good leg.

All but two weeks of my entire time in France I have spent doing front line service, and it's been a wonderful experience. At times we were six miles from the front line; from our post we could see the Boches' observation balloons, and frequently saw them fall in flames.

While I've been doing operating work we have had to do many things differently than we were trained to do. When you remember that every wound is an infected wound, that will account for it. In removing foreign bodies, quantities of mud, dried hard clothing, and even weeds have been removed. We have one ward with nothing but Balkan frames, and it's called the Argonne forest.

I will be so glad to get back to civilization again, and get some American food. If anybody ever says French cooking, French maids, or French laundry to me again, I shall give my opinion of those three articles.

It is a wonderful thing to see the work that your colleagues are doing abroad. It is the one bright spot in France, the one thing that leads you to lift your eyes from the mud rakes, and the steel and iron of it all, to the stars and to the cross. It seemed to give promise that faith, honor, peace, and charity are not to be torn from the hearts of men. I have never seen more conscious devotion to duty than I have seen among the nurses in France.

The story of Bellevue in World War I would be incomplete without some mention of Jane A. Delano, who ranks in the forefront of her profession along with Florence Nightingale and Nurse Edith Cavell. Miss Delano's first public service came just two years after her graduation from Bellevue. In 1888 yellow fever was raging in many of the southern states. Miss Delano was offered the superintendency of the Sand Hills Hospital near Jacksonville, Florida.

She went from this most difficult position to the still more exacting one of superintendent of the School of Nursing at Bellevue. There, in a four-year stay, she restored the school's standing to conform with the ideal that had characterized it during its early days under Sister Helen Bowdin and her faithful little band.

In 1910 Miss Delano helped in the creation of the National Committee on Red Cross Nursing Service, and was subsequently made chairman, which gave her a golden opportunity to exercise her genius for consolidating the work of the many different volunteer nursing groups. During the Mississippi floods of 1908, and the Omaha cyclone and Ohio flood of 1913, Miss Delano proved the incalculable value of her carefully laid organizational groundwork. She next went into the Army Nurse Corps, and in 1911 carried out an inspection tour of American military hospitals in Hawaii and the Philippines. On this trip, while she was making a side-excursion through China and Japan, the Japanese Red Cross gave her a decoration.

In 1912 Miss Delano resigned from the Army Nurse Corps to devote her entire time to building up the Red Cross Nursing Service. To this end she traveled extensively through the United States, speaking at training schools, graduations, and before nurses' alumnae meetings. To increase the prestige and multiply the numerical strength of the Nursing Service became her dominant desire. It was almost as if she sensed approaching crisis and was trying with all her might to prepare her country to meet it. But this is only sentimental conjecture, and there can be little doubt that when nurses of the period pledged themselves as ready to serve "in time of epidemic, fire, flood, or war," the last contingency did not seriously figure in their thoughts.

With the greatest war man had known up to that time came an amazing humanitarian response. A myriad of agencies to promote mercy were marshaled and made to work together. In the forefront of these hosts of mercy was Jane Delano of the American Red Cross. Through her office approximately 20,000 nurses were supplied to the Army, Navy, the American Red Cross, and the United States Public Health Service. In 1914, even before America joined forces with the Allies, the Red Cross had organized and sent abroad medical and nursing units. Intricate and arduous details accompanied their selection for strictly neutral missions. Trouble on the Mexican border, where nurses were needed for the cantonments, was an added complication. From August, 1914, to May, 1916, Miss Delano held in her powerful hands strands of policy and administration extending from Washington to the fifteen nurse supervisors located in England, Russia, Germany, Austria, Hungary, Serbia, and Belgium.

Even in the months preceding America's declaration of war had come an expansion and extension of the responsibilities of the chairman of the National Committee on Red Cross Nursing Service that made a reorganization imperative. In order to afford adequate and expert assistance and to divide the burdens, a bureau of nursing service was established at national head-quarters. Miss Clara D. Noyes, who had been associated with Bellevue as general superintendent of the Training Schools of Nursing, was appointed director of this group. Later, under the exigencies of World War I, it became obvious that nothing less than the creation of a department of nursing functioning from national headquarters in Washington under the department of Military Relief would help to solve this pressing problem. Jane Delano was appointed director of this department, and a Bureau of Field Nursing was created to supplement it.

Imagination can scarcely conjecture the enormous pressure and duties devolving upon the Red Cross Nursing Service during those strenuous days of mobilization, of epidemics in cantonments and in the country at large. While the welfare of the Army and Navy came first, nevertheless the needs of the civilian population could not be neglected. Hospitals and public health work had to be maintained at an even higher degree of efficiency in order to provide for the families of soldiers and sailors, and, above all else, to keep up preparedness by recruiting and training the future supply of nurses.

Early and late, throughout the period of the war, Miss Delano labored at her desk. Sundays and holidays brought no respite. The volume of details to which she must attend was monumental; the responsibilities hourly augmented; day after day some one hundred complete applications from nurses ready for service were sent to the War Department through the Bureau of Field Nursing. But for the efficient and harmonious functioning of this branch of the department of the nursing service, it would have been humanly impossible for Miss Delano to carry on. As a member of the Council of National Defense, still other urgent demands were made upon her. In December, 1918, Miss Delano embarked on a tour to the overseas hospitals of the A.E.F., and it was in February, 1919, that she was stricken with mastoiditis. On April 15, in the bare barracks hospital at Savenay in Brittany, she passed away.

The War Department record reads:

> Hard as it was to lose Miss Delano, it seemed fitting that the nurses that she had organized, the soldiers for whom they were enrolled, and the people whom both had crossed the ocean to help, should have surrounded her at the last. Even the enemy, for whom Miss Delano had labored in the days before the United States had entered the European War was present. For as the funeral procession wound up the hill, it passed groups of German prisoners, who saluted.

· XXIII ·

THE GREAT FLU EPIDEMIC

When the Bellevue authorities, about the time of America's entry into World War I, told Miss Brink that she was too old for overseas service, she accepted their decision with a wry smile. It was not the first time she had been disappointed by arbitrary board rulings. But, as fate decreed, she was to perform prodigies of service as great as any recorded in the military hospitals. Indeed, she was to lay down her own life that others might live.

The Bellevue Nurses Unit sailed for France, made a splendid name for itself, and was expecting an end to the great conflict when, in 1918–19, a world-wide influenza epidemic hit the United States.

As a rule, influenza is a relatively mild virus disease which appears pretty much regularly every couple of years. But occasionally, for reasons unknown, the pathogen becomes lethally virulent. The first such recorded waves of the deadly form of influenza occurred in 1889, with original foci of infection at Athabaska in Upper Canada, in Greenland, and in Central Asia. The second great outbreak occurred in 1918. It was first noted in Chungking, a little later in Meshed in Persia, then in the Allied port of Brest, and presently in Sierra Leone in West Africa. Following the sea route, it spread over the entire world. At one point the British navy was so badly hit it could not have put to sea. The United States was not spared the viral scourge, which eventually killed off about one per cent of the world population.

It is believed that a mutation in the ordinary strain of influenza virus caused both the 1889 and 1918 pandemics. The exact method of transmission is not known. But it would seem that the disease was carried from person to person, since people in isolated places such as lighthouses did not fall sick, providing that they kept away from their base. At any rate, there was no known countermeasure for the disease except good nursing, as shown by the great disparity between the death rate in civilized and primitive regions of the world. In New York, Carrie Brink showed the profession what a gifted and courageous nurse could do to mitigate disaster.

First among the flood of victims that was to fill every available bed in Bellevue were thirty sailors sent over by the Navy from Brooklyn Navy Yard. In a few days the hospital was jammed. Even the new tuberculosis boat, successor to the *Southfield*, moored at the foot of East Twenty-ninth Street had to be turned into a flu hospital. The operating rooms closed down, except for emergency operations. To make matters worse, other New York hospitals refused to accept flu cases, until Bellevue became so crowded that the city was driven to ordering other hospitals to open their doors. The municipal lodging house was filled with flu patients, and the medical students were assigned to look after them. Wards with a bed capacity of 34 had 75 patients. There were no bedside stands between beds, because there was no space for them. Balconies and halls were filled to the elevator doors. Ten deaths a day per ward was the average. A patient would sit up at the end of the ward, call for the nurse, and by the time the nurse got there the patient would be dead. A children's ward with a capacity of 50 had 150 patients, three in a bed. In the admitting office, the nurses would rouse incoming patients long enough to get their names and addresses, and rush them to bed so that they might die in bed rather than on the stretchers. After the morgue was filled, a former alcoholic ward, then vacant, was used for the overflow of bodies.

The hospital became so crowded that the hospital authorities cut down daily admissions to 250. Doctors pleaded with people to stay at home if they had anyone to take care of them. During this terrible epidemic many maternity cases admitted to Bellevue with the flu went through delivery, only to have both mother and child collapse and die. The nurses were shocked by nature's gratuitous cruelty, and many had to struggle with their feelings to keep on. But always there was Miss Brink, unshakable, a woman of iron will.

In addition to her superintendent's duties, Miss Brink took over the ordinary duties of a ward nurse. She started a snack bar in the nurses' residence which was kept open the clock 'round. Waitresses regularly fell sick, and replacements were afraid to go near the nurses who were in contact with the flu. Miss Brink presided at the steam table the morning the cafeteria opened, and appeared there every morning throughout the epidemic. Her feet and ankles swelled until she was finally forced to wear cloth-covered canvas shoes over plaster casts. Every night one of her nurses went to her room with ice bags for her terribly aching feet. But she worked on.

The effects of influenza were terrifying to watch. Dr. Rufus Cole tells of the first onslaught of the epidemic in an army hospital:

> The only time I ever saw Dr. Welch really worried and disturbed was in the autumn of 1918, at Camp Devens, near Boston. . . . It was cold and drizzling rain, and there was a continuous line of men coming in from the various barracks (to the hospital), carrying their blankets, many of the men looking extremely ill, most of them cyanosed [blue] and coughing. There were not enough nurses, and the poor boys were putting themselves to bed on cots, which overflowed out of the wards on the porches. We made some inquiries about the cases, went to the laboratory, and then on down to the autopsy room.
> Owing to the rush and the great numbers of bodies coming

into the morgue, they were placed on the floor without any order or system, and we had to step amongst them to get into the room where an autopsy was going on. When the chest was opened and the blue, swollen lungs were removed and opened, and Dr. Welch saw the wet, foamy surfaces with little real consolidation, he turned and said, "This must be some new kind of infection or plague," and he was quite excited and obviously very nervous. . . . It was not surprising that the rest of us were disturbed, but it shocked me to find that the situation, momentarily at least, was too much even for Dr. Welch.

One incident provided a grim sort of comic relief to that first fearful day. When Dr. O. T. Avery, who had been rushed from the hospital of the Rockefeller Institute, searched the lung sections for influenza germs, he used for the crucial Gram test the bottles labeled "alcohol" which were already in the laboratory. To his amazement, the expected reaction did not take place. More and more sections were brought in for analysis. At last Dr. Avery had used up all the alcohol, and he sent to the storeroom for a fresh supply. At once the correct reaction appeared. Someone had drunk the alcohol from the first batch of laboratory bottles and refilled them with water.

By the middle of October the flu was raging throughout New York State, and by December, 263,519 cases had been reported to the state department of health. During the fall and winter of 1918–19, according to figures compiled by Dr. Biggs, 51,000 people died of the disease.

This 1918–19 influenza epidemic saw the sudden return of a mortality experience typical of medieval times. In Connecticut, for example—and conditions in New York State were essentially the same—because of the flu, the over-all death rate shot up to 63.9 deaths per 1,000 persons, more than double the figure for the worst month of the previous pandemic of influenza in 1890–92. Chroniclers of the Connecticut experience wrote:

> . . . these cold figures present but a faint picture of the actual extent of the tragedy. We must go back to records of

bubonic plague to find a parallel for the conditions which existed in many . . . communities during the height of the epidemic. Emergency hospitals were improvised . . . and nurses and physicians, largely supplied by the U. S. Public Health Service, were themselves stricken down by the epidemic; the lack of medical and nursing care was in many cases acute. Many persons died without any medical attention, and there were not a few instances of whole families being wiped out within a few days. In the cities most severely affected, the great problem came to be the burial of the dead. At ———— and ————, for example, coffins remained for days on the ground, until in the latter case the mayor assigned the engineering force of the city to the task of digging graves.

The experience of New York City was anticly reflected at Bellevue. Of Miss Brink's nursing staff, 144 came down with the flu and six of them died. The trustees held an emergency meeting in the hope that someone might come up with an idea. A few doctors even suggested that the hospital be closed, or at the very least refuse new patients. The board, however, quickly voted down these drastic proposals, and the Bellevue tradition of being able to face up to any emergency remained intact.

The board's only concession was to close the hospital to visitors for a few days to relieve the desperately overworked nurses from the added strain of dealing with panic-stricken relatives. As it was, the nurses' eyes, as seen over their cheesecloth masks, were black-ringed with fatigue. During the epidemic Bellevue cared for more than 3,000 cases in the first three months. The daily census was often over 1,100 patients. Through it all, Miss Brink was everywhere, her very presence a guarantee that the system would not, could not, break down.

Of all Bellevue nurses, Carrie Brink will live longest in the hearts of a whole generation of women who either trained or served under her while she was either superintendent of nurses or head of the Bellevue Nurses' Training School.

One student wrote of her:

She was like a mother to all of us. As we checked in at the bulletin board in the morning, before breakfast, Miss Brink

would be watching for us. She would examine us on one side
as we approached her, and on the other side as we went away.
She always noticed whether our hems were proper and our
aprons straight, and whether our collars buttoned up high
enough not to annoy the interns, and whether we had rubbers
on or not on rainy days. She even sensed whether we had had
breakfast. How, I never knew. But if she determined that we
hadn't had breakfast, she would send us back to the dining
room, saying that we couldn't take care of sick people with
empty stomachs.

She was a stern disciplinarian, she had dignity, poise and
understanding. She felt responsible to our parents for our
welfare, while we were in the city. She visited her sick nurses
every day, and the critically ill in the hospital, and she would
know each nurse's name, and where they were on duty and
how long they had been on, when they were due to be
changed, and exactly what grades they were making. She
could tell the amount of gauze used in Bellevue in a week,
and she didn't have to keep notes, they were all in her head.

At our infrequent dances Miss Brink was more than a
mother. When midnight came she would gather all the nurses
back of her, and say to the interns, now you must go home,
these girls have to get to sleep. At one Halloween party, I
remember, an intern spiked the punch to see what would
happen. Miss Brink, not knowing it had been spiked, took a
full cup, then a sip and made no comment. She walked away
without a word. At that same party, one of the interns came
disguised in a striped student nurse's uniform and a cap. Because everyone was masked, no one recognized him, but Miss
Brink unerringly knew that something was wrong, and decided at 12 o'clock every one must unmask. However, the
intern got the word, and by 12 o'clock he was gone. Miss
Brink never knew who he was, although he is one of Bellevue's most respected doctors today.

If a nurse were to be operated on, Miss Brink was there
to hold her hand while she went under the anesthetic, and
she was there again when she came out of the anesthetic. No
one ever knew when Miss Brink would appear on a ward, nor
what she would ask to see. Perhaps it would be the supply
cupboard, or the linen, and then she would make her way
through the ward, smoothing the pillows of the seriously ill
patients, or giving them a drink, or some little kindness.
When one of us nurses would meet Miss Brink on the street,
or on Broadway, or at the most formal function, we would
automatically stand up and say yes, Miss Brink. This was not

from a sense of fear, but out of respect and admiration. She was very much beloved, and in the event that a nurse had to be sent home for an infraction that involved an intern, Miss Brink deeply resented the fact that the intern was allowed to stay and the nurse had to go. She backed her nurses to the limit.

Miss Amy Hilliard, who during the war held the position of general superintendent of the Training Schools of Bellevue and Allied Hospitals, has this to say:

How well I remember when we finally prevailed upon Miss Brink to conduct some of the practical examinations for the New York State Regents certificates. One day, after examining a particularly unresponsive group, she came in very tired and depressed. I asked what had happened, and she just grinned and said, "I wish I could give them brains, you can't get anything out of the head that doesn't have anything in it." It seems she had asked one applicant to enumerate some of the avenues that were now open to graduate nurses. And the immediate answer was, "Fifth Avenue." To another question, what would you do for a case of drowning, her candidate had brightly replied, "Bury it."

Perhaps Miss Brink was too old for the war, but she saw the flu epidemic through. One night in 1920, she dropped to the floor at the foot of the stairs in the main entrance of the nurses' residence, and shortly afterward passed away. From the time of her death until her burial a few days later, there was an honor guard of graduate nurses in constant attendance, an honor which has never been paid to a Bellevue nurse before or since.

XXIV

THE MEDICAL EXAMINER'S OFFICE

The law says that every cadaver must have an explanation. Usually this is a simple certificate of cause of death filed by the attending physician. But a city the size of New York also turns up a considerable number of bodies that are not so easily explained. These mute victims of accident, suicide and, often enough, of murder then become the problem of the city— specifically, of the chief medical examiner and his staff. These men work out of Bellevue, where they have at their disposal the hospital's modern laboratories and technical experience.

The office of the medical examiner was created in 1918 to supplant the old elective coroner system that for so many years had been notorious for inefficiency, graft, and high cost to the taxpayer. Until replaced by the one medical examiner's office, there had been eleven coroners all told: four in Manhattan, two in Brooklyn, two in Queens, two in the Bronx, and one in Richmond. Each was allowed a full-time personal clerk and a retainer fee of $3,000 to be paid to a physician. A special investigation conducted in 1914 under the direction of a reform mayor, James Purroy Mitchell, found that the cost of the coroners ran to some $175,000 per year; and Commissioner of Accounts Wallstein, who was in charge of the probe, added that maintaining the system was a "sheer waste of public money."

Of sixty-five men who had been coroners since the consolidation of Greater New York in 1898, the investigators found that nineteen had been physicians. Of these physicians, Wallstein said: "Not a single one was a man of any professional standing or reputation in this city. Generally speaking, they have been doctors chiefly noted for their political activity." Among the remainder, eight had been undertakers; seven, professional politicians; six, small real-estate brokers; two, saloonkeepers; two, plumbers; a lawyer, a printer, an auctioneer, a contractor, a carpenter, a painter, an expressman, a butcher, a wood carver, a marble cutter, a labor leader, an insurance agent, a musician, a milkman, a dentist; and several had had unknown occupations. Wallstein concluded:

> The elective coroner system in New York City represents a combination of power, obscurity, and irresponsibility which has resulted in inefficiency. . . . With constant temptation and easy opportunity for favoritism, and even extortion, with utter lack of supervision or control, and without the slightest preparation and training to create in the coroner's mind a scientific and professional interest in the performance of his duties, the present system could not have been better devised intentionally to render improbable, if not impossible, the honest and efficient performance of the important public function entrusted to his office.

Wallstein blamed the coroner system for the shielding of criminal abortion, the packing of coroner's juries, extortion by coroner's physicians, and the covering up for all types of criminal activity. The coroners as a class were so abysmally incompetent that "infanticide and skillful poisoning" could be "carried on almost with impunity."

Mayor Mitchell, as a result of this inquiry, decided to recommend legislation abolishing the entire coroner system, replacing it with the responsible medical-examiner procedure, originated and most successfully practiced in Suffolk County, Massachusetts —that is, the Greater Boston area. Not only would his project, Mayor Mitchell contended, save the city some $50,000 a year; far more important, it would safeguard it from incompetence

and corruption and materially assist it in the prosecution of criminals.

In Albany, the legislature acted swiftly to pass the bill creating the new position and abolishing the coroner system in New York City. It was signed into law by the Governor on April 14, 1915. But the parasitic old office, long a favorite among the ward heelers and politicians, did not die that easily. For better than two years, the constitutionality of the new law was tested in court, and it was not until after a final decision by the Court of Appeals that the first chief medical examiner took office in early 1918.

The coroners were now replaced by a chief examiner and a deputy located at Bellevue in Manhattan, and one examiner for each of the four other boroughs. A small secretarial staff was also provided. It was stipulated that the chief examiner be appointed by the mayor, through the city civil service system, and be subject to his removal. It was further decreed that he would have to be a physician, a skilled pathologist, and an expert microscopist. The chief examiner was also given the authority to appoint his deputy and the other examiners.

He was further required to keep detailed records—the old coroners' files had been farcically inaccurate—to report his findings to the board of health and to work closely with the police department.

By this time Mayor Mitchell had been succeeded by the Tammany mayor, Thomas Hylan, who appointed Dr. P. J. Riordan as first chief examiner. For a while it looked as though politics was to play as big a part in the new setup as it had under the coroner system.

Riordan had hardly taken office when H. W. Harden of the Civil Service Reform Association protested most vigorously, pointing out that the eligible list was headed by Drs. O. H. Schultze, Charles Norris, and Douglas Symmers of Bellevue, one of whom should have been chosen for the job above Dr. Riordan, whose name did not even appear on the list. The city countered by acting to have these three doctors removed from the list in favor of Dr. Riordan. The Reform Association then obtained a Supreme Court injunction restraining the city comptroller from paying Riordan's salary on the grounds that he was not a skilled pathologist, as required by the new measure.

A few days later the three doctors who headed the list were summoned by the Civil Service Commission to a hearing on charges that in connection with qualifying for appointment to the medical examiner post they had performed illegal autopsies. On January 29, the Reform Association announced that it was preparing a suit to compel the appointment of one of the three doctors. At this point Hylan capitulated, explaining that he had never meant to give Riordan the job permanently anyway. He then named Dr. Charles Norris to the new post. Norris, who had been chief of the Bellevue laboratories, took office on February 1, and was succeeded at the hospital by Dr. Symmers, who had been third on the list.

Dr. Norris' appointment, according to the new law, was for a three-month probationary period. When the three months were up, the law required the mayor either to confirm him permanently in the post, or name a successor. Despite two or three violent disputes with the city, Dr. Norris remained as chief examiner until his death in 1935. During these seventeen years he became a legendary figure and the model for scientific sleuths in countless detective yarns. This reputation was thoroughly merited. He brought to his new office an intelligence and probity that did much to revolutionize criminal investigation in New York City. Many other cities adopted Norris' techniques with excellent results.

With Dr. Symmers, who succeeded him as director of laboratories at Bellevue, Dr. Norris was to enjoy the first of several important collaborations in his operation of the chief medical examiner's office. The association of these two men was one of the oddest in Bellevue's history.

"Doc" Norris, or "Chief," as he was known to the New

York police, newspaper reporters, lawyers, and criminals, was a powerful figure of a man well over six feet in height. "If I had only started drinking when I was fourteen years old," he liked to say, "I'd now be seven feet tall." He sported a long, pointed goatee and looked at the world with infinite suspicion through a pair of chillingly penetrating, deep-set eyes. He would descend upon scenes of mayhem with a flourish, like some enormous Mephistopheles about to subvert Gretchen.

If the entire city of New York had been combed, it could not have produced a more exact opposite to Doc Norris than Dr. Symmers. A brilliant pathologist, like his spectacular colleague, and a meticulous technician, Symmers was a small, crotchety wren of a man. Rumor had it that he hated Norris, but actually the reverse was true. He harried the big man like a terrier snapping at a great Dane. Norris, who feared neither criminals nor politicians nor crooked cops, was terrified of his tiny colleague.

When Symmers was made director of laboratories, he at once made himself unmistakably at home. And when Dr. Norris presumed to set up a little office in a corner of the lab, Symmers made him sign a paper saying that he would return the space whenever Symmers demanded. Norris signed without protest. Norris went to Wanamaker's and there bought a desk and some chairs. He also brought down, from a storeroom, a bloodstained old rug upon which murder had been committed. These, and a microscope which Norris paid for out of pocket, were the only appointments of his new office. Even so, they were too sumptuous for Dr. Symmers' Spartan taste.

"What in hell is this?" he inquired. "A country club?"

He forbade Norris, who was seldom seen outside the laboratories without a big cigar, to smoke in the autopsy room. Norris was compelled to conceal his toddy, for he was fond of a pick-me-up during the long day's press. Later, when Dr. Milton Helpern became an assistant to Norris, the burly "Chief" used to call on his aide to intercede with Symmers for the things he needed. When the fiery little man baited him, as he did almost daily, Norris would quietly wait until Symmers departed and then ask mildly: "Helpern, now what do you think of that guy?"

At one time Dr. Norris was seeking a position for his nephew, a brilliant young doctor whose talents were perfectly suited to the Bellevue laboratory service. For some days Dr. Norris struggled to get up enough courage to ask Symmers to hire the young man. He got to the point of standing for some moments before Symmers' closed door, but then hurriedly retreated to his own office, where he said: "Helpern, I can't do it."

The fact that Dr. Norris was a wealthy man in his own right, as well as a rarely gifted and exceptionally industrious public servant, also helped to make the medical examiner's office a resounding success. Having an independent income enabled him to compile a fine private library of works on pathology, toxicology, and criminal investigation which he kept at his home on West Seventy-second Street and where he spent most of his time when not at the hospital or at the scene of a crime. Not needing his professional salary to make ends meet also made it possible for him to keep his office free from political pressures. Out of his salary of $7,500 per year, it was estimated that he spent at least half on books, equipment, and expenses incurred in running his office. Sometimes this unfairness angered him and while Hylan was still mayor, he resigned in a huff over finances. Hylan refused to accept his resignation and finally succeeded in calming him down. Later, when the McKee administration took away his automobile, he walked out again, but in a week he was back.

The author of many monographs on scientific criminal investigation, and in later years a professor of medical-legal pathology at New York University, Dr. Norris was also the ghost writer of a number of popular murder mysteries. But it is doubtful if any of these surpassed in colorful detail the cases he uncovered in real life.

There was, for example, the celebrated Elwell "perfect murder" of June 11, 1920. Joseph B. Elwell, one of the first Americans to play and teach bridge for a living, had built a sizable fortune out of lessons at $10.00 per hour and by playing for high stakes with well-to-do patrons. He was also a man for the ladies. In spite of the fact that he was nearing fifty and wore a toupee and false teeth, at his West Seventieth Street apartment he often dallied with socially prominent matrons and debutantes.

This interesting career suffered catastrophic interruption. One morning at seven-thirty, Elwell was found by his housekeeper in his ground-floor study, groaning and unconscious. He was slumped, minus wig and false teeth, in an overstuffed chair. Wrapped about him was his old bathrobe. Between his eyes was a neat little bullet-hole. On the floor near him was a single revolver shell.

The police had already decided it was suicide when Norris appeared at nine. Puffing his long cigar with machinelike regularity, the chief examiner went methodically to work, and soon satisfied himself there was enough evidence of a struggle to discount suicide. The old-style telephone, for example, was smashed. Reconstructing the crime, Norris speculated that Elwell had been surprised while going through his morning mail, and then had seized the telephone to defend himself. An autopsy confirmed Norris' on-the-spot conjecture. "Even a contortionist," he later said, "couldn't hold a .45 four or five inches from his head and shoot himself straight into his head."

Norris always claimed he knew Elwell's murderer, but he carried this secret and many others with him to the grave when he died in 1935. During the long investigation, some of New York's brightest society names had flashed through the news. And it was said that one of Elwell's prominent paramours, the daughter of a Wall Street financier, tripped up the back stairs of Elwell's house, quite unaware of the murder, and was bundled out again by the police before her identity became public. At all events, it was Norris' feeling, one shared by public opinion, that there had been a cover-up because of the importance of the figures involved.

The unsolved Elwell murder case was very much the exception, however, during Dr. Norris' regime. In many instances when the untrained coroners of earlier days would have certified "accident" or "suicide" or "cause unknown," Norris put down "murder," and made it stick. More than one killer went to the chair as a result of the doctor's diagnosis. On the other hand, of course, there were quite a few innocent persons whose lives were saved by Dr. Norris' impartial diligence. One of these fortunates was a longshoreman named Joseph Trapia, whose guilt Norris had refused to accept, despite as damning a set of facts as was ever placed in a prosecutor's brief.

The Trapia affair began on a cold winter morning, when Patrolman James Anderson saw a man with a bulky package under his arm making his way furtively toward India Wharf in Brooklyn. Anderson stopped him. The man said he was a longshoreman and that the bundle contained his work clothes. The policeman then allowed him to proceed, but ducked into a doorway to keep an eye on him. He saw the man stop and look back over his shoulder to see if the patrolman was still observing him. This alerted the policeman still further.

Anderson hurried after him and saw him dump the package into the river, then run. Anderson fired his pistol and followed in hot pursuit. Another policeman cut the fugitive off. The pair hustled the suspected man to the station house. Here the man gave a wrong name. He refused to explain his actions or what was in the mysterious bundle. A hack driver, however, finally identified the prisoner as Joseph Trapia and led them to Trapia's home at 56 Caskett Street.

Bursting into Trapia's squalid flat, the detectives were horrified by the sight of a limbless torso of a woman propped up in one corner. The head, starey-eyed, lay nearby.

In a matter of minutes, Dr. Norris was bulling his way into

the swarm of detectives and policemen in the longshoreman's apartment. After a long inspection of the grisly remains, he coolly said, "This isn't a murder. It's carbon monoxide poisoning."

The district attorney for once was unimpressed. A decapitated lady without arms or legs, to his literal mind, strongly suggested homicide. Trapia was put on trial for murder. The woman turned out to be a neighbor's wife who had been having a love affair with Trapia.

During the trial the prosecution attempted to brand Trapia a "fiendish ripper." In vain. Dr. Alexander O. Gettler, Bellevue toxicologist who often collaborated with Medical Examiner Norris, without qualification certified death had come by carbon monoxide poisoning, thus substantiating Trapia's story that the woman had been overcome by fumes while they both lay on the bed in a drunken stupor. Trapia got off with three years for illegal disposition of the remains.

Reporters wanted to know how Norris, without an autopsy, had so quickly known that death was due to carbon monoxide.

"Simple," he said. "Carbon monoxide poisoning always leaves a pinkish discoloration of the skin and a pinkish tinge to the blood."

In another hotly contested case, Norris helped acquit an impoverished woman of infanticide. In this affair, the accused had been charged with disposing of her two-month-old baby by putting it in the oven and turning on the gas. Norris, however, certified death by pneumonia.

"The poor creature," he later explained, "felt the child grow cold, not realizing it was the chill of death. She put it in the oven, the fire unlighted, to try to warm it."

A remorseless seeker after facts when dealing with a suspicious corpse, under other circumstances Dr. Norris could show great compassion. Although a member of the aristocratic Norris family who founded Norristown, Pennsylvania, he felt keenly for the city's unfortunates, whose last acts were so often played in the autopsy room at Bellevue. It was his belief that never should wealth or position serve as a shield.

It was one of his strongest opinions that autopsies should always be performed when prominent people came to a violent end through what was believed to be suicide or accident. He felt that in such cases it was only too likely that an insurance beneficiary might have sped them into oblivion.

By the time he died in 1935, Dr. Norris had created, out of the shambles of the coroner system, a smoothly functioning instrument of justice that has survived every change in New York's stormy political history and emerged triumphant from every attempt to corrupt its operation or impugn its integrity. Of equal importance, Norris left behind a corps of highly skilled medical investigators, men who had been won by his gruff humor and kindliness as much as they had by his ever questing intelligence.

It was one of Norris' assistants, in fact, who broke the most celebrated case in the brief history of his office. This was Dr. Howard W. Neall, who was called as an expert in the Ruth Snyder case. Mrs. Snyder's alibi in the brutal murder of her husband was that she had been lying in a dead faint for six hours during the time the crime was committed. The alibi stood up until Neall told detectives that no faint could last that long. It was then that she admitted that she and her lover, Judd Gray, had first attempted to poison Snyder's whisky, then chloroform him, and had finally finished him off with a sash-weight. Because she failed with her story of the "long count" faint, Ruth Snyder and Gray went to the electric chair.

Next to Norris himself, the name which the public came to associate most commonly with the office of the chief medical examiner was that of Dr. Thomas A. Gonzales, who succeeded him to that post in 1935 and remained there until his retirement in 1954. Dr. Gonzales, a Bellevue graduate and the New York-born son of a Spanish tobacco merchant, already had acquired a name in fourteen years of work in pathology when, in 1918, a few months after Norris' appointment as chief, he became an assistant medical examiner. All in all, Dr. Gonzales spent thirty-six years in the office, having been promoted to deputy chief in 1926, and finally to chief two years later (only after taking an examination so stiff that only one other man was qualified to compete).

Dr. Gonzales, on account of his severe expression, at first was likely to be thought of as a martinet. Actually, he was a patient, kindly man, and one of the great scholars in his specialty, medical criminology. In addition to his duties with the examiner's office, Dr. Gonzales taught forensic medicine at the New York University-Bellevue Medical College for many years, and co-authored *Legal Medicine and Toxicology,* a massive 700-page compilation of every case that had come under the scrutiny of the medical examiner's office since its creation.

Like Norris, Dr. Gonzales was equipped with a natural suspicion that refused to accept violent death at its face value. Dr. Milton Helpern, present chief medical examiner, recalls a case back in the twenties, when Dr. Gonzales "scratched a suicide and found a murder." This was a carefully simulated piece of work on the part of a husband who had strangled his wife, then meticulously set the stage to make it look like a suicide by gas. Dr. Gonzales, however, noted barely perceptible marks on the neck of the victim and also observed that the skin coloration belied the suicide theory. Autopsy confirmed his verdict of death by strangulation.

Another of the dedicated group that grew up under Doc Norris was Dr. Alexander O. Gettler, who figured decisively in the Trapia case. For many years he presided as head of the city's toxicological laboratories at Bellevue. Norris had received much of his training in Germany and Austria, and was a great admirer of the crime labs in those countries. Through him, the best European methods were incorporated into the Bellevue laboratory, which eventually became the largest of its kind in the world and a model throughout the United States. Dr.

Gettler, who served under both Norris and Gonzales, was of Austrian birth but was educated in this country. He had been at Bellevue eight years when Norris set up the first medical examiner's office there.

Though from the two thousand autopsies a year in which he participated Dr. Gettler probably had as intimate a knowledge of the human body as anyone in the hospital, he was not a doctor of medicine, but held a Ph.D. in pathological chemistry. Quite apart from his vast contributions as the city's toxicologist, Dr. Gettler was a distinguished biochemist, and taught the subject for many years at New York University. But it was through his connection with many of the city's most sensational crimes —he testified in some fifty murder cases a year—that his name became widely known to the tabloid readers of the Big Town.

The Vivian Gordon, Starr Faithful, Costello, Becker, and Snyder murder cases were only a few in which he and the toxicological laboratory at Bellevue figured. It was Dr. Gettler's final examination in the Ruth Snyder-Judd Gray case which supported Dr. Neall's findings.

But murder and suicide are not the only ways in which true cause of death comes disguised. There have been times when the "detectives" of the Bellevue laboratories have been handed puzzlers in the form of accidental deaths in which the killer was as difficult to track down as the wiliest living assassin. Dr. Gettler always considered the most baffling case he ever handled was one in which an elderly, prosperous couple was found dead in their apartment in a Brooklyn residential hotel. They had returned the previous night from a Florida vacation. A maid discovered the bodies the following afternoon. There was no lead at all at the scene to indicate how they might have died, nor could police unearth any motive for a twin slaying. It soon became evident that if there were to be a solution, it would have to come from the Bellevue autopsy room, where the bodies had been sent for study.

Painstakingly Dr. Gettler and his staff analyzed each organ

for every known poison, but found nothing until a highly sensitive series of tests revealed slight traces of cyanide in the lungs. Gettler bore down on this clue and finally came up with a sure answer: the couple had died of hydrocyanic acid gas poisoning. But who had administered the lethal dose, and how?

The police and toxicologists went back to the hotel. There they learned that the couple resided in an annex of the hotel which the manager had believed was unoccupied. The couple had, upon their arrival from Florida, gone directly to their rooms without notifying the desk of their return. The following morning the manager had put fumigators to work in the apartment directly below the one which they were occupying, and a seepage of gas sufficient to kill had drifted up into the room where they were sleeping.

This case was but one of hundreds of murder, suicide, and accident deaths that could not have been solved by the police until the establishment of the medical examiner's office, with its invaluable liaison with the Bellevue laboratories.

In Dr. Gettler's words:

> The scientific determination of the cause of violent deaths is beyond the power of the old-fashioned coroner. The causes of death are not always so obvious as they would seem to the inexperienced. . . . In these days chemistry plays a prominent part in the detection of the agencies used to kill. Science will aid justice, if given a chance.

XXV

AWAKENING IN PSYCHIATRY

Through its long and lively history, Bellevue has come to mean many things to many people.

To doctors, researchers, nurses, the name suggests immeasurable contributions to our store of medical knowledge, as well as the dedication of the men and women responsible for them. To the medical student or young woman embarking on a nursing career, Bellevue means a place to learn. To intern or train at Bellevue is widely considered a privilege, and confers a distinction that lasts a professional lifetime.

To the countless thousands restored to useful lives, and to their families, Bellevue also has a very special and personal meaning—particularly to the unwanted and underprivileged who in affliction have found at Bellevue surcease from pain and the way back to health.

Still, to a surprising number, including most New Yorkers who have never entered the famous portals, the mere mention of Bellevue evokes fear and nightmare visions of the horrors which are supposed to lurk in the long corridors, especially in the psychiatric and alcoholic wards.

Abetted by sensational fiction and low jokes, the concept of Bellevue as the nation's number one "snake pit" has spread to the extent that there are even some who think of Bellevue as nothing more than an insane asylum—and a pretty inhumane one at that.

That Bellevue's highly advanced psychiatric division of today has had unfortunate antecedents is undeniable. In the days when mental illness was regarded as a mark of shame, rather than an affliction to be treated like any other, Bellevue was no better and no worse than any other bedlam. But the grim past should not blind us to the fact that Bellevue pioneered in the rational treatment of the alcoholic and the mentally ill, and today is considered one of the foremost centers for therapy and research in these fields.

The first signs of improvement at Bellevue in the care of the mentally afflicted date back more than eighty-five years. Important strides had already been made in many medical fields, particularly in surgery and the control of hemorrhage, but treatment of psychotic and neurotic patients was not much different from what it had been in medieval times, when madness was thought to be a sign that the Devil had taken possession of the sufferer's body.

Until the latter part of the nineteenth century, mental patients brought to Bellevue by relatives or by the police were penned in two basement wards, one for men and one for women. The violently disturbed, the sexual pervert, and the alcoholic were all herded into the same quarters, together with bewildered and inoffensive patients. Here they were frequently held for long periods while lawyers, alienists, and families debated their sanity. At this period it was commonly said in New York that a few days in Bellevue's insane ward would drive even the most normal person out of his mind.

These appalling conditions prevailed until 1870, when Dr. Stephen Smith won a long fight to wring from his reluctant or indifferent colleagues on the hospital Board recognition that something had to be done to better the lot of Bellevue's mentally ill.

Since Dr. Smith was one of the best-known alienists of his day, and an able man in the light of then-existing knowledge, his arguments carried sufficient weight to speed up the long, slow reform movement initiated earlier by Dorothea Dix in America and the Scot, Sir Thomas Smith Clouston, in Britain. The times at long last were ripe for betterment. Surplus profits had become available for altruistic disposition. The democratic ideal, quiescent during the decades of intense material growth following the Civil War, was again in the air. Dr. Smith's monograph *Who Is Insane?* created great interest among thinking people, and is still considered by medical historians to be a significant contribution to early psychiatry. Most important, Dr. Smith interested a number of young doctors in the mentally ill, who hitherto were considered outside the medical pale.

Dr. Smith was a humanitarian, as well as a pathfinder in psychiatry. In later life he founded the American Public Health Association, as previously noted, and his name was linked with New York's earliest welfare and slum-clearance projects. Concerned by the high mortality of the city's poor children during the summer heat, he urged a tree-planting program. Needless to say, he was unable to penetrate the politicians' granite ignorance of the marvels of plant respiration. Some were heard to mutter that surely Dr. Smith had spent one year too many in the loony bin.

Another of Dr. Smith's reforms would have released paupers, who were wards of the city, from wastefully expensive desuetude in custodial institutions. Dr. Smith wanted to settle them on farmlands where, he felt, they could not only regain their self-respect, but in so doing contribute to their own support. This "county farm" idea, needless to say, was too far ahead of its time to be acceptable.

Co-operative developments or bank-financed housing projects, much like those which were to come along many years later, were urged by Dr. Smith as slum clearance measures. During the brief tenure of the reform mayor Seth Low, in 1902-3, it looked as though Dr. Smith, who had been named head of the city's department of municipal institutions, would be able to put some of his farsighted proposals into practice. But a Tammany victory in the next election cost him his job and put a sudden end to his vision of civic improvement.

The first concessions won by Dr. Smith in 1870 for the insane at Bellevue amounted to no more than the establishment of a separate division for the care of mentally ill patients, with quarters in a little building near the Twenty-sixth Street entrance. There were still only two wards, one for either sex, but patients were at last placed under care of a doctor who was qualified as an alienist. This doctor was aided by nurses and a rotating crew of interns from the hospital's other branches.

Some of the more violent sufferers were still confined with the tractable patients, but the sexual deviates and more objectionable alcoholics were now quartered in the old basement wards, and the criminally insane were fenced off from the others and guarded by a police officer.

The lot of the mentally disturbed at Bellevue and Blackwell's Island, however, which had been gradually improving thanks to Dr. Smith's unremitting pressure on the Board, suddenly got a spectacular assist from a series of stories called "Ten Days in a Madhouse" which came out in the *New York Post*. Those exposés were written by the famous woman reporter Elizabeth Cochrane, known under her pen name as "Nellie Bly."

She was assigned by her editor to get a firsthand account on conditions in Bellevue's insane pavilion and on Blackwell's Island, where patients certified *non compos mentis* at Bellevue were sent for confinement.

While it may be true that Miss Cochrane's descriptions of the suffering and callousness behind Bellevue's walls were deliberately lurid, basically her scathing indictment had the ring of truth. As her stories appeared day after day, the sensation-hungry public ate them up, and in the end were revolted. The administration began to quake.

Miss Cochrane told how her "examination" had turned out to be a farce. The four physicians supposed to examine her certified her offhand. While awaiting removal to Blackwell's

Island, she nearly froze to death in the unheated pavilion. She told of physical beatings by nurses and attendants at Bellevue for the most trifling offenses, of sadistic teasing by the staff, and of the utter indifference of those in charge.

After her commitment to Blackwell's Island, her insanity still unquestioned by Bellevue, she proceeded to relate of the endless nightmare of those who would spend the rest of their lives licking from their fingers, hideous slops picked from common dishes, and sharing one another's bath water.

She told of female inmates lashed together into "rope gangs," of strong drugs being forced on the disturbed, of ice cold baths for the recalcitrant. During her whole stay, once confined, Miss Cochrane acted as sanely as she knew how, to see if this would bring attention and release. But like the rest, she was ignored. She would have remained at Blackwell's indefinitely had not her newspaper revealed the ruse to the authorities who, in great alarm, then had her speedily released.

While he no doubt deplored the sensationalism of "Ten Days in a Madhouse," the series greatly strengthened Dr. Smith's hand. The public rose up in arms, really frightening the municipal authorities. The following year's million-dollar-a-year appropriation for treatment of the city's insane came as a surprise to no one.

Yet progress in care of the mentally ill in New York, as elsewhere, was slow and halting. In 1901, an investigating grand jury found that among 700 patients which Bellevue had delivered to Manhattan State Hospital for custodial care, more than 250 had contusions on the body, and many others severe facial bruises as well. A study of the records showed very clearly that they must have been beaten while at Bellevue, and the situation was referred to the courts.

The *American Monthly Review of Reviews* for March, 1901, summarized the grand jury's findings:

> Nurses were found to have had no instructions as to the care of the inmates and to have been left to their villainy

without supervision . . . hideous and obsolete devices . . .
were used for restraint of the patients . . . Bellevue had sunk
deep into the mire of brutal officialism, degraded politics and
a heartless and mercenary type of professionalism.

The upshot of the investigation was that three nurses were
dismissed and indicted for manslaughter, and other, graduate
nurses, five of them now, were put in their places. Even so, the
gross negligence continued. It was not long after the new nurses
arrived that an inmate who suffered from an acute form of
religious melancholia burned himself severely by holding his
face on a hot radiator. The nurses had been given very explicit
instructions about this patient, but investigation disclosed that
at the time the accident took place, they had been happily engaged in hazing a new attendant.

And so it went for some time, with Bellevue in an unenviable
middle position between the sluggish city administration and
the sensational daily press, for after the success of the *Post* series,
the hospital became a regular whipping boy for ambitious city
editors and reformists.

For a few years more, much was said and written but little
or nothing done about the insane pavilion. Then, in 1904, the
hospital began to feel the impact of a very strong personality,
a man who, during his more than thirty years there, piloted the
Bellevue psychiatric division to its present eminent position in
the care and treatment of the mentally ill. This man was Menas
Sarkis Gregory, a young physician who came to the great East
Side establishment from Kings Park State Hospital, to replace
an ineffectual administrator for whom the post was much too
onerous. Hardly more than five feet tall, Dr. Gregory was once
described by Mayor Jimmy Walker as "the greatest little man
in the world." This little dynamo from Armenia electrified the
insane pavilion from the very day of his arrival.

Born in Turkey, where his father was massacred, young
Gregory (or Boulghurjian, to use his proper and less pro-
nounceable Armenian name) first came in contact with medi-

cine at a missionary hospital. As a young man he made his way to America. He was graduated from Albany Medical College in 1898, and chose psychiatry, the least desirable and remunerative department of medicine, as his field. Having interned at Craig Colony for Epileptics in Sonyea, New York, and worked on the staff at Kings Park, he had already established a reputation as a first-class alienist before coming to Bellevue.

From the outset his magical warmth, though he spoke with an accent, brought a response from even the most depressed mental cases. The nervous strain and physical hazards of his work never got him down. While he was always frank and open with the press in discussing Bellevue's problems, he absolutely refused to talk about himself.

Not long before his death, Dr. Gregory was described in the *New York Sun* as a "Dante in the shadowy hell of shattered minds." The phraseology was perhaps a little on the florid side, but apt nonetheless. From 1904 until his resignation over an administrative difference in 1936, he worked intensively among the psychotic.

One of his first moves was to have women installed as head nurses, with rapid improvement in morale resulting. By careful study and screening of his personnel, little by little he built up a competent and compassionate staff. Many was the time a nurse would come off duty suffering from a black eye or an even more serious beating at the hands of a violent patient. On one occasion, he himself was chased up the street by a former inmate, who was firing a pistol at him as he ran.

From earlier experience in state institutions, Dr. Gregory knew that many of the patients under his care suffered from psychoses which proper treatment could cure in a relatively short period. Many of these sufferers had in years past been shipped off to spend the rest of their days in custodial institutions, when even the simple therapies available in those days could have returned them to the outside world. He gave special effort to salvaging these people.

He recognized, too, that the ward environment had a great effect on the patients' will to get better and go home. And so he hung the gray walls with cheerful pictures, rounded up some comfortable furniture, and even placed indestructible artificial palms, which he wheedled from the board of health, in the dark corners. A little later, he had phonographs installed.

He got rid of the old restraining devices and clamped down on the indiscriminate use of narcotics. He removed most of the barred windows, installed clean toilet facilities. Most important, perhaps, he separated the severe from the mild mental cases.

A new relationship was established with other branches of the hospital, for Dr. Gregory found that many of the patients who were sent to him were suffering from purely physical depressions incurred after childbirth, influenza, rheumatism, scarlet fever, and tuberculosis. The care which other branches of the hospital provided to these cases, he believed, could have a permanent effect on their mental health.

Instead of trying to conceal Bellevue's problems from the public, Dr. Gregory took his story right to the people in a candid public relations campaign designed to acquaint New York with the seriousness of the psychiatric problem at Bellevue. He fought hard to dispel the taboo and disgrace surrounding mental illness, and counseled that mental diseases could often be curbed if caught in time.

Over and over, he urged sufferers and their families not to await court action before seeking help at Bellevue. He and his ever-growing staff tried everything they knew to avoid legal entanglements. Bellevue, he insisted, had no interest in holding nonviolent cases against their will. The hospital's aim was to help before it was too late.

Dr. Gregory thought of mental cases just as other physicians regarded accident cases. To enable him to reach patients before their personal crises became more serious, he persuaded authorities to let him conduct an outpatient mental clinic. Here friends and relatives brought persons showing psychiatric symptoms, for early treatment, which often cured the patient without the necessity of confinement in the already overtaxed wards.

During Dr. Gregory's tenure, it was estimated that nearly one-third of all patients admitted to Bellevue were alcoholics. In these people and in drug addicts, he was as much interested as in psychotics. Together with Dr. Alexander Lambert, who became a national authority on alcoholism, Dr. Gregory laid down many of the procedures which are still in practice at Bellevue and numerous other hospitals around the country. With the same evangelistic spirit with which he carried the facts on insanity to the public, he also preached that alcoholism was an illness, not a sin. Much of present-day understanding of problem drinking can be attributed to his pioneering fervor.

In 1911 when the alcoholic ward came under his jurisdiction, his first step was to segregate those who were actually ill or merited further examination, from the one-third who were just passingly drunk and in need of nothing more than a place to sleep it off. In this connection, Dr. Gregory once attempted to put through the idea of a city-operated sobering-up station where the Bowery bum types could flop for the night without cluttering up his wards. He failed in this, but at least his system of handling alcoholics speeded up the turnover during a period when Bellevue had a reputation along skid row for spreading the welcome mat for drunks.

Dr. Gregory's assembly-line method was first to separate the sick from the merely intoxicated. The latter group was then given sedatives and vitamins and was usually discharged before the day passed, only to be replaced by a score of new arrivals within the next twenty-four hours.

Those who were sent to the psychiatric division, however, were carefully studied for some clue that could lead to their recovery. In Dr. Gregory's belief, the only permanent cure for alcoholism lay in the sufferer's ability to replace drink with another interest that would wholly absorb his attention and his will. He felt that religion was the best bulwark, and studies made at the city's mission houses further convinced him of this.

In examining alcoholics classified as "sick," Dr. Gregory and his staff were greatly aided by the vast, detailed statistical study of alcoholic patterns prepared at the hospital under the direction of Dr. Lambert.

These analyses, which Dr. Lambert based upon ward studies and hospital records, brought to light many startling facts. It was found, for example, that there was a considerable variance between the drinking biographies of men and women. While admissions by numbers amounted to about the same, most female alcoholics were either youthful (mostly in their twenties), or quite advanced in age. There was a sharp falling off during the age years from thirty-two to thirty-seven. Strangely, these were the peak years for male alcoholics. It was learned, too, that nearly twice as many young women died of alcoholism as young men, and that women sufferers were usually harder to manage and more abusive.

Weather conditions, Lambert discovered, also had a considerable effect on New York's drinking habits. The period from September through December showed the highest incidence of delirium tremens; summer months had the lowest. Heat waves invariably brought about a decline in these cases.

Occupational surveys, domestic and environmental studies of patients, painstakingly broken down and analyzed by Dr. Lambert and his co-workers, added to the bank of information upon which Bellevue physicians could draw in the treatment of alcoholic cases.

For Dr. Gregory, Bellevue did not end at the big iron gates. He thought the hospital's services should reach out into the city itself, into the homes of the problem drinkers, the drug addicts, the mentally and nervously disturbed. He felt that misunderstandings in the home were frequently the cause of patients' being sent to Bellevue, and vainly asked the city for a staff of social workers. When that failed, he turned to the voluntary committee of the Social Service Bureau, to Mrs. Willard Hyde, Miss Ruth Morgan, Miss Cornelia Brice, Mrs. Grant LaFarge, and others. They provided him with Jane Nash, an extraordinarily gifted nurse who was to become a moving spirit in Dr. Gregory's clinical work.

Dr. Gregory ranged from the medical and social fields to sweep away a few legal cobwebs too. Frequently called as an expert witness in criminal and civil cases where an individual's sanity was in question, he had a better-than-average working knowledge of the law—and a less-than-average patience with its cumbersome procedures.

In this connection, he made two important improvements in the interests of aiding the mentally ill in their dealing with the courts. The first involved the City's old practice of holding criminally insane suspects in jail until a commission could get around to examining their cases and passing on their mental health. This often took weeks, even months. Dr. Gregory succeeded in having the commission system abolished, instead having the suspects sent to Bellevue for an examination which could usually be accomplished in a few days.

His other legal triumph was having court, for ill persons, held at the hospital. Until his time, sick prisoners were forced to stay in prison wards until deemed able to go to court, or until they died. Today, a Supreme Court magistrate visits the hospital twice a week, and the ailing inmate is either cleared of charges or is allowed to remain in the ward until well enough to be remanded to prison.

With all his innovations, Dr. Gregory's physical plant was shrinking. In 1911, he had been able to secure a $20,000 appropriation which enabled him at least to make a better separation of the violent from the milder cases. But it was far from adequate, and so while Dr. Gregory dreamed of shiny new buildings, on the practical level he had to scheme constantly for ways to make the old quarters more efficient. More than 3,200 cases a year were already passing through the psychiatric division, and Dr. Gregory felt that, if the hospital were to render fullest service to the mentally ill of the city, there would, and should, be many times that number coming under his care.

It was not until 1933, the year before his resignation, that Dr. Gregory was to see his vision realized in the new eight-story plant that rose to occupy the entire block between Twenty-ninth and Thirtieth streets. It was built for what, in that depression year, was the staggering sum of $4,300,000, and it could accommodate 600 patients.

Having seen the psychiatric division expand from the draughty little pavilion on Twenty-sixth Street, where abuse was the accepted therapy, to these fine new quarters, staffed by a carefully picked corps of men and women especially trained and qualified for psychiatric work, could be called career enough for three men. But it was not enough for Dr. Gregory.

Barely two years after his resignation, he was called back to Bellevue as a psychiatric consultant and he remained in that capacity until his sudden death in 1941 while playing golf in Westchester.

Dr. Gregory was sixty-three years of age at the time of his death, and virtually until the moment he was stricken he remained as bristling with cheerful energy as the day when, a stripling doctor in his mid-twenties, he arrived to restore health to a branch of Bellevue that was itself sick.

Dr. Gregory was a lifelong bachelor—his work at Bellevue was his entire preoccupation. As he said in a newspaper interview some years earlier:

> My only interest is in the hospital. It is my aim to make people know that there is such a hospital and have them take advantage of it when they or their families need it . . . [but] people cheat themselves. They wait until they're hopeless. They won't come to the hospital unless driven to it. If

nervous people would come to us as soon as trouble shows, they could be helped.

Bellevue still practices what Dr. Gregory preached. "The story of psychiatry at Bellevue," his *Times* obituary said, "is the story of Dr. Gregory's life."

· XXVI ·

ANESTHESIA ADVANCED

Emery Andrew Rovenstine was born, 1895, in the small town of Atwood, Indiana, a trading center for the farmers of the district. Fifteen years had passed since the death of the dentist Dr. Charles Thomas Jackson, last of the triumvirate of Jackson, Wells, and Morton who had ushered in the era of anesthesiology. The elder Rovenstine was Atwood's only anesthesiologist, and sole proprietor of the community's ether supply. But he was not, himself, a physician. Son of a prosperous pioneer and medicine man, he kept store in the pleasant little crossroads town, and sold dry goods, groceries, shoes, notions, candy, drugs, and medicines.

The son, Emery Andrew, organizer of Bellevue's great school of anesthesiology, was fond of reminiscing on his "medical heritage." His grandfather John A. Rovenstine, a Civil War veteran, had homesteaded in both Arkansas and Indiana, but by nature was a rover. Much of the time he went off peddling a homemade concoction called "Rovenstine's Liniment," from the sale of which he realized substantial profits. C. A. Rovenstine, Dr. Rovenstine's father, used to strum a banjo to draw customers to his father's wagon.

When Emery, oldest of four children, was big enough to look the part, his father used to deck him out in a Santa Claus outfit and post him in the store window at Christmastime. His job was to point out, as ingratiatingly as he knew, the various seasonal attractions there on display.

This early background of salesmanship probably stood Dr. Rovenstine in even better stead than his "medical heritage" when, many years later, he entered into the new and controversial field of anesthesiology. It was an area of medicine beset by the twin foes of progress—charlatanism and ultraconservatism. Dr. Rovenstine was to need all the persuasion at his command to gain support for the daringly modern techniques which it became his life's work to develop and advance.

Medicine was not one of Rovenstine's youthful dreams. While attending high school in Atwood and later in Blue Island, near Chicago, where he had moved to live with an uncle, he had ambitions of being a schoolteacher. But it was during these years that he had his first encounter with anesthesiology—by way of a butt in the stomach followed by a thrashing. At Blue Island, Rovenstine engaged in athletics and made something of a name for himself. On one occasion he was playing with the Blue Island basketball team against a nearby school. The referee was Dr. Arthur Guedel, himself an anesthesiologist then instructing at the University of Indiana, who picked up a little money on the side officiating at high school basketball games. At a particularly tense moment in the final period young Rovenstine, angered by an adverse decision, took out the physician-referee by lowering his head and ramming him in the stomach. The astonished Guedel, when he recovered his wind, got off the floor and gave Rovenstine a sound walloping. Guedel vividly remembered the incident years later when Rovenstine became one of his students.

By dint of studying summers at Winona State Teachers College in Indiana, Emery Rovenstine succeeded in becoming an elementary school teacher at the age of seventeen. A year later, helped by an athletic scholarship, he enrolled in Wabash College, from which he was graduated in 1917, qualified to teach mathematics, physics, and chemistry, and to coach athletics.

Young Rovenstine was a versatile and energetic young man. To finance his education after leaving high school, at different times he was a hunter and trapper, a college waiter, a ballplayer, and a cucumber buyer for a pickle company. However, teaching school was still his main interest when World War I took him to France, where he served as an officer-courier at the front in the Saint-Mihiel and Argonne campaigns.

It was the pain and suffering he saw during the war, he often recalled later, which first stirred his interest in medicine and anesthesiology.

Also in France during the war, though Rovenstine was unaware of it, was the man whom he had attacked in the basketball game. Dr. Guedel was in charge of a hospital behind the lines. Out of his work with war casualties in this hospital came the first complete study of the physiological effects of anesthesia. Among other things, Guedel discovered that many of the patients died from the anesthesia itself. It was the work of Guedel and other pioneers with the wounded of World War I that initiated the great advances in anesthesiology made in the postwar years.

Rovenstine, however, after demobilization, taught and coached at high schools in Michigan and Indiana for four more years before he made his final decision to enter medical school at the University of Indiana, and study anesthesiology under Guedel.

For four years Rovenstine put everything he had into his medical studies. He supported himself by working afternoons and evenings in a drugstore in the Negro district, and played semi-pro baseball Sundays. Summers, he held down a job with the Heinz Company as a vegetable buyer.

In 1928, following a year's internship, he hung out his shingle as a general practitioner in La Porte, Indiana, with anesthesiology a sideline. Already, however, signs of the impending financial crash had appeared in the Midwest. Rovenstine, in the first part of 1929, decided it was time to close up shop and concentrate on a secure post as anesthetist.

His first preparatory step was to sign up for a short course under a Dr. E. I. McKesson, a prominent anesthetist and the well-to-do inventor of anesthetic dispensing equipment. Upon completion of this refresher course, with Guedel's help, he secured a residency at the University of Wisconsin Hospital, and an opportunity to study under Dr. Ralph Waters.

Bellevue's great anesthesiological department, as well as those at teaching hospitals connected with Harvard, Pennsylvania, Iowa, and Stanford, has its roots in Waters' "pilot plant" at Madison. Waters' maxim was: "A poor surgeon needs a good anesthetist, a good surgeon deserves one." Through his brilliant teachings, the subject of anesthesiology became a specialized department in leading medical schools, and the anesthetist found his important place in the operating rooms of the great hospitals.

Under Waters, Rovenstine came to see that the scope of his chosen field was far greater than even he had imagined. It extended into every branch of medical science and pharmacy, into chemistry, physics, and even into mechanical and electrical engineering. Whatever lingering doubts Rovenstine may have had about his future career were dispelled at Wisconsin. He plunged into all the ramifications of his subject with a dedication that thereafter never flagged. "Being a Rovenstine anesthesiologist means being a damn good doctor," a Bellevue surgeon was later to say of the young man from Indiana. "It means spending your whole life finding out what makes people live." It was this spirit that Wisconsin fired.

This same Dr. Waters it was who, with the help of his disciple, Dr. Rovenstine, eventually brought about the acceptance of the modern doctrine that the anesthetist, and not the surgeon, must be in over-all command of the operating room. For, as one surgeon who had been sold on this theory by Rovenstine remarked, "After all, he [the anesthetist] administers the blood, the saline, the anesthetic. He's the fellow who looks over the patient and decides how he's going to put him to sleep. He's the fellow who says, 'the patient is getting depression of the vagus, he's going to die,' or, 'we're switching from cyclopropane to ether.' " In up-to-date hospitals, it is the anesthesiologist who is the "take-charge" man, while the surgeon does the cutting.

Rovenstine, when he went to Wisconsin, was far from being a "Rovenstine anesthesiologist" himself. But during his five years under Waters, he discovered his own gifts and came to believe that the conquest of pain was the highest goal to which a doctor could aspire.

It was in 1935 that Rovenstine was called to New York from Wisconsin to organize the school of anesthesiology at New York University, and head the department at Bellevue. By this time Wisconsin methods enjoyed wide medical acceptance, and Dr. Waters had been asked to recommend a man from his staff to take the New York post. Rovenstine was his choice. He had just turned forty when he arrived in New York with his wife. They took a tiny mid-town apartment, from which Rovenstine, while off duty, seldom ventured except to go to an occasional show, football or baseball game.

At Bellevue and New York University Rovenstine soon ran into heavy sailing. The new Midwestern techniques had been embraced by an advanced minority in the East, but the much more numerous standpat school rebelled against Rovenstine's upstart novelties.

The newly appointed Rovenstine more than once was told bluntly that he and his ideas were not welcome in New York. He was even threatened with professional ruin if he did not resign. However, obstructionism did not dismay Rovenstine. He had worked too hard to get where he was in the field of anesthesiology to give up without a fight. Early in the game he made up his mind never to quit Bellevue merely because of the hostile attitude of jealous, stick-in-the-mud colleagues. Turning a deaf ear to his critics, he began to set up a new school of anesthesiology with typical dispatch.

Suddenly personal tragedy intervened. One fall afternoon Rovenstine returned from a football game and found his wife dead. The taps of the gas stove had all been turned on.

From that day on for many years Rovenstine buried himself in work. Bellevue and anesthesiology became his obsession. He often worked and wrote for more than eighteen hours a day. That Bellevue is a world center for the study and practice of anesthesiology is a tribute to these Herculean labors, and a deeply moving reminder of a tragic loss.

Rovenstine's courses in anesthesia at Bellevue characteristically start with an examination of the nature of pain itself. He has been described as having a dispassionate, scholarly approach to the problems of suffering while in the classroom, but great commiseration with the sufferer when actually in the presence of pain. Once, when a number of victims of a fire were brought to Bellevue for treatment, he was heard to cry out: "My God, how they must have suffered before we got to them!" This reaction was revealing of the man. The good anesthesiologist, though he must be cold and calm while at work, at the same time must have great empathy, and sense what is happening to the patient from the least flicker of a sign.

Anesthesiology, as taught at Bellevue, is a vast, complicated subject. Rovenstine himself admits that it is no easy matter keeping abreast of the field. Research results on the endless parade of new anesthetics and sedatives constantly appearing from the laboratories of the big pharmaceutical houses must be evaluated. New techniques in blocking nerve trunks, in hypnosis, freezing, are studied by the teacher even as he hands them on to the student. Anesthesiology is still a very new science. There are only a few hundred full-fledged anesthesiologists in the country, though Bellevue and other schools are regularly adding to their numbers, and each thinks of himself as a student rather than a master, even Rovenstine himself.

In operative surgery five main anesthetic methods are used singly or in a variety of combinations. Commonest is the insufflation, or breathing in, of ether or vinyl ether. In most cases this is the easiest, least expensive, and safest method. Its prime advantage is that if anything goes wrong, breathing usually stops before the heartbeat, thus giving the anesthetist warning to take counter-measures. Nitrous oxide induction, often in combination with oxygen and ether, is a second method. Nitrous oxide, or laughing gas, is often used to start general anesthesia, and is sometimes desirable alone, or with oxygen, in a short operation. Spinal injections of certain anesthetics are desirable where the patient's heart or lungs are in poor condition. Intravenous injections of pentathol and other drugs are also valuable under the same conditions. Cyclopropane, another gas, is swift and strong like ether, and has fewer side-effects.

Used separately, and in many different combinations, these are the anesthetist's principal means of inducing unconsciousness. During surgery, he must also keep a running check on the patient's condition, and be alert at any instant to supply saline, plasma, or whole blood, and if necessary to order the operation halted.

Some anesthetic gases are highly explosive and require the greatest caution on the part of the anesthetist. Certain schools and hospitals go in for mechanical gimmicks to prevent static electricity from touching off a fatal blast. Not so Bellevue. Rovenstine says: "We never leave any loopholes for static. We place responsibility directly on the anesthetist and no one, or nothing, else. We don't trust mechanical devices. Our anesthetist must keep contact with the patient at all times and be grounded."

Violence during the early excitement phase of anesthesia is another danger against which the anesthetist must guard. Dr. Rovenstine admits he has never regretted his days on the gridiron and diamond, for many times his brawn has stood him in good stead when a husky patient acted up under anesthesia.

Almost anything can happen during an operation, even in routine surgery. No two patients react exactly the same to an anesthetic, and the anesthetist must watch closely for signs of allergy or other toxic side-effects while surgery is in progress. In some cases, it is necessary to make a quick change of agents; in others, the incision must be closed swiftly, the patient revived, and the entire operation postponed or cancelled.

One of the most dangerous areas in surgery is the chest. In chest surgery, thanks to the work of Rovenstine and his colleagues, Bellevue has made a national reputation. And just as World War I supplied Guedel and earlier pioneers of anesthesiology with a mountain of invaluable data, so World War II advanced new anesthetic techniques, particularly in chest cases.

As a member of the Army Advisory Board, and as an active anesthetist in several general hospitals in the European theater, Rovenstine wielded an influence that saved countless lives. With characteristic energy he drove home the idea that the anesthetist must control the operating room. "About the time of the Bulge," one army surgeon recalls, "another doctor and I handled four hundred consecutive chest cases, including forty-two heart operations, without one death. In the first World War, two-thirds of the men whose chests were opened died." He gave Rovenstine a full share of the credit for the fact that these men survived.

Today, Rovenstine, his able young assistant Dr. E. M. Papper, and their Bellevue colleagues are breaking through new pain barriers. Much of the work that is going forward there now is concerned with the relatively unexplored possibilities of the so-called "nerve block"—or the anesthetizing of nerves which transmit pain. This technique is used in treating arthritis, angina, bursitis, and many other inoperable conditions. Nerve blocking has made an intimate knowledge of neurology another anesthesiological requirement. In order to block a nerve successfully, the practitioner must know exactly where each nerve center is located in order to place the injection where it will be effective. The use of nerve blocks is now spreading to many disorders previously inaccessible to treatment. Dr. Papper, for example, has had notable success with this method in curing shingles.

Anesthesia by freezing is another technique under investigation by Rovenstine and his colleagues. Not one for fooling around with fancy gadgets, Rovenstine "froze" his first patient by putting him in a bathtub full of ice cubes!

Use of hypnosis, too, for minor surgery, is also being tried under Rovenstine's direction at Bellevue. One of his earliest subjects was his secretary's mother, who had gangrene of the toe and was successfully operated on after having been hypnotized by Rovenstine.

Rovenstine, now happily remarried to a successful executive in the chinaware business, still works on a staggering schedule. It is nothing for him to put in a full day in the classroom or operating theater, take a quick nap, then work through most of the night on a new paper. Even in the few hours he takes out for relaxation on such rare occasions as his wife's busy program happens to coincide with his own, he is likely to be reminded of his work. He likes to tell of going with Mrs. Rovenstine to a night club where the prosperous owner was also acting as master of ceremonies. As soon as the man appeared, Rovenstine asked his wife where he had seen him before. She suggested either in the newspapers or in the hospital. On the way home Rovenstine suddenly remembered. The man had once been a Bellevue case, an alcoholic who had to be operated on.

Rovenstine also likes to tell about an elevator operator at the hospital. Again and again he would bring up the subject of anesthesia, and often astounded Rovenstine with the range of his knowledge. Not until the man's death did Rovenstine learn that the operator had himself been a doctor who, disheartened by the suffering he had seen, had abandoned his practice. However, the students, Rovenstine says, must have known the operator's secret, for they used to ply him with questions on anesthesia while on their way up to exams.

Despite the pain he has witnessed in three decades of anesthesiology, there is nothing calloused about Rovenstine or the doctrine he teaches at Bellevue. Long experience has not dulled his sympathies. Always he has remained a soft-spoken, affable man, passionately in love with his work. People meeting him for the first time often notice an absent look about him. This, a writer friend of his has explained, is "because he is thinking ten years ahead."

· XXVII ·

AGAIN BY WAR IMPELLED

In 1942 Bellevue for the fourth time was drawn into the vortex of war. Again the familiar pattern was repeated; the staff raided, surgical and medical units recruited for the field. A vast fund of new experience was accumulated under pressure, leading to rapid postwar advances in all fields of medicine.

Dr. John Mulholland, assistant to Dr. Arthur Wright, chief surgeon of the Third Division, was one of the first Bellevue doctors to be called up. He was assigned by the War Department to head and organize a Bellevue unit to serve in World War II. In short order he had organized a basic staff consisting of Dr. Benjamin Ashe of the Second Division, to head the medical section; Dr. Currier McEwen, dean of New York University College of Medicine, to serve as executive officer; and Miss Thelma Ryan, later Lieutenant Colonel Ryan, as chief nurse. The new unit was named United States General Hospital No. 1, in memory of the old Base Hospital Unit Number 1 of Vichy fame, which had continued as a reserve unit during the intervening years of peace.

By the end of the year, General Hospital No. 1 was in training at Fort Meade, Maryland. Meanwhile, the Services were rapidly stripping Bellevue of medical and nursing personnel, a depletion which the Board tried in some measure to counteract by introducing a system of nine-month internships. Bellevue next took on the responsibility of giving special courses for the Service medical corps. The members of old Base Hospital Number 1 felt a paternal interest in its World War II successor. Dr. Charles H. Nammack, director of the Fourth Medical Division, who had been young Lieutenant Nammack in 1918, presented to the unit a stand of colors. One of the flags was that of the city of New York, which the unit had been given permission to carry.

Again the Bellevue unit sailed forth into a sub-infested Atlantic. But this time the destination was England instead of France. The unit's first task was to set up a hospital in Hertfordshire, just outside of London. Up until D-day this hospital took care of wounded airmen of the Eighth Air Force bomber squadrons, then daily softening up the Continent for the invasion. They also cared for ground force and other victims of the London bombings. Some of the hospital's huts for enlisted men were hit in a German raid, and the unit suffered its own first casualties.

The next move was across the channel to Omaha Beach, where a landing was made, in typically bad weather, from LST's. By stages the hospital advanced through the Normandy mud to Paris, and was finally quartered in seven buildings formerly used by the Germans as an A.A. artillery school. The buildings were new and modern, but had been thoroughly vandalized by the departing Germans. For two weeks 650 French civilians and 250 German prisoners worked at clearing away mines and unexploded ammunition, and on November 12, 1943, the members of the staff were ready to open a well-equipped hospital of nearly two thousand beds.

These extensive accommodations proved inadequate. A month or so later, during the Battle of the Bulge, the patient load became so heavy that hundreds of beds had to be set up in the corridors. The surgeons, working around the clock, in April alone performed 1,142 operations.

As the hospital was near the only airfield from which planes flew directly to the United States, it was a rendezvous for Bellevue men scattered all over the battle area. V-E day came and went. Plane after plane took off for New York, but no sign of orders for General Hospital No. 1. Scuttlebutt had it that the next stop was Tokyo, not home. Morale began to sag a little. But before V-J Day, the Army finally acted.

Dr. McEwen was detached to become chief medical consultant of the European theater. The unit itself was sent off to the Pacific. Dr. Mulholland and most of the original staff, however, were relieved, and came home to Bellevue. The First General Hospital was awarded the Meritorious Service Unit Plaque for "outstanding devotion to duty . . . in keeping with the highest traditions of service."

Hair-raising stories of life in the Medical Corps and the Nurse Corps are endless. One of the many who had narrow escapes was Lieutenant Blanche Sigman, a head nurse who was aboard the brightly lighted Allied hospital ship, *Newfoundland* when German bombers set it afire in Salerno harbor, October 13, 1944. All 103 American nurses were reported saved, though some British nurses and doctors were killed. After the bombing, the nurses were taken to North Africa, and then ordered to rejoin the American Fifth Army evacuation hospital in Italy.

The following account of the bombing was cabled to the New York *Herald Tribune* by UP correspondent Don Whitehead:

"The British sailors were marvelous," said Lieutenant Blanche Sigman of Cambridge, Ohio. "They were as calm as though nothing had happened and kept kidding all the time. But the girls acted wonderfully, too. The sailors said they never could have saved us if the girls had become hysterical." Lieutenant Sigman said she awakened at 5 A.M. when a bomb hit the ship, which was lit brightly with white, red and green lights aglow.

"I got up and dressed and started up on deck," she said. "I met two girls and they said they had not heard a bomb, so

I decided not to awaken the others. I got back in bed and then the bomb hit. It blew the doors off the hinges, shattered the walls, broke all the mirrors. By some miracle, none of the American girls were killed, although some British doctors and nurses died."

Nurses living in a ward over which the bomb exploded were awakened when the walls collapsed and the ceiling fell in. None of them was able to say why they were not seriously injured. Debris blocked passage to the ward room.

They thought they were trapped until Lieutenant Sigman brought a flashlight down and sailors came to guide them through another passage to the deck. They grabbed what clothes they could find. Some came on deck naked to climb into lifeboats, only to find some of them damaged by the explosion, and unseaworthy. Other hospital ships in the area sent lifeboats over, and the girls climbed down rope nets and ladders into them. There were 76 in one boat. The bomb had punctured the bow of this boat and the girls had to bail with helmets to keep afloat. Many of them had severe rope burns caused by sliding down into the rescue craft.

"Some of the girls would start down the ladders nude, and the sailors would pull them back and give them their pants," Lieutenant Sigman said. "They were dressed in the strangest assortment of garments ever seen at sea. One of the girls had only a jacket and others were wrapped in sheets."

But the ship was abandoned in good order, without further loss of life, and the nurses were taken aboard another hospital ship which carried them back to a North African port for rest and treatment.

The New York *Herald Tribune* of January 28, 1944, carried this story:

Salerno. The first group of American nurses arrived at this beachhead today and underwent two German air raids in rapid succession before they had time to dig fox-holes. They numbered more than 100. One group that installed itself in hospital tents was headed by Chief Nurse First Lieutenant Blanche Sigman of St. John's Place, Brooklyn, a graduate of Bellevue Hospital of New York. "We slept on the decks coming over," she said, "and had several alerts during the night. We came ashore without getting our feet wet, and ran into two air raids before we had even unpacked."

Then came the screaming headlines of February 8: "American Hospital Bombed and Two Nurses Killed." Then, after three weeks, a letter from Colonel Blanchfield:

> It is impossible to put into words our deep feeling of sympathy, or to express the gratitude of a nation for the spirit in which Lieutenant Sigman completed her assignment as a member of the Army Nurse Corps. She typifies the very finest in American womanhood. Had she known that she was to die, she still would have said, "I must go, it is my duty." The nurses are like that in this war. They fear nothing. They beg to go forward as far as possible, because they feel they are needed so urgently. In her death there is only one consolation we can give. Before she gave so much, she helped to save so many.

Lieutenant Sigman was posthumously awarded the Purple Heart, and the nurses' quarters at Fletcher Hospital in Cambridge, Ohio, her birthplace, were named Sigman Hall in her honor.

Once again letters from Bellevue nurses give a graphic and heartbreaking picture of the aftermath of battle. First Lieutenant Kathleen Dean wrote home during the height of the Iwo Jima and Okinawa campaigns:

> If my letters have fallen off it's because the flesh has been weak. I wonder how much longer we can stand this pace— but as usual no one has complained. The month of March was a nightmare. It started when the *Solace* arrived from Iwo Jima on February 26th, bringing the bloodiest and most broken load of patients we'd ever nursed—and most of us have nursed battle casualties from several campaigns. They are veterans of 18, 19, and 20 years of age—and, the most incredible of all, it has not made them too bitter. They can still laugh and tease, whistling at a nurse they think is "well stacked." They've all got into the habit of calling me Cookie. I grin through hidden tears at that. They are 19 and 20, and I am 23, but I feel years and years older.
> They started coming in about 7 P.M. Sunset time here, and the clouds were like pink, lacy streamers over the bay as we sat in the mess hall listening to the public address calling us back to duty. We thought we couldn't do much that night until we got there and saw them—and then there were a

thousand voices calling for a drink of water, a thousand voices asking for an aspirin, anything to help ease the pain.

At least we had quonset huts in which to put them in beds with white sheets. Their bodies were black. It looked like coal dust, but they said it was the volcano ash from Mount Surabachi. It was ground into the soles of their feet, as we found out the next day when we tried to wash it off.

The long hours slipped by—I think we got a few hours sleep that night—and the next morning we were up on the hill again. It was an endless round of giving plasma, whole blood, changing dressings, putting on casts, taking X-rays, sending patients to surgery, trying to do a million little things for them. They were still pouring in, brought down from Iwo in anything that would sail on water as well as in the hospital ships—and some of the combat ships carrying wounded were subject to attack on the way down. They were dazed and suffering, most of them, but glad to be off the ship.

They were all Marines, and more than a bit startled to find themselves in an Army hospital. "What the hell—is this a Doggie Hospital?" asked one 19-year-old. "OK, Gyrene, if you don't like it you know what you can do," I said, shooting him in the bottom with 5 cc. of penicillin. He grinned at me, a crooked Irish smile, "No, I ain't calling you a Doggie, you're a *woman,* Cookie." And that started the whole ward calling me Cookie. Nothing has warmed my heart so much since I've been out here, as Cassidy with his broken neck and wired jaw calling me Cookie.

I've been working in Orthopedic surgery, and for Iwo campaign casualties, we had the amputation ward. During the first days, we worked much too hard to listen to the patients talk—and they were much too excited. When I did get around to listening, they all seemed excited about an article they had seen in the *New York Times,* announcing the availability of penicillin in pill form. They had all been getting penicillin every three hours, day and night, for a couple of weeks, until they felt like pin cushions. "Why can't we get pills instead of needles? I suppose all the big shots are getting the pills. I'd rather be back at the beach at Iwo than take any more of these needles. Boy, you sure play a good game of darts, Cookie," were a few of the comments. God knows I didn't like to do it. Neither did any of the other girls, but how can you tell a bunch of heroes about infections they didn't get?

The days went on and on, more and more Marines came in on litters, cargos of American youth, pathetic in their helplessness. One blue-eyed kid from Texas had both hands gone. I never saw that boy without a smile on his face. We stuck a wooden applicator into the bandage upright, and a cigarette on the other end of it, so he could smoke.

Again, Nurse Dean wrote on the Twenty-sixth of April, 1945:

The Iwo operation was called Hot Rock, and it sure was the hottest thing that has happened here to date. Marine Pfc. ———, age 19 with freckles, who said they wouldn't serve him drinks in a San Francisco bar, lost his left leg from the burst of a Jap mortar—their new thousand-pound mortars, used for the first time on Iwo. He told the other patients in all seriousness, "You should have seen the tattoo I had on that leg." They're not long in coming around. I guess it's the American in them.

I thought those days of back-breaking drudgery would never end. After you've been on the receiving end of this thing for a long time, and see their brave efforts and undeniable heroism and their quiet cheerful acceptance of their losses, it does something to you inside. . . . It's shudderingly real if you just look beneath the surface. They are hopelessly handicapped before their lives have begun . . .

I know what civilian patients can be like, especially some of the old ones at Bellevue—and they need a lot of care—but if some of the young nurses only knew how good these kids are, they would want to be the first to try to do something for them.

The Army Nurse Corps is not a bed of roses. No one ever said it was. *Time Magazine* listed complaints they got from the Army Nurse Corps. Drilling and field training was one of them. "Rank has its privileges" was another; being treated by Chief Nurses like school children was another—and they are all true. I've come up against every one of them at some time or another since I have been in the Army. But they make me laugh—griping about those things to newspaper people. How infinitesimal those things are beside the picture of the G.I. who puts up with the same things—gets his leg blown off at Iwo or Okinawa or Saipan or Kwajalein or France or Italy—and then has to be at the tender mercy of an overworked, dead tired "angel." Draft nurses? Yes, that's the way we feel about it out here."

Nurse Dean wrote on May 1, 1945:

The hospitals here are stretched to capacity again, filled with patients—mostly Navy, from the Okinawa campaign.

The patients from Okinawa are not as appallingly young as were the Iwo veterans, and from what they say, Okey is a much better piece of real estate, with hills, grass, green trees and numerous villages. One infantry captain back with a compound fracture of the tibia fibula told me his men were fighting in and out of ancient family tombs all the time. The Okinawans are said to have some Chinese blood and some of their traits. Ancestor worship is one of them. The natives were mostly old women and children, the young men presumably being in the Jap army, and the young women working on the Japanese mainland. All were terrified of the Americans and had to be dragged forcibly from foxholes and houses, and put into compounds, screaming and holding back . . .

We heard today the Jap suicide planes had hit the hospital ship *Comfort*, killing 20 patients and 6 nurses. Those crazy Japs, what have they got to look forward to? The big bombers that thunder out of here day after day are laying waste and destruction to their cities and industries. I cannot understand the psychology of these suicide attacks. Sure hit, and sure death. They say those pilots are all royally entertained for several weeks at Tokyo's best whorehouses, with finest food and the most charming geisha girls, before they go out to attack our ships. My brother's ship took five suicide hits, but got itself back to San Pedro for repairs—with half the crew missing.

On May 8, 1945, she wrote:

The United States must be electrified today—V-E day! On this hot little island in the Pacific, it was to us just another day. There was no rejoicing, no stopping of work; everything went on as usual. We got in a hospital ship with 500 more patients from Okinawa. I think the feeling is the same everywhere out here. It is because our minds are too small to comprehend the whole picture.

The patients heard the news when I did, this morning at 7 A.M. They were having trays served them, as usual making cracks about the dehydrated rubbery eggs and the salty bacon, when the San Francisco broadcast came crackling through with its news.

It has been a usual sort of day. We had stew and canned pears for lunch. The patients hobbled to the PX on crutches, bought candy bars, cigarettes, and the latest copy of *Yank*. A few B-29's soared lazily overhead through the white banked clouds. At 4 P.M. the nurses gathered in our little officers' club for a cold bottle of beer, discussing V-E day, and stressing the thoughts uppermost in our minds. One was, how soon will they send us help, and when will V-J day be? There is a lot of work here, especially in the hospitals. How much more will there be after the first salvo for the battle of Japan is sounded?

Quotations of this moving sort could be multiplied a hundredfold. But at long last the guns fell silent, for a little while, at least, and the Bellevue unit came home. The older physicians and surgeons, men of the First World War who had been called back to active service from the consulting lists, went into retirement. Dr. Adrian Lambert was succeeded by Dr. Frank Berry. Dr. Wright, on the operating staff for a quarter-century, retired to his Maryland farm from his post as chief of the Third Surgical Division, and was replaced by Dr. Mulholland.

Of the changes that had occurred during the war, one was the affiliation of the Fourth or Open Division with New York University Post Graduate College of Medicine. The purpose of this merger was to supplement the hospital's teaching staff, which had been badly depleted by the war. Dr. Charles H. Nammack, who had succeeded Dr. Alexander Lambert as division director, insisted on keeping the division open to all comers so that interns might be competitively selected from all over the globe. Before this, Fourth Division had occasionally conducted undergraduate courses for Cornell Medical School and postgraduate courses for Columbia. The whole program of the Fourth expanded so much during and after World War II that Dr. Nammack had one of his interns serve as co-ordinator of students—among other things, to prevent them from getting lost in the endless corridors.

Before the Fourth Division became linked with New York University, Dr. Nammack had devised an ingenious way of circumventing the rule that all gifts to Bellevue must revert to the hospital's sinking fund. Divisions affiliated with the medical schools get around this obstacle by seeing that gifts for them are given to the schools, and so marked for the division in question. But the Fourth Division, before it came to have such affiliations, incorporated itself as the "Society of the Fourth Division, Incorporated."

As a result of this arrangement, it received from Mrs. Jessie Woolworth Donahue a beautiful sunny ward for women patients, in memory of her father, Frank Woolworth. The walls are painted a soft green, the drapes are gaily flowered chintz, the equipment is of the latest design. There are soundproof floors, adustable beds, bed tables, reading lamps—everything that could be devised for the comfort of the patients. Another gift was a plasma tank, donated by Mrs. William B. Leeds.

BELLEVUE TODAY

Of the score and a half of social service institutions financed and run by the city of New York, Bellevue is the largest. Indeed, it is the largest city hospital in the world. It is a free hospital— that is, it must accept any patient without demur, though the patient who can pay must pay, according to ability, up to a maximum of $25.00 a day. The matter of being admitted for care at Bellevue is not arbitrated, as in thousands of privately managed American hospitals, at the bursar's window. The Bellevue system is to get the sick to bed, and explore their pocketbooks later.

Very naturally a hospital with a daily caseload of 2,700 costs money to run, even though in the world's richest city far, far more is spent on cigarettes and liquor than on Bellevue, multiplied by ten. The food bill, for instance, approaches a million and a half dollars annually. The daily cost of keeping a patient on a Bellevue ward works out at around $20.00 a day for food, laundry, nursing care, depreciation of equipment, and other expenses. This is leaving medical care out of account; also, the services of physicians, surgeons, and technologists, and the use of X-ray machines, chemical testing apparatus, microscopes, fluoroscopes, and countless other laboratory devices. Likewise, drugs cost the patient nothing, and they are a big item in the usual hospital bill.

As for the system of billing the patient, anyone who earns $125 a week or more must pay the full $25.00 a day. But if this patient has a family, he is charged correspondingly less, down to a minimum of $2.00 a day. Charges have steadily risen as first depression-spending and then two wars inflated the dollar. Back in 1936 the Bellevue charge was $3.00 a day. Ten years later the rate had risen to $7.56, and in the next decade again it more than doubled, with no end in sight. However, most of Bellevue's patients are either very poor people or social casualties. The great influx of Puerto Ricans in recent years has burdened the facilities of Bellevue and offset a diminution in caseload pressure that might otherwise have been expected. Actually, only 7 per cent of the total flow pay the full $25.00 a day. Those who feel they have been overcharged can appeal to the reviewing board of the New York Department of Hospitals.

In the public mind the prospect of hospitalization at Bellevue is still fraught with apprehension. The "black bottle" legend dies hard; likewise, the broader idea that Bellevue patients are regarded as so much human meat to be cut up and plied with drugs for the mere sake of experiment. But even among the most ignorant the truth is slowly spreading—the truth that scientific experiment, by definition, is not callous, but extremely cautious, watchful, and aware of pain. The fact is, the spirit of experimentation at Bellevue is all to the good, a tremendous advantage to the patient. It is the same spirit, exactly, as that found at the Mayo or Leahy clinics. And to such places flock the well-to-do and educated from all over the world. But this analogy is hard to sell to people sorely beset, and ill-equipped in any case to appreciate it.

It must never be forgotten that Bellevue gets far more than its share of difficult and terminal cases. This is true of a city hospital anywhere, but especially true of Bellevue, which serves the largest and most socially complex metropolis in the whole world. In any event, unavoidably the death rate per thousand at

Bellevue is slightly higher than at other New York hospitals. Even so, the mortality rate is only 4.7 per cent of all patients admitted, or six to seven deaths a day. This is astonishingly low in an institution where extremity is chronic. And it must also be borne in mind that over 20 per cent of Bellevue admissions die within forty-eight hours, for the reason that they are in such poor shape when they arrive. If this consideration were applied to the average mortality rate, it would approach the figure shown by the finest private hospitals, many of which would not even open their doors, as Bellevue must, to the impoverished moribund.

All told, some 50,000 patients are treated and cared for each year in all the departments, including the outpatient clinics, of Bellevue. Four-fifths of these people belong to the white race, and the bulk of the remainder are Negroes from Harlem. A breakdown of admissions by religion shows that about 60 per cent are Roman Catholics, a figure in considerable measure accounted for by the recent influx of Puerto Ricans; 25 per cent are Protestants; 12 per cent are of the Jewish faith; and the final 3 per cent represent other creeds.

Out of the 50,000 total, about 3,700 are children under two years old; another 3,700 are between the ages of two and fifteen; and the rest range all the way up to the century mark. The bulk of the admissions, some 17,000 or 34 per cent of the whole, come into the psychiatric division, a figure that most graphically indicates the pressures and worries of life in the atomic age. Several categories of admission run between 2,000 and 3,000 annually in each—delivery cases; eye, ear, nose, or throat surgery; gynecological; TB and other pulmonary diseases. Cancer is, of course, a tremendous problem, and accounts for a vast amount of surgery.

Ten years or so ago, interns at Bellevue were not paid for their unceasing labors, beyond receiving a monthly stipend of $15.00, plus room and board. Today, a Bellevue intern is paid about $72.00 a month over and above room, board, and other perquisites. The interns' living quarters have also been improved beyond recognition. It was not so long ago that interns slept four in a room. And since on-duty hours were almost always staggered, one of them would always be disturbing the others as he came or went, or pursued his studies. All this has changed, and necessarily so, for a doctor's training today demands every ounce of strength and concentration he can muster.

Whereas Bellevue never lacks for interns, and annually turns down hundreds of applications, the nursing situation is as clouded here as everywhere else. Nursing at Bellevue is a particularly tough job, a real challenge, for Bellevue is a hospital in the full sense, not a rest home or spa. Everywhere nurses are underpaid, and everywhere the sense of vocation which has always drawn fine young women into the noblest of callings has been undermined by the cynicisms and doubts of our troubled times. But at Bellevue, in addition to these factors, the rigors of the job also militate against having an adequate nursing personnel. On the other hand, it is well known throughout the United States that a Bellevue-trained nurse is absolutely the best, bar none. A Bellevue nurse has seen every imaginable human condition, and has learned how to deal with it. Out of this intensive experience arises a certain Bellevue stamp, an air of self-assurance and competence that sets Bellevue women just a little bit apart from their sisters in the profession. This elite tradition to some degree still attracts young women of superior character.

In actual fact, according to the national scale, Bellevue nurses are quite well paid, though it cannot be too often reiterated that they deserve much, much more. This you would readily admit if you followed, say, a nurse assigned to pulmonary surgery or to the psychiatric disturbed wards, through eight hours of duty for a week. At any rate, a head, or chief, nurse gets $5,990 a year; a registered, or trained, nurse, $4,500; a practical nurse or ward attendant, $3,650; and a nurse's aide, $3,400.

Meanwhile everything has been done to attract student nurses to Bellevue. Theirs is perhaps the most carefully planned, and certainly the most attractive, building in the whole huge establishment.

The Bellevue nurses' residence contains 902 rooms, of which 727 are for women, 150 for male students at the Mills School of Nursing for Men, and 25 provide accommodations for faculty members. In this hotel—for actually it is a kind of better-class hotel—live some of the trained personnel and all the trainees. Each floor is equipped with a modern kitchen, where the girls can fix snacks, and eat them, if they wish, while watching TV in the adjacent lounge. At their disposal, too, is a big gymnasium, also bowling alleys, and a 75-foot swimming pool. The classrooms are in the form of amphitheaters, ensuring everyone a good view of the instructor's demonstrations. For off-hours study and relaxation, there is an excellent library from which French doors give out on a terrace furnished with deck chairs.

The only feature that mars this physically attractive setting is the trainees' low monthly allowance. Students are paid about $20.00 a month during the three-year training period. Of this amount, even the most saving must spend at least $10.00 on small essentials, which leaves only $10.00 for fun. This, of course, is a stupidity. It makes no sense to be so niggardly when young draftees, for engaging temporarily in an occupation of incomparably less difficulty and human importance, get up to five times as much. However, until the general public understands its own basic, long-term needs, the inequity will certainly continue.

The spiritual factor in the cure of disease has always been present in the Bellevue scene, though never as actively as today, when both psychosomatics and the lessons learned in times of national peril have again affirmed the age-old truth that faith in a benign and loving God is often the difference between success and failure in the struggle against the body's infirmities. The first Protestant chapel at Bellevue was built in 1889; the first Catholic chapel in 1893. Then, in 1940, three modern chapels were constructed as part of the new administration building.

Since most patients are Catholic, the priests of that faith are most active at Bellevue. Some years they make nearly 50,000 bedside visits, and they are on call at all hours of the day through the switchboard operator. They administer the sacraments of confession, communion, extreme unction, and baptism, and keep as busy as the pastorate of many a fair-sized city. Occasionally a patient will even be confirmed in the hospital, though this sacrament may be given only by a bishop.

A very important and only recently developed aspect of the Bellevue program is the rehabilitation service, where patients who have suffered amputations, blindness, paralysis from strokes, and similar afflictions may learn how to function usefully despite their handicaps. The moving spirit behind this new Bellevue rehabilitation service is Dr. Howard A. Rusk, whose name is familiar to millions all over the country through his columns on veterans' health services appearing weekly in the *Sunday New York Times.*

Having seen how well Army rehabilitation worked, and noting that civilian disabilities in peacetime greatly outnumbered those service-connected in war, Dr. Rusk was inspired to work for modern rehabilitation centers in civilian hospitals. At the time Dr. Rusk was with the Army, Dr. George D. Deaver was doing comparable work on a smaller scale at Bellevue among disabled cases on the wards. After the war, Rusk and Deaver worked together for a separate department of physical medicine at Bellevue with its own wards and staff, and succeeded in interesting the department of hospitals. In 1947 their ideas were put into effect. Rusk became head of service, Deaver clinical chief, for the two brand-new, spick and span, 40-bed wards made possible through a grant of $250,000 from Bernard M. Baruch. The rehabilitation service worked so well it grew almost of its own accord. Today it also has a 20-bed ward for children and a 60-bed ward for TB victims. Beyond this, ten more rehabilitation centers have sprung up in city and voluntary hospitals throughout New York, and others are projected. More than 1,500,000 people in the United States are suffering from some degree of paralysis from cerebral hemorrhage and allied vascular failures. A very large percentage of these people could be made ambulatory and employable. Very plainly, rehabilitation is an economic as well as a humanitarian necessity. Preventive medicine and clinics, at the other end of the spectrum, are equally important.

And so, at Bellevue and everywhere else, more beds are required and new pavilions are sorely needed. But these days it costs $25,000 to build just one hospital room. And people are living much longer, thanks to tremendous progress in medicine and nursing care, which means that the chronic diseases and disabilities of old age are on the rise. It has been estimated that by the end of this century, if all the chronically ill were left on their own, each American worker would have to support one chronically ill person.

The only logical way to forfend this alarming prospect is to put more and more disabled people back into jobs. An employment-for-the-handicapped movement was started at Bellevue by a group who call themselves J.O.B.—Just One Break. This organization, supported by donations, has a salaried full-time director and an executive assistant, but is otherwise made up of nonpaid volunteers. Henry Viscardi, the director, was born legless, but he actually succeeded in organizing a subcontracting business in Long Island called Abilities, Incorporated, which is staffed exclusively by the handicapped. J.O.B. takes care of sixty to seventy applicants a month, and has undertaken an impressive program of employer education through articles and speeches. This program has set in motion a groundswell of interest throughout the whole nation. With surprising ease the public has been educated to the fact that a handicapped worker, because of the self-discipline he has necessarily achieved in the rehabilitation process, is almost always more dependable, and also more productive within the limits of his working scope, than his unhandicapped competitor.

But the main function of Bellevue is to care for the acutely ill, to handle immediate physical and mental crisis. To this end, every imaginable organ and complex of tissue in the human body at one time or another has been intimately explored and functionally analyzed. Innumerable studies of disease are conducted year in, year out, at Bellevue, and new drugs tested. A close watch is kept on therapeutic and surgical trends. Promising innovations are rapidly subjected to analytical research. The brain-wave clinic set up in 1938, for example, was among the first to be established in a major hospital for the routine diagnosis of brain conditions. Its facilities, greatly expanded in the interim, are in daily use as a check on other diagnostic findings in brain tumor, epileptic, and related cases.

In the radiation therapy department, headed by Dr. Sidney Rubenfeld, the hospital has one of the few cobalt rooms in this country. It houses a radiocobalt isotope generating a 2,000,000-volt beam useful in treating tumors, cancers, and endocrine disorders. All therapeutic results are carefully tabulated and forwarded to the Atomic Energy Commission. Bellevue also has a disaster unit which will attempt to go into action should an atom bomb land on New York and, needless to say, miss the East Side.

A combined project of the radiation therapy service and the chest service was recently launched to study modified techniques in the X-radiation of cancer of the lung. The plan calls for experiments in keeping the diseased lung in a collapsed state so as to avoid damage to the sound one.

Bellevue is also carrying on continued studies of the effects of head injuries from World War II and Korea; in the use of chloromycetin in the therapy of chronic ulcerated colitis; and in the use of the new anti-TB drug, isoniazid, as applied in the therapy of tuberculous meningitis, a particularly virulent form of TB. Other studies range from all aspects of care of the heart, changes in penetrative wounds of the heart, studies on the tape recording of heart and lungs, through projects to aid hay fever sufferers, such as testing the drug Ampigen for the treatment of highly sensitive hay fever patients. Research is being conducted on the effect of the new ataraxic, or tranquilizing, drugs in the control of hypertension, menopausal symptoms, and psychosis. Not even the common cold sore, *herpes labialis,* is overlooked at Bellevue, with the result that the use of cortisone for this harmless but disfiguring ailment is being studied.

Once again turmoil and strife, charge and countercharge, have come to Bellevue, just as so often happened in the past. On April 30, 1957, Dr. Dickinson Richards, director of Bellevue's First Medical Division, and a Nobel Prize winner, leveled a shocking charge at the city. Dr. Richards stated that the city had "shamefully neglected" Bellevue for the past twenty years, and that the city "allows us neither the physical facilities nor the personnel to permit adequate care . . ."

A few days later eight more doctors, the medical and surgical heads of Bellevue's four divisions, issued a statement backing Dr. Richards and greatly amplifying his charges. They recommended that the present Bellevue be torn down and rebuilt from the ground. They said:

> The buildings are old and antiquated; the plumbing is faulty and totally inadequate. Steam pipes break. The tiny elevators are ridiculous in a hospital the size of Bellevue. There is an ever-present fire hazard which will some day take lives. The whole hospital is dangerously overcrowded.

Mayor Robert Wagner promptly answered that an architect would be paid $85,000 for a detailed plan for Bellevue's expansion and rebuilding. To this the Medical Board replied:

> It should be remembered that in 1940, and again in 1946, architectural plans for a new hospital were actually completed, but never resulted in the construction of a new plant.
> These plans were then given No. 1 priority among the city's needs for hospital construction, yet they were arbitarily set aside by previous city administrations.

We are most anxious that the plans resulting from the new survey, for which appropriation has just been made, should actually lead to the construction of the urgently needed new hospital.

From all the furor and recriminations these facts emerged: that the physical care received by Bellevue's patients is far below standard; that the medical and surgical care is the very best in the world.

The *New York Times Magazine* said of the controversy:

Bellevue is being scored solely for its lack of physical comfort and beauty, and for conditions that create the needless difficulties under which its staff must minister to patients. As a result of the recent furor, the city has begun expediting plans for reform, but it is unlikely that any of these will be put into effect right away. Dr. Morris A. Jacobs, Commissioner of Hospitals, explains that the rebuilding of Bellevue will have to be done in stages.

"We can't tear down a hospital like this in one fell swoop," he says. "Where will we put all the patients?"

But with all its faults, where else can a patient get the benefit of such all-encompassing medical care? Again the *Times* comments:

A case that serves to illustrate the extraordinary facilities Bellevue has at its command is that of an adolescent victim of a street attack.

Wheeled into the emergency ward, this girl was unconscious and in such bad shape that the nurse in charge dared not move her onto a bed. Ten doctors worked over her for two hours—a neurologist and a neurosurgeon concentrated on her head, which had been smashed by a piece of pipe; two thoracic surgeons attended her many chest and neck wounds; an ear, nose, and throat man performed a tracheotomy; the girl had been raped, calling for the presence of a team from gynecology; a surgeon attended to minor fractures; an anesthetist was in constant attendance; consultants in surgery and medicine stood by to offer guidance. Of the 300 or so admissions to the emergency ward each month, about 275—many of them in just as bad shape as this attack victim—are pulled through.

The city has promised a new hospital, and this time Bellevue people mean to see that the hospital becomes a reality. The new structure will symbolically complement the United Nations building a few blocks to the north, and no doubt serve as a constant reminder that life is tough enough without the additional torments of war, either at home or abroad.

In hope of keeping up with the new Bellevue, New York University is trying to raise funds for a massive $15,000,000 medical center to be built on an East River site four blocks north of the hospital. This new group will include a separate building for the rehabilitation center, room for new laboratories and research projects, and greater teaching space. It will also contain a hospital for middle-income families, who always seem to be left out in social advance. As matters stand, most of these people are too well off to go to Bellevue, but cannot afford services offered by privately run hospitals.

Also in bright prospect is a scheme for making the new hospital and medical center an international center of medical education. This, too, would complement the U.N. Through a fellowship plan the center's facilities would be opened to the whole world. Animating this project is a wish to do something for the famous European centers of medical learning from which American medicine, in earlier times, gained so much.

The old Bellevue spirit of Mott and Francis, of Biggs and Welch, will not be lost as the hospital undergoes a physical metamorphosis. This spirit is indestructible, for it arises naturally out of nurturing the sick and helpless. So long as Bellevue cares for the endless stream of poor, sick people cast off by the city, so long will it thrive and live. "And now abideth faith, hope, charity, these three"—says Paul—"but the greatest of these is charity."

INDEX

Abbe, Dr., 102
acute appendicitis, surgical technique for, 140
age of advance in medicine, 125
Albany Medical College, 241
alcoholism, recognized as illness, 243, 244
Almshouse of 1816, 15
ambulance, origin of, 82, 83
ambulance system, inaugurated, 83
American Academy of Art, 29
American Base Hospital Unit Number 1, 205
American Lancet, 40
American Medical Association, 38, 88
American Public Health Association, 74, 237
American Red Cross, 80, 103, 115, 184, 208, 213
amputation, improvement of, 80
anatomical research, opposed by Church, 17
anatomy, 8
Anatomy of Drunkenness, 59
Anderson, Alexander, 11
Anderson, James, 229
anesthesia, development of in Bellevue, 252 ff.
anesthesia, local, 143
anesthetic, discovery of, 124, 125
Aristotle, 7
Armstrong, T. F., 189
Army Nurse Corps, 212
Art of Cross-Examination, 170
Ashe, Benjamin, 258
Asiatic cholera, epidemic, 43 ff.
Astor, John Jacob, 72
Avery, O. T., 218

Baglivi, 7
Baker, George F., 179
Bamber, Beatrice M., 203
Bard, John, 19, 21, 26, 27
Bard, Samuel, 21, 28, 29
Barker, Fordyce, 55, 90
Barlow, General, 120
Barton, Clara, 184
Baruch, Bernard M., 273
Bayley, Richard, 22, 26
Beck, John, 40
Bellevue doctors in World War II, 258, ff.
Bellevue Establishment, 15
Bellevue Hospital, as teaching center, 62

caseload of, 3
children's clinic, 86
clinical lectures at, 62
conditions in, 45, 46, 55, 56, 107 ff., 139, 172-175
night wards, 119
cost of operation of, 3
costs, 268, 269
death rate in, 94, 95, 96, 269, 270
description of, 1, 2
first laboratory at, 131
first medical college, 55
first woman doctor, 194, 195
future of, 278
improvement in mental care, 241 ff.
insane ward, conditions in, 236
interns, conditions for, 270, 271
investigations of, 2
involved in murder trial, 169-172
location of, 1
Medical College, 78, 88, 133, 137, 150
combined with New York University, 159
described in 1860, 79
medical school affiliations, 3
nurses, conditions for, 271, 272
opened to all students of medicine, 51
organized into house services, 51
origin of, 6, 9
outpatient department, 86
pathology research laboratory, 135
population of, 3
problems of, 2
progress and research, 275, 276
reforms in, 76
religion in, 272, 273
renovated, 176
reorganization, 86
School, 125, 126
separated from Almshouse, 48
types of patients and diseases, 270
Bellevue Medical Board, 54, 62, 80, 94, 113, 117, 120, 121, 176, 276
Bellevue Nurses' Registry, 163
Bellevue Social Service Department, 191

Bellevue Training School for Male Nurses, 170
Bellevue Training School for Nurses, 113 ff., 165-168, 180, 213
origin of, 80
Bellevue unit, World War I, 203 ff.
Belmont, August, 72
Berry, Frank, 266
Biggs, Hermann M., 133; 138, 149 ff., 168, 199, 200, 202, 208
Biggs-Loomis report on tuberculosis, 152
Blackwell, Elizabeth, 80, 103
Blackwell, Emily, 103, 123
bleeding, 7
Bly, Nellie, 169, 238
Board of Charities, 117
Board of Health, 71
Board of Visiting Physicians and Surgeons, 48
Boerhaave, 7, 19, 45
"Bone Bill," 52
bones, Wood's collection of diseased, 52
Bowdin (Sister) Helen, 118. *See also* Sister Helen.
Bowen, General, 105, 113
Brannan, J. W., 157, 172, 186, 188
Brice, Cornelia, 245
Brink, Carrie J., 203, 215 ff.
Bryant, Joseph B., 151, 152
Bryant, William Cullen, 69
Bull, William T., 95
Burdick, Carl G., 204
"Bureau of Medical and Surgical Relief for the Outdoor Poor, The," 86
Burr, Aaron, 28, 30

Campbell, Mrs. Helen, 84
cardiac clinic, 178
Carnegie, Andrew, 135
Carnegie Laboratory, 150
Carr, Walter Lester, 132
"Case of the Girl with the Charcoal Scales, The," 89
Cavell, Edith, 212
Chambers Street Hospital, 142
Chandler, Charles F., 75
Charity Hospital, 99, 100, 101, 142
charlatans, 7
Cheseman, Dr., 40
childbirth, 13
mortality rate, 142
cholera epidemic, 129, 151, 153